PICTURE CHORDS

Book 1

John Brimhall's

ADULT PIANO-CHORD COURSE Complete

The chords in Book One are graphically illustrated for left and right hand. Names of the notes are shown next to each chord and written mostly in the root position. This book may well serve as a perfect note speller and as an easy reference chart for study purposes.

Every effort should be made to memorize these picture chords in each hand by spending a few minutes each day just playing chords.

John Brimhall
for the publisher

CHORDS FOR LEFT OR RIGHT HAND
(M, m, dim, aug, 6, m6, 5, 7)

CHORDS FOR BOTH HANDS

T5716

ISBN 0-8494-3018-6

VISUAL CHORDS

Book 2

John Brimhall's ADULT PIANO-CHORD COURSE Complete

In the second book of this chord method we present a melody line with chords above each song. The chords are to be played with the left hand and you will note that the chords are inverted to give a smooth transition from one chord to another. These tunes are all top lines extracted from published Kiddie Sheets of each title.

John Brimhall
for the publisher

CONTENTS

MELODY CHORD Arrangements

Book 3

John Brimhall's ADULT PIANO-CHORD COURSE Complete

This third book is quite unique in that it gives the player an opportunity to play a melody line with chords in the right hand! You will notice that the chords in each song contain the notes in various inversions and at times with notes missing. The left hand will play the root of each chord. Use the pedal when playing and change the pedal with each chord change.

A fingering tip – be sure to hold all notes for their correct time values and adjust the fingering accordingly.

These arrangements should give the player a brand "new sound" and therefore add to one's enjoyment in playing these songs.

George Volpe
for the publisher

CONTENTS

PICTURE CHORDS

Left Hand Chords On C

C
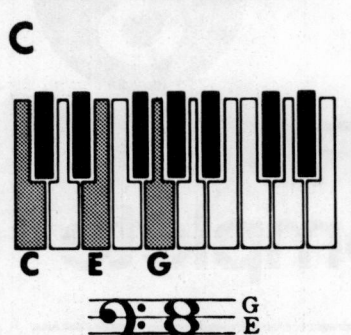

Cm
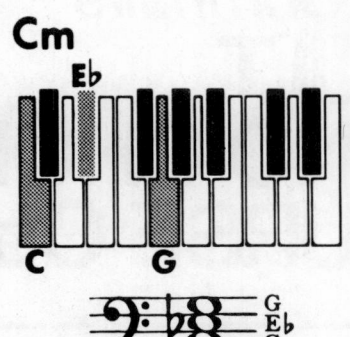

Cdim
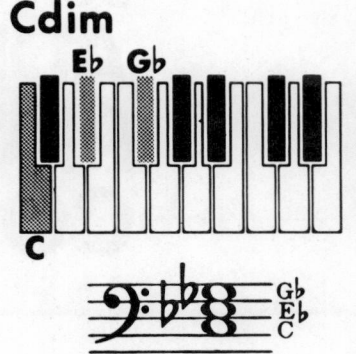

C+
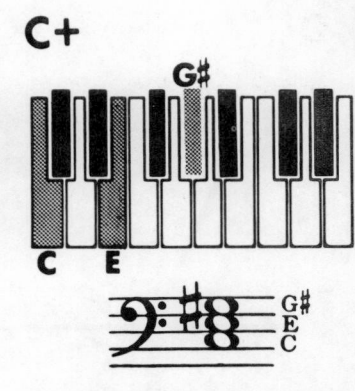

C6
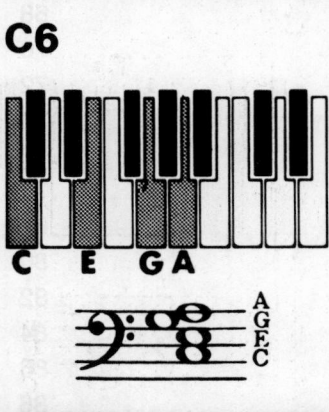

Cm6
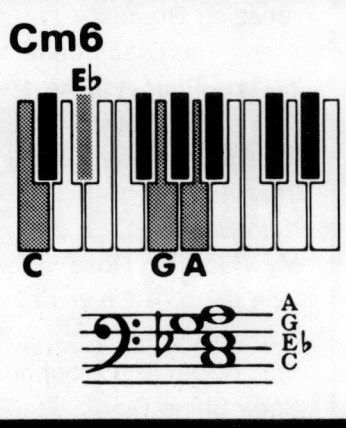

C(♭5)
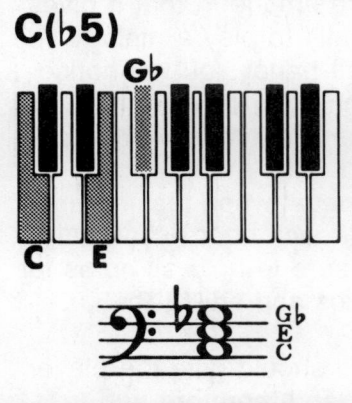

C7
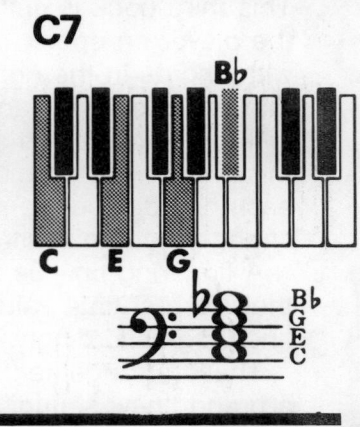

Cm7
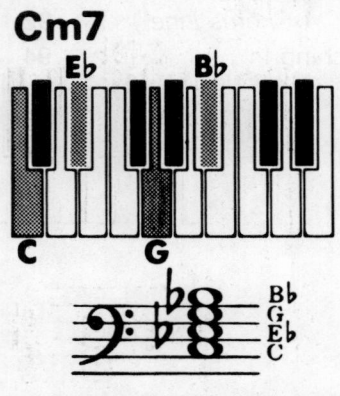

Cdim7
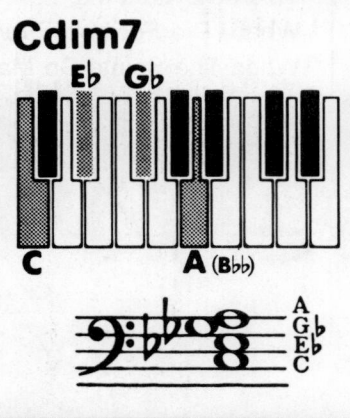

Cmaj7
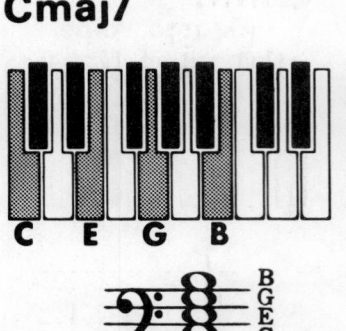

C7♯5
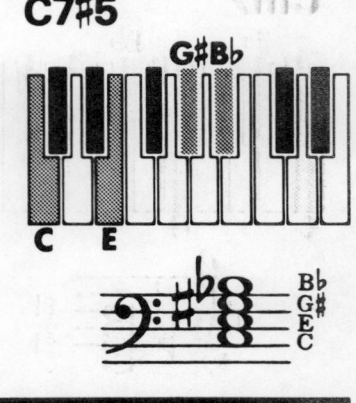

C7♭5
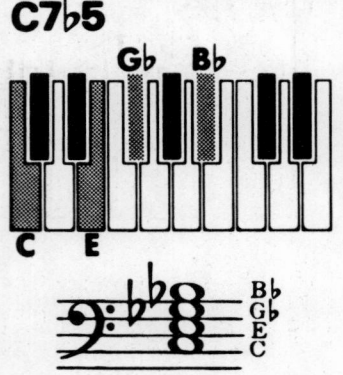

C7(sus)
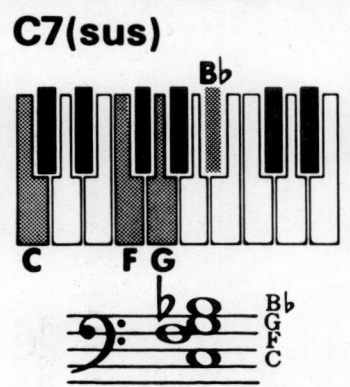

Cmaj7♯5
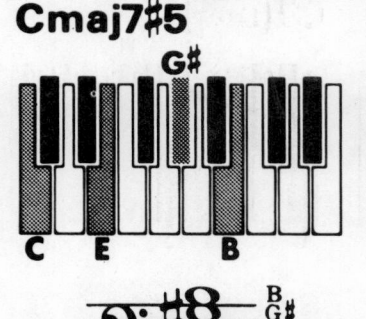

Cm7♭5
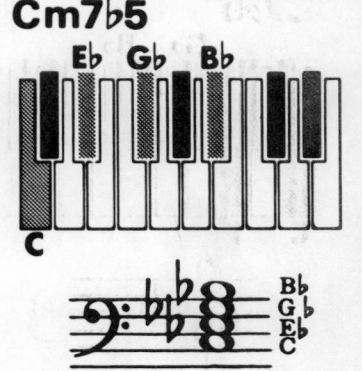

C 𝄞

Right Hand Chords On C

C

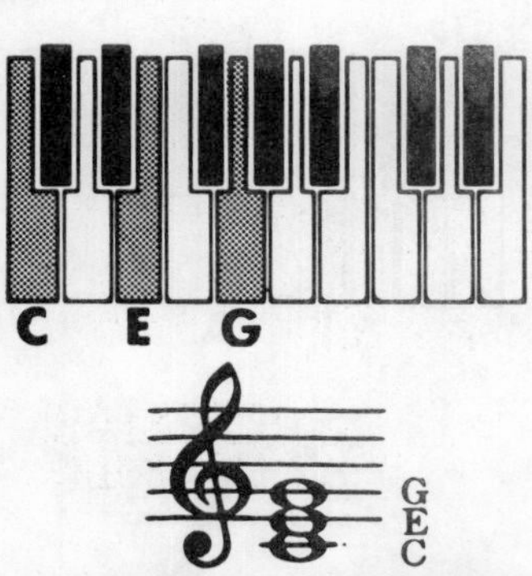

C E G

GEC

Cm

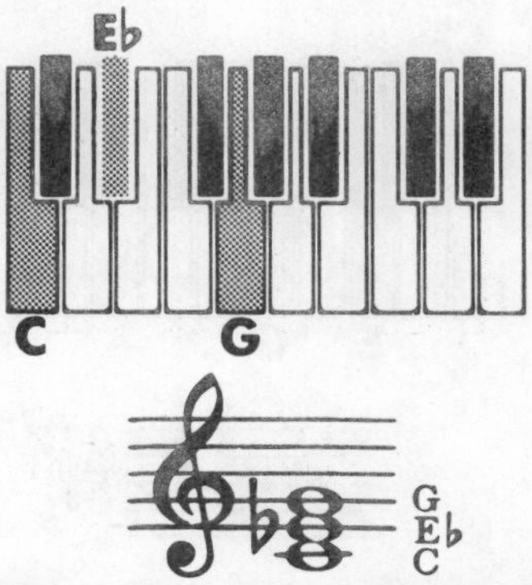

Eb

C G

GEb C

Cdim

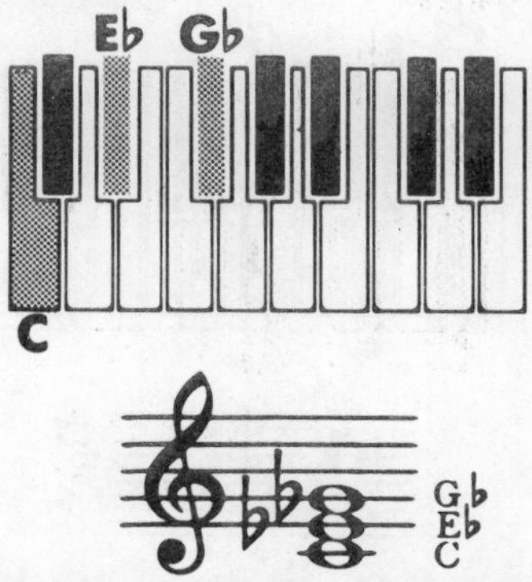

Eb Gb

C

Gb Eb C

C+

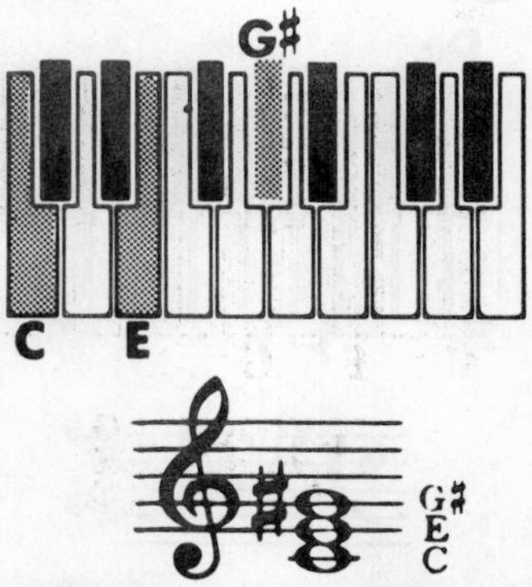

G#

C E

G# E C

C6

C E G A

AGEC

Cm6

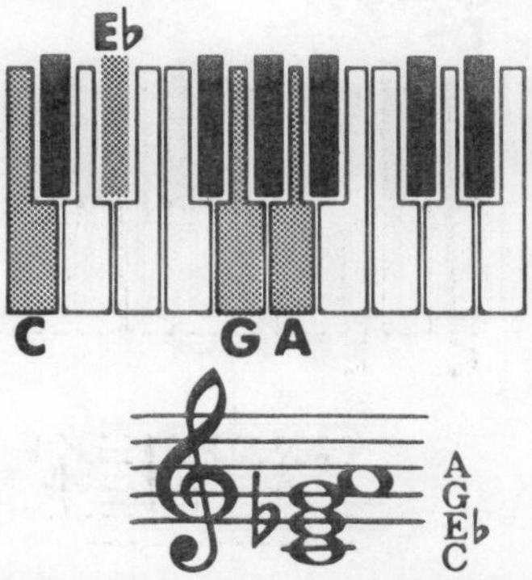

Eb

C G A

AGEb C

C(b5)

Gb

C E

Gb E C

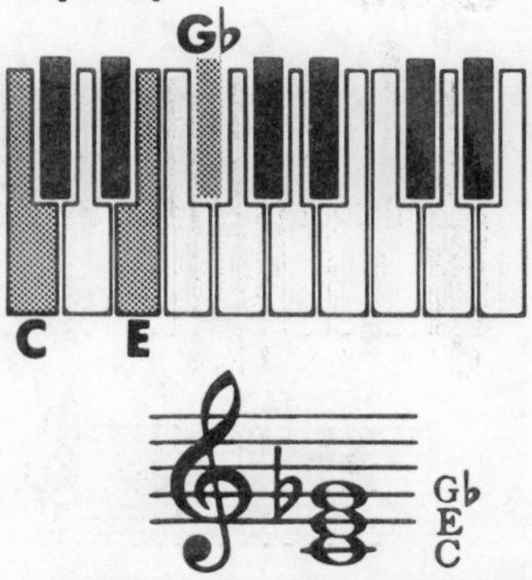

C7

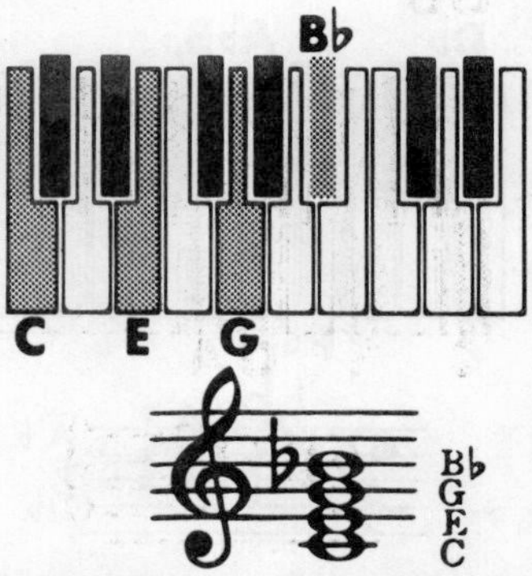

Bb

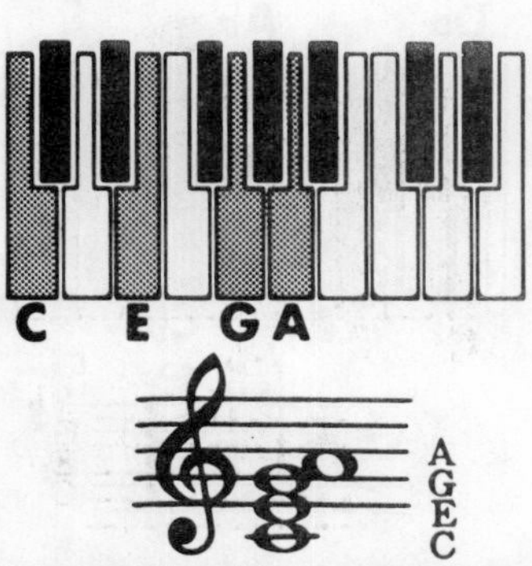

C E G

Bb GEC

Cm7

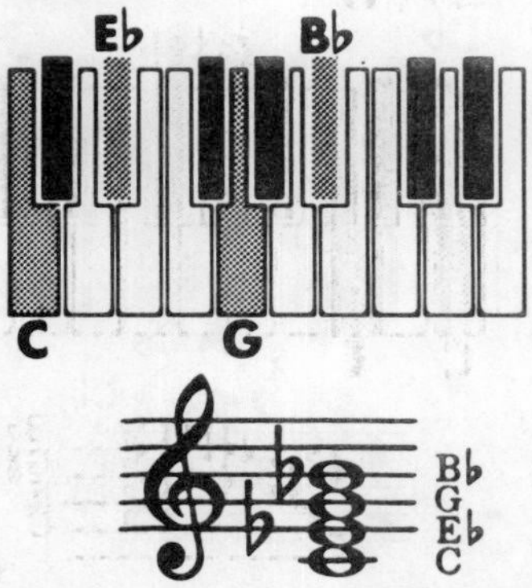

Eb Bb

C G

Bb GEb C

Cdim7

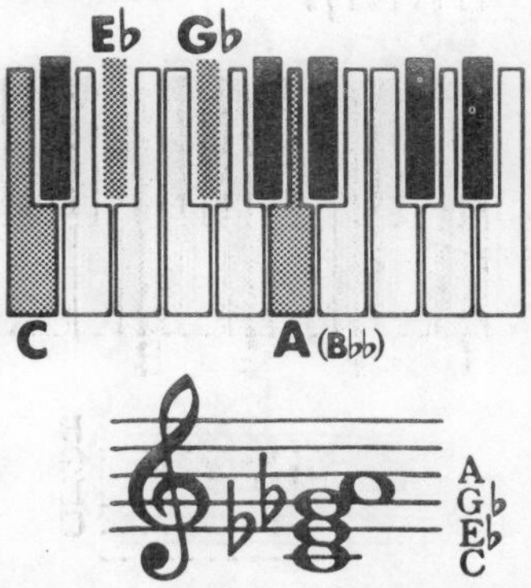

Eb Gb

C A (Bbb)

AGEb C

Cmaj7

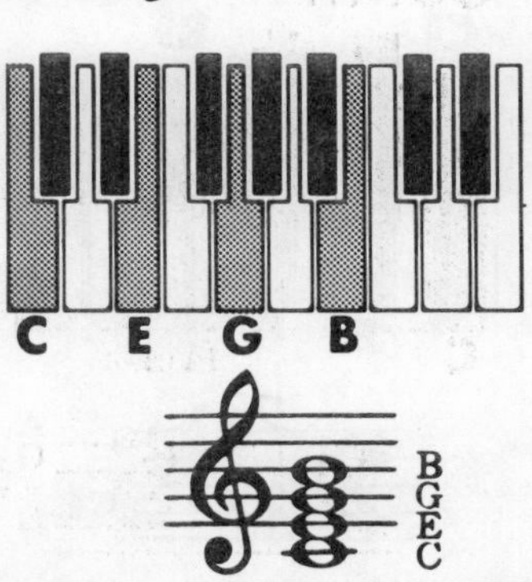

C E G B

BGEC

C7#5

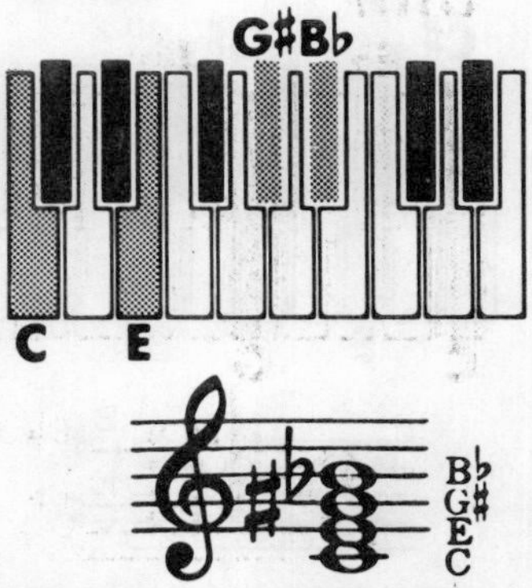

G#Bb

C E

Bb G# E C

C7b5

Gb Bb

C E

Bb GbEC

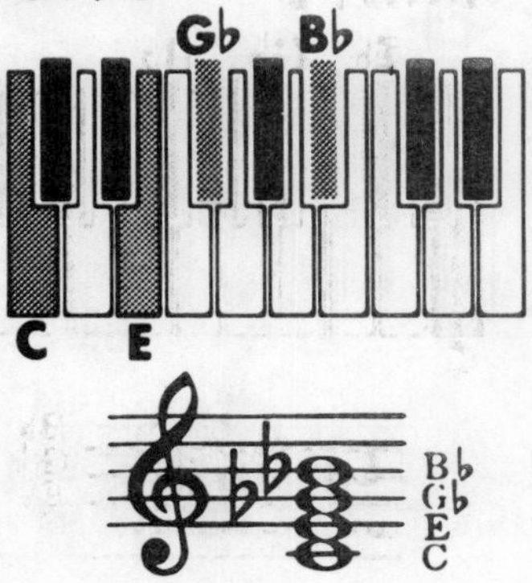

C7(sus)

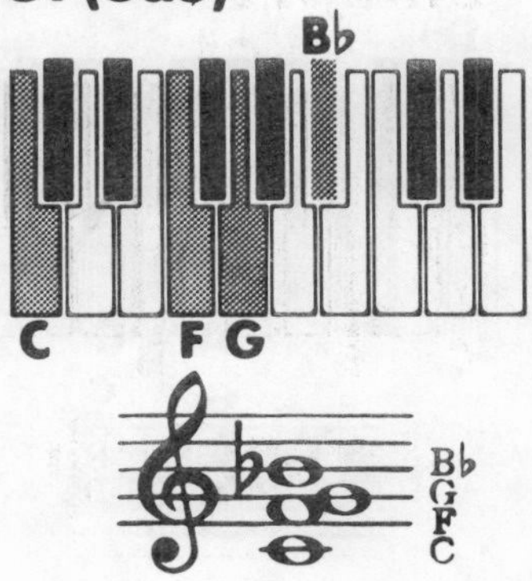

Bb

C F G

Bb GFC

Cmaj7#5

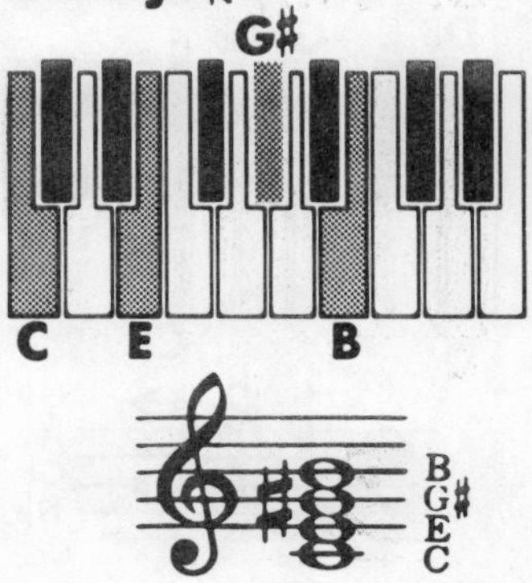

G#

C E B

BG#EC

Cm7b5

Eb Gb Bb

C

Bb Gb Eb C

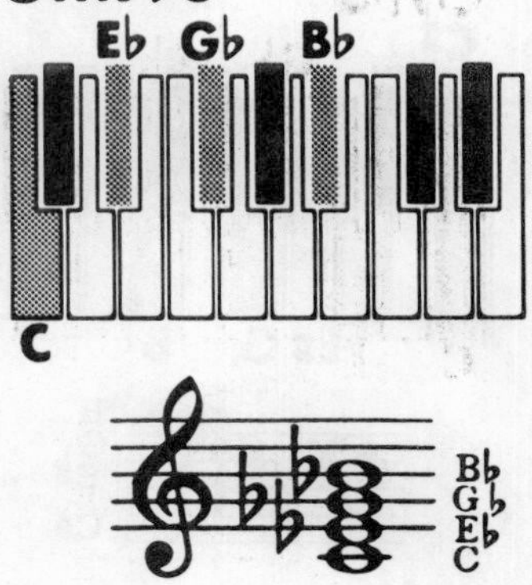

6

Left Hand Chords On D♭(C#)

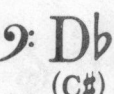

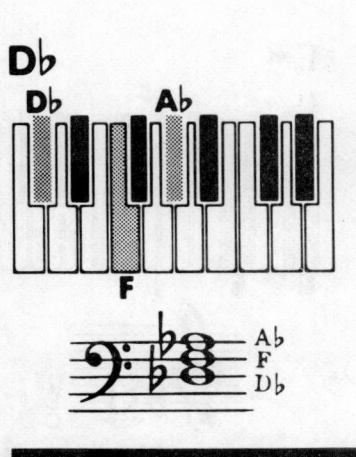

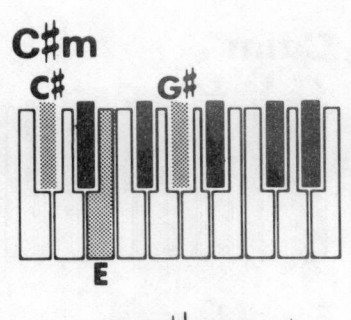

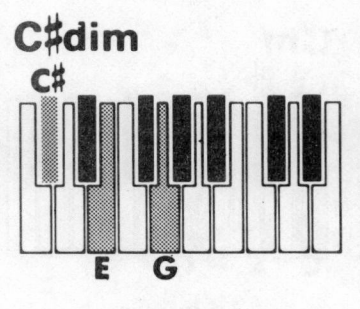

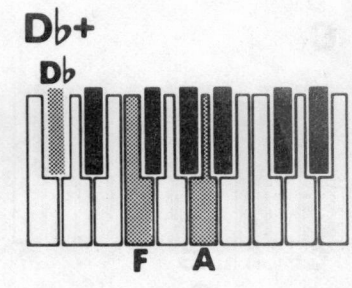

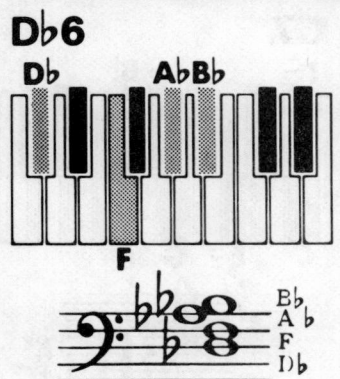

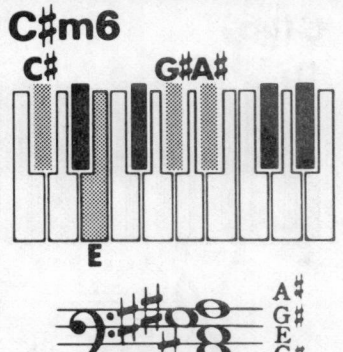

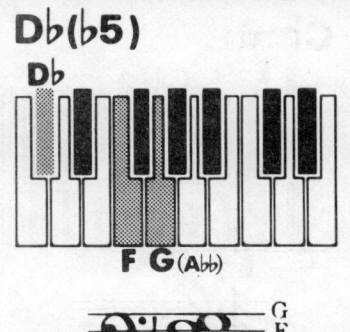

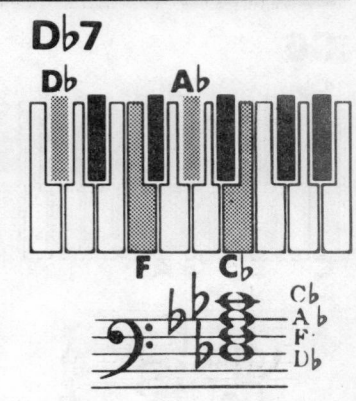

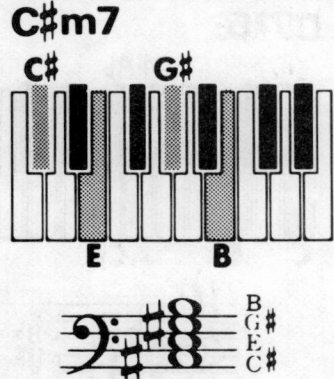

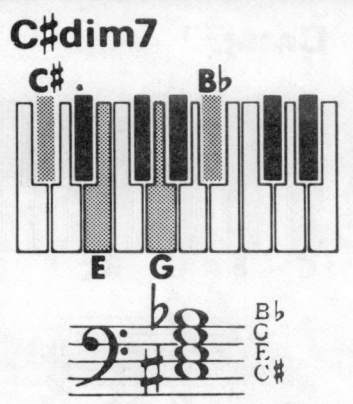

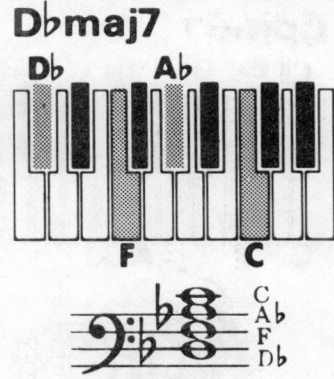

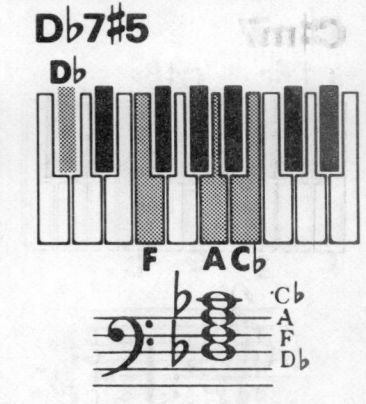

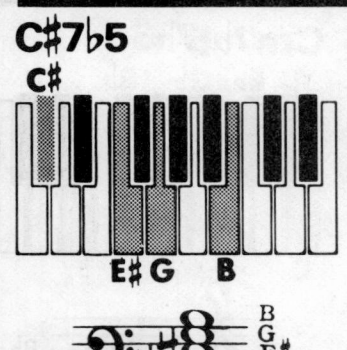

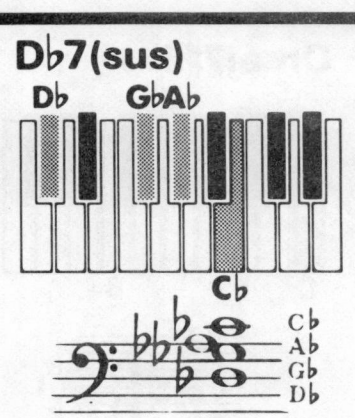

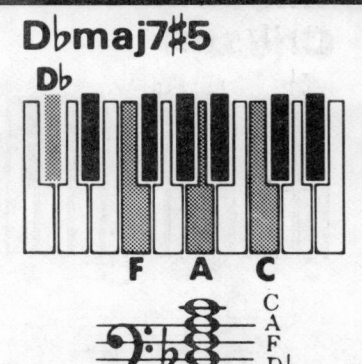

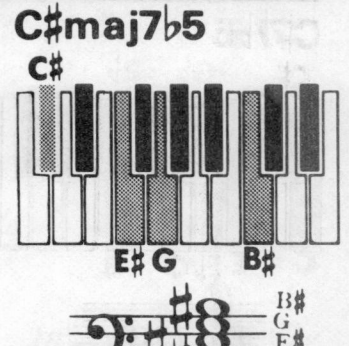

Right Hand Chords On Db(C#)

Db

C#m

C#dim

Db+

Db6

C#m6

Db(b5)

Db7

C#m7

C#dim7

Dbmaj7

Db7#5

C#7b5

Db7(sus)

Dbmaj7#5

C#maj7b5

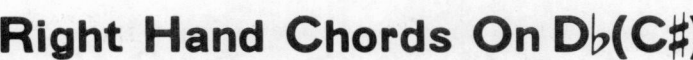

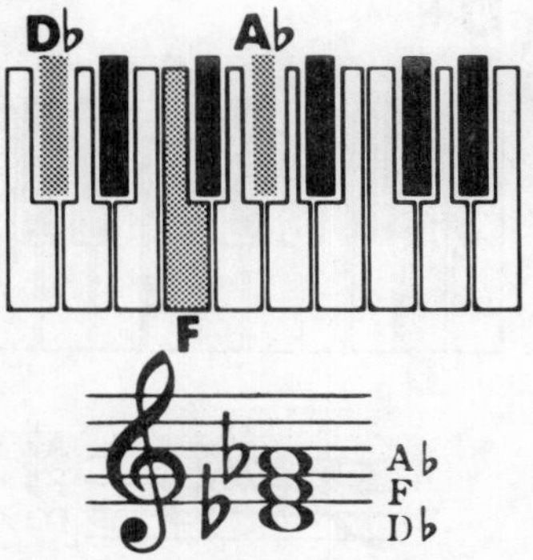

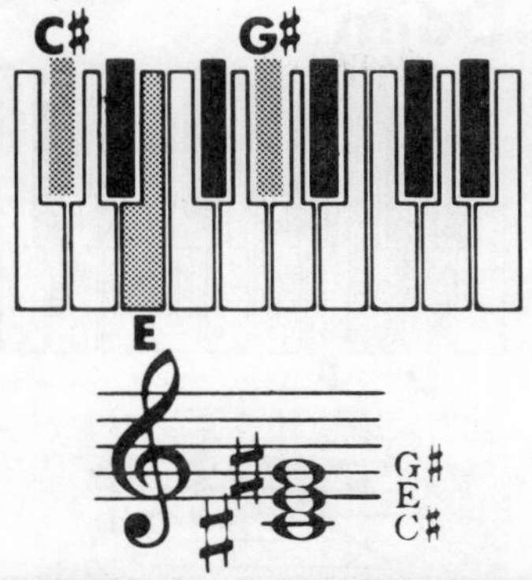

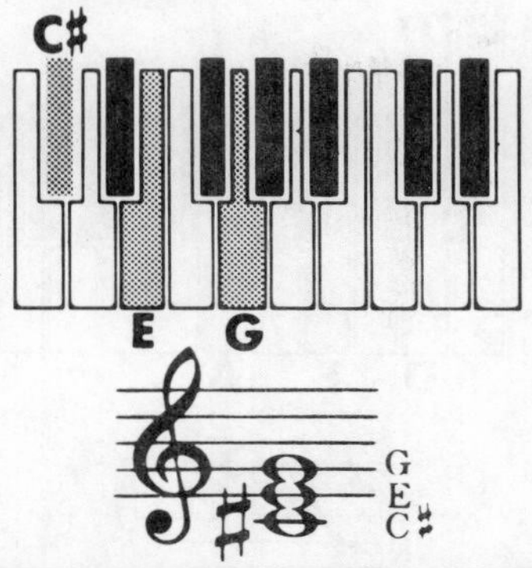

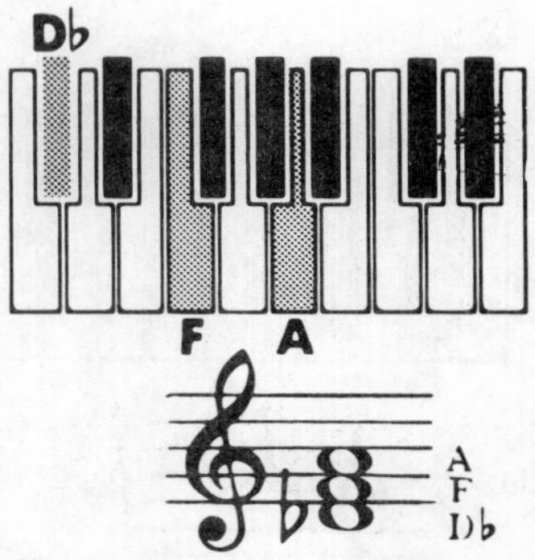

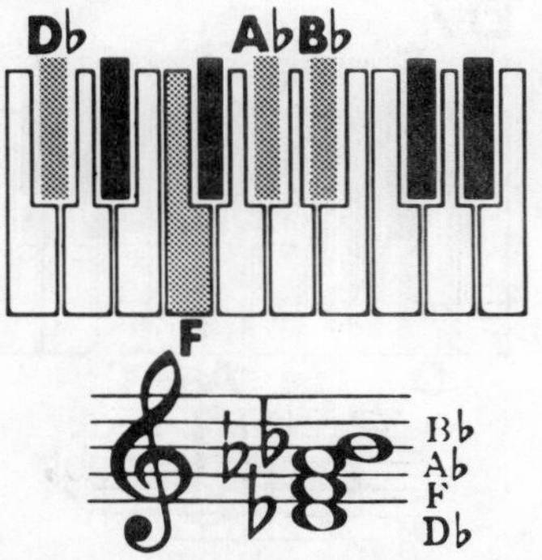

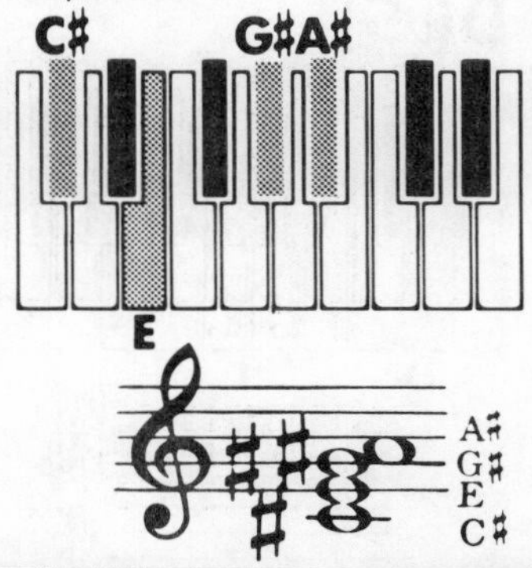

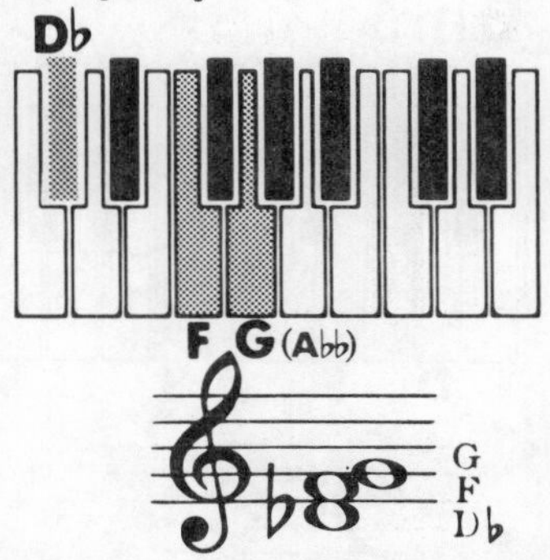

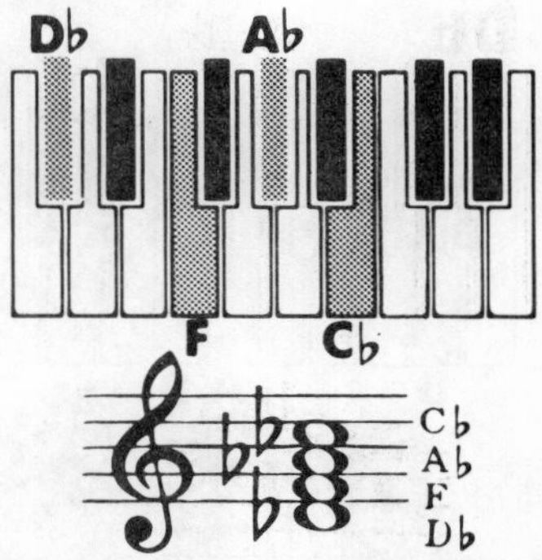

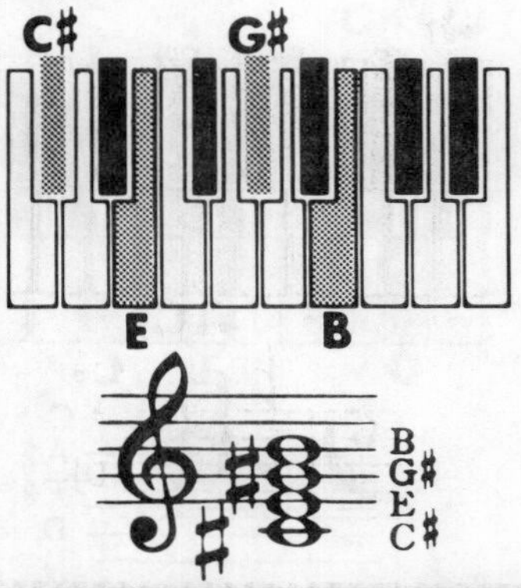

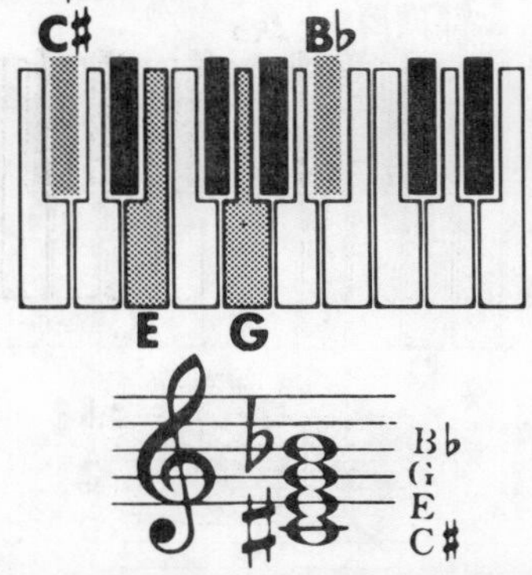

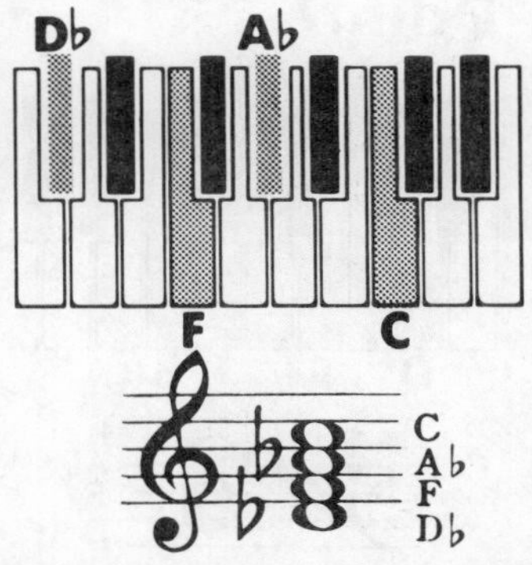

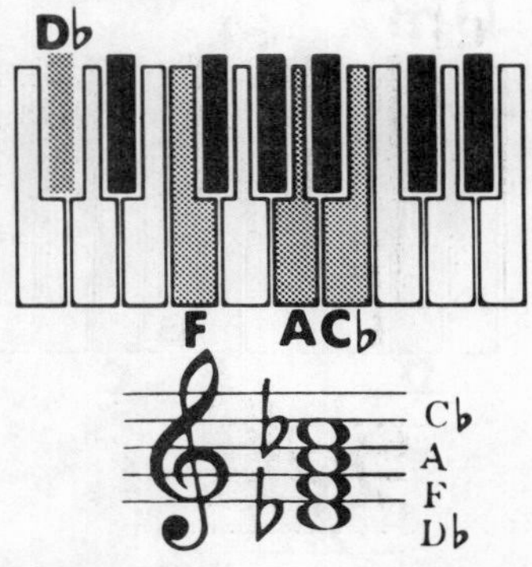

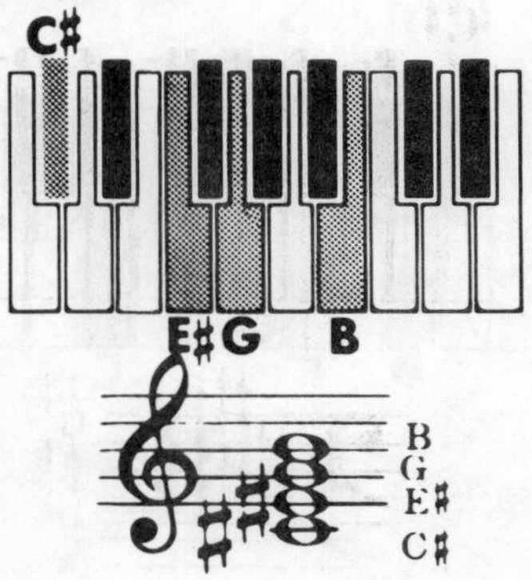

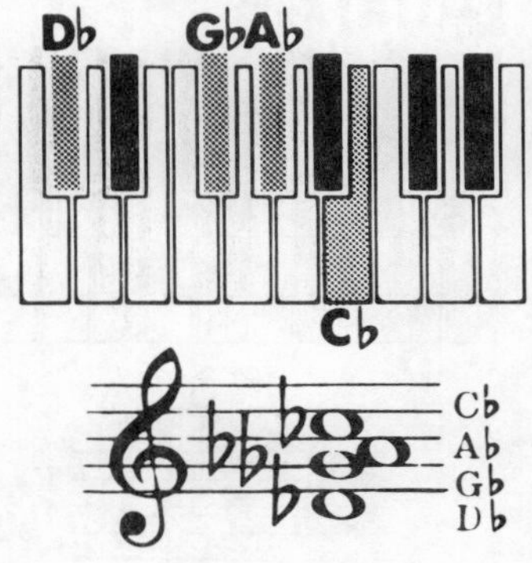

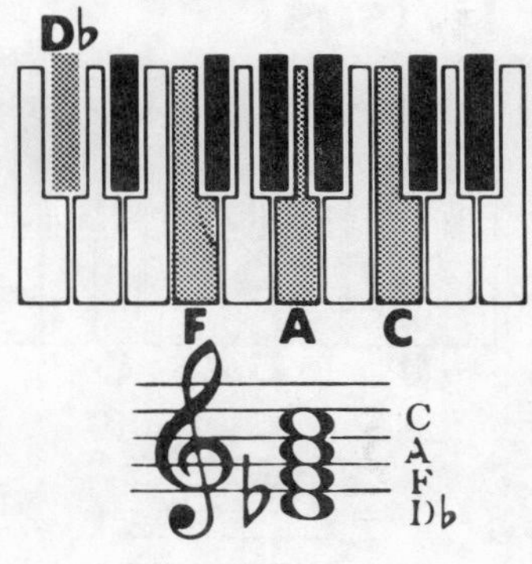

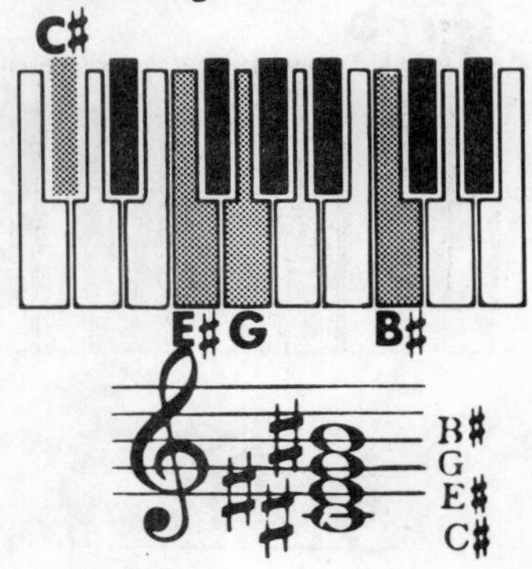

Left Hand Chords On D

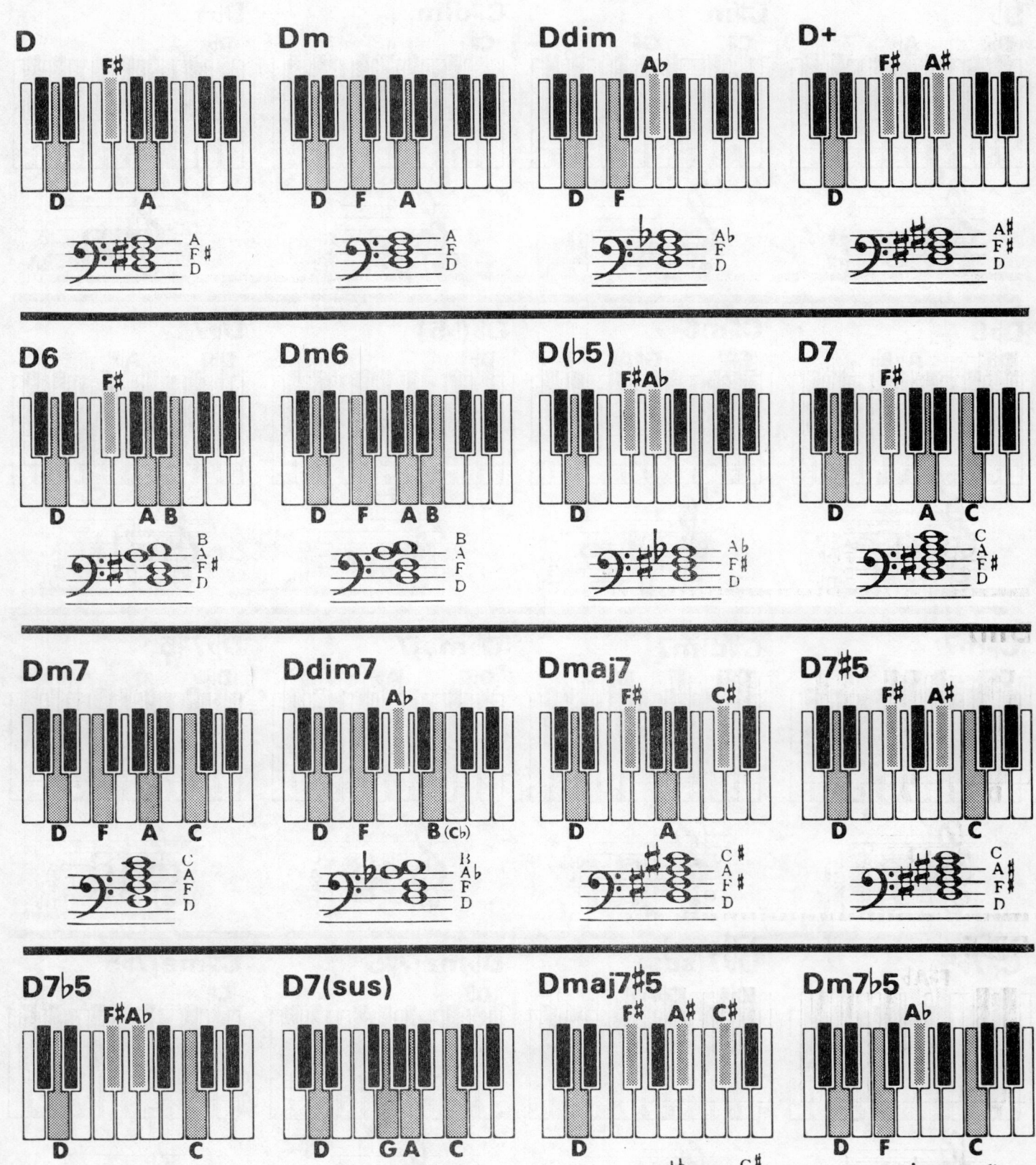

Right Hand Chords On D

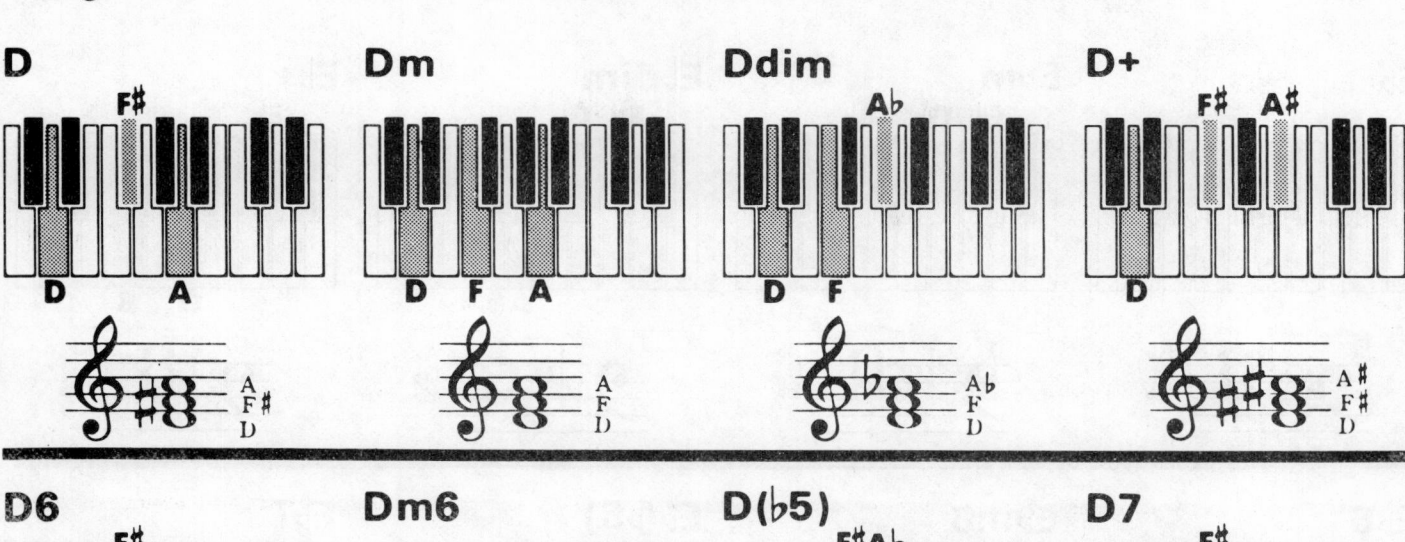

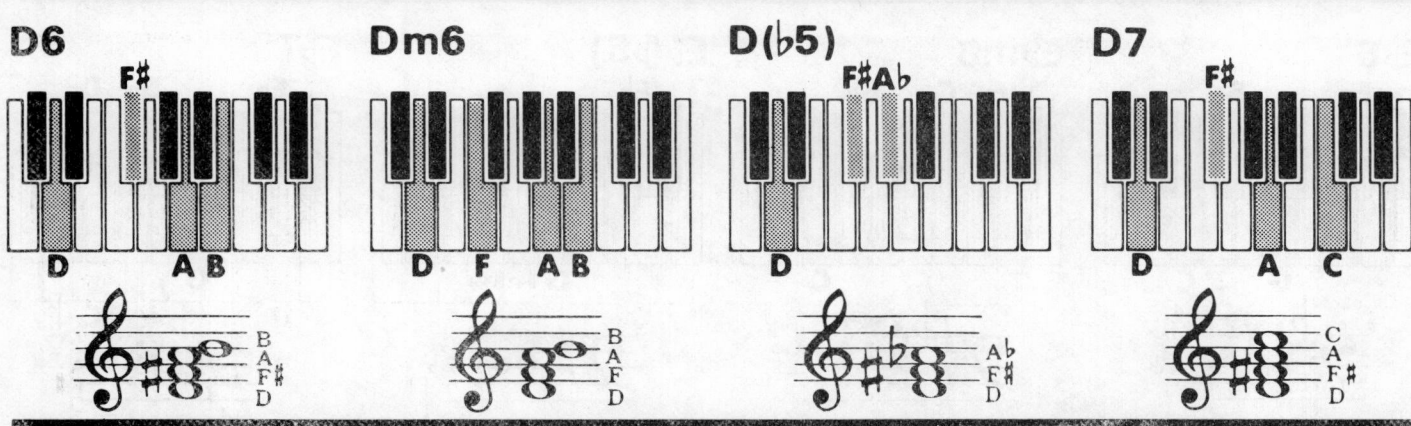

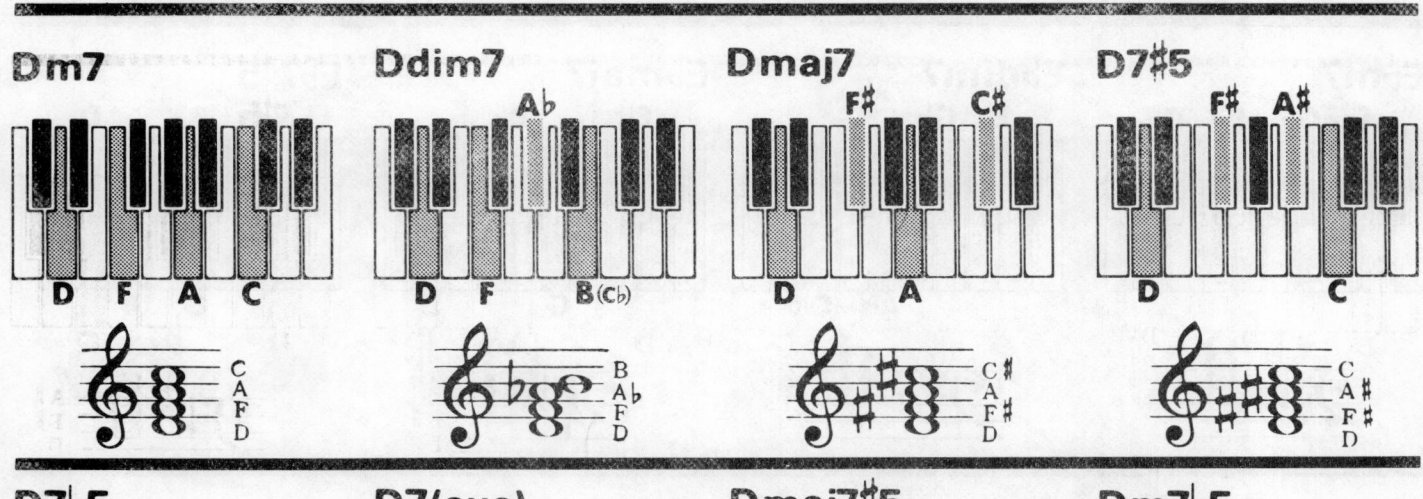

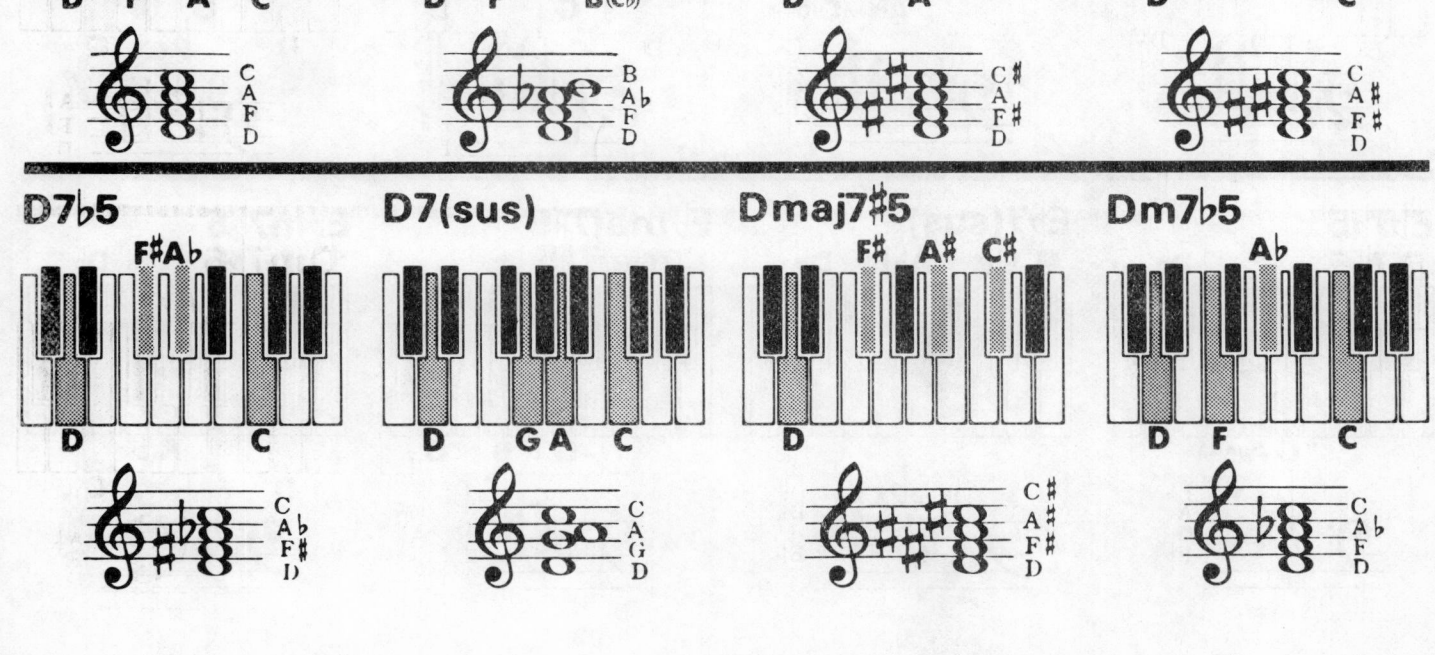

Left Hand Chords On E♭

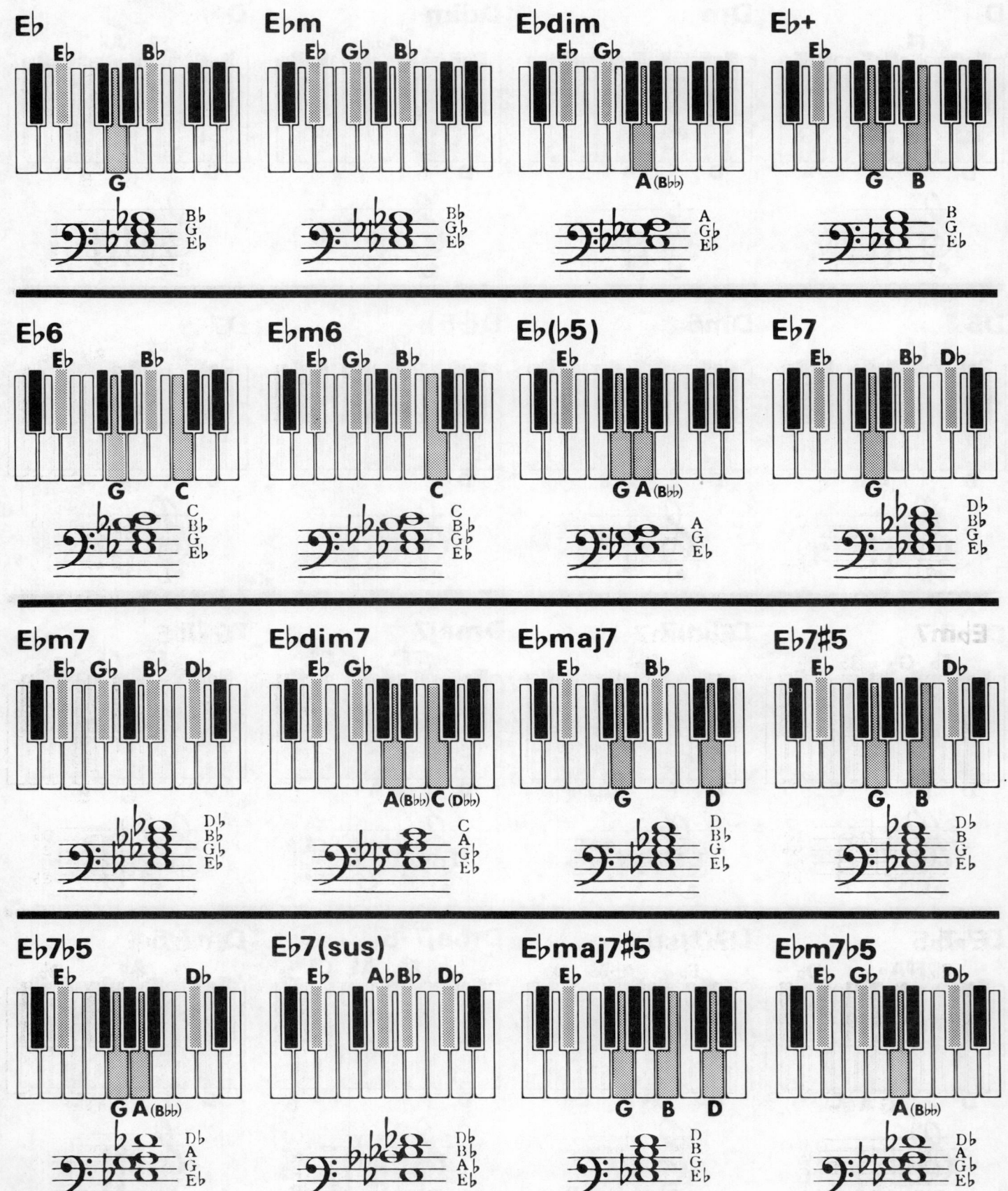

 Eᵇ

Right Hand Chords On E♭

E♭

E♭ B♭
G
B♭ / G / E♭

E♭m

E♭ G♭ B♭
B♭ / G♭ / E♭

E♭dim

E♭ G♭
A(B♭♭)
A / G / E♭

E♭+

E♭
G B
B / G / E♭

E♭6

E♭ B♭
G C
C / B♭ / G / E♭

E♭m6

E♭ G♭ B♭
C
C / B♭ / G♭ / E♭

E♭(♭5)

E♭
G A(B♭♭)
A / G / E

E♭7

E♭ B♭ D♭
G
D♭ / B♭ / G / E♭

E♭m7

E♭ G♭ B♭ D♭
D♭ / B♭ / G♭ / E♭

E♭dim7

E♭ G♭
A(B♭♭) C(D♭♭)
C / A / G / E

E♭maj7

E♭ B♭
G D
D / B♭ / G / E♭

E♭7♯5

E♭ D♭
G B
D♭ / B / G / E♭

E♭7♭5

E♭ D♭
G A(B♭♭)
D♭ / A / G / E

E♭7(sus)

E♭ A♭B♭ D♭
D♭ / B / A / E♭

E♭maj7♯5

E♭
G B D
D / B / G / E♭

E♭m7♭5

E♭ G♭ D♭
A(B♭♭)
D♭ / A / G♭ / E

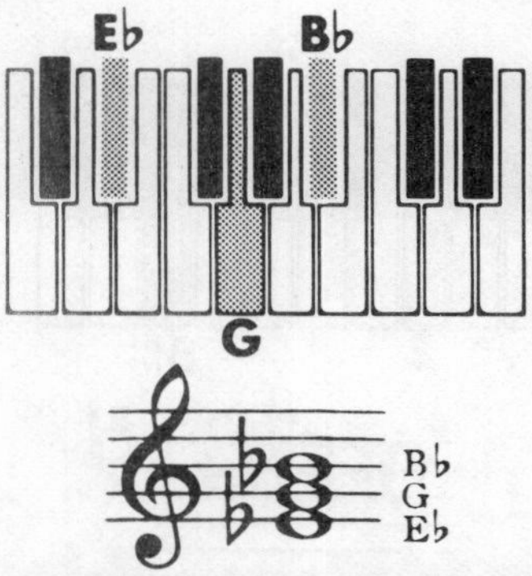

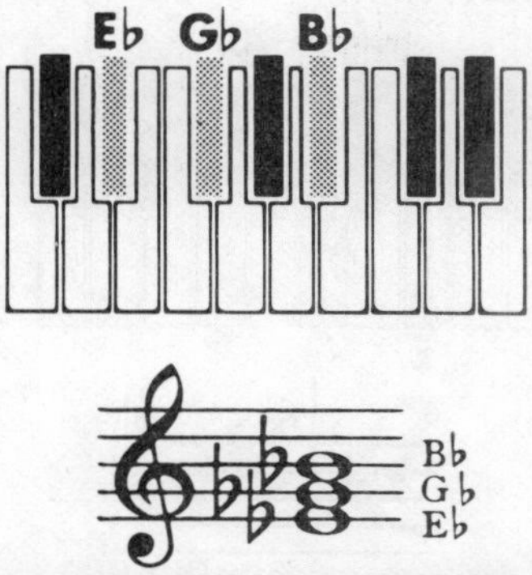

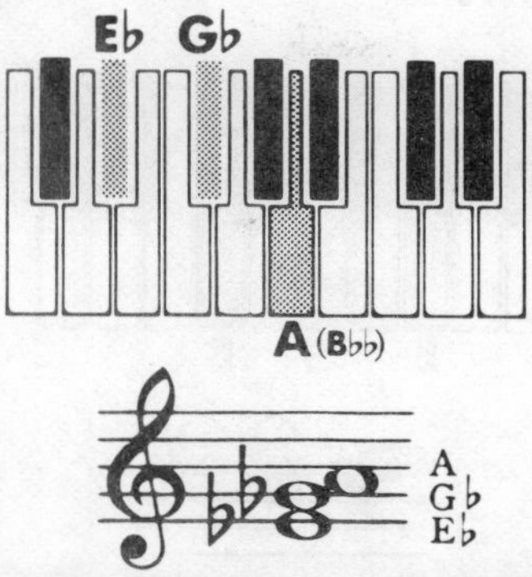

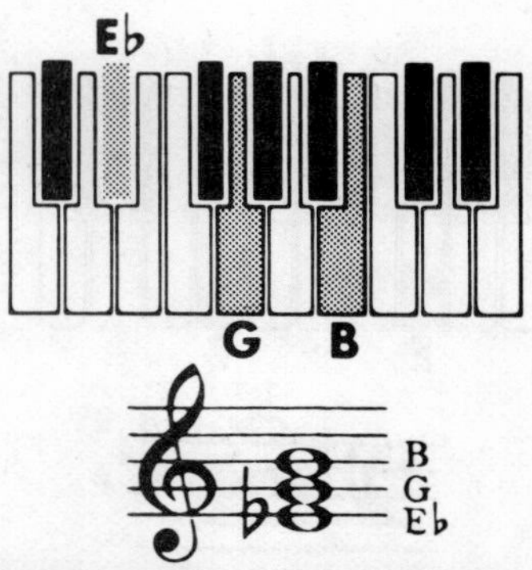

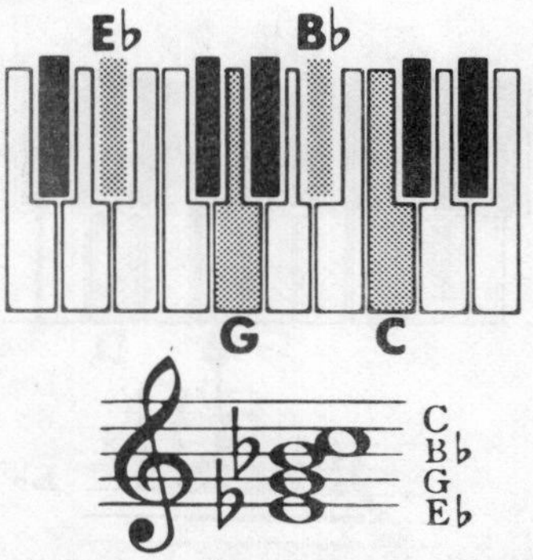

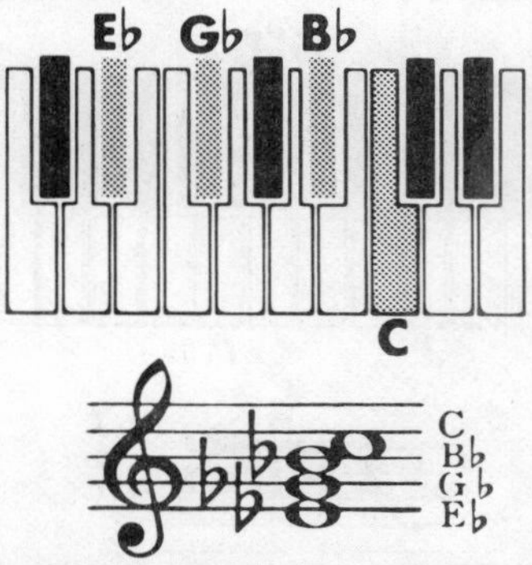

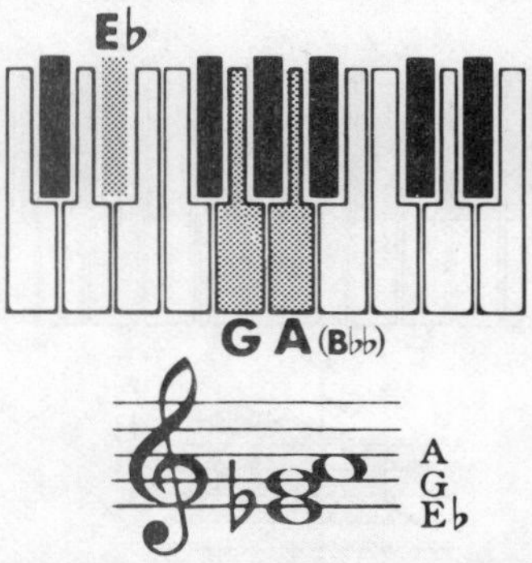

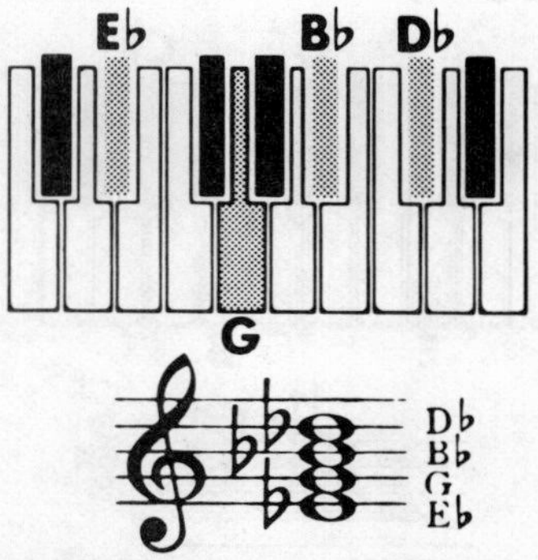

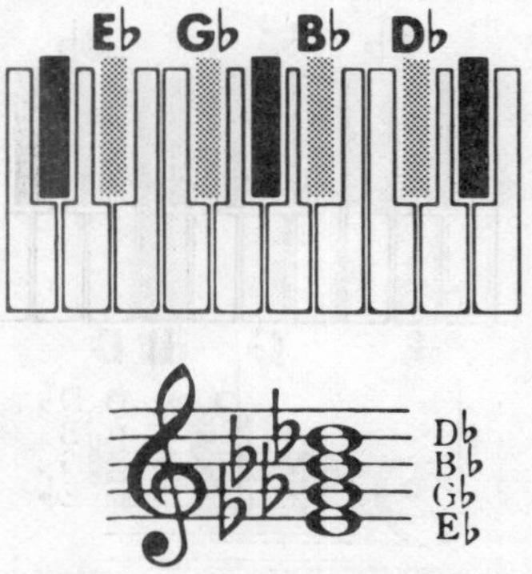

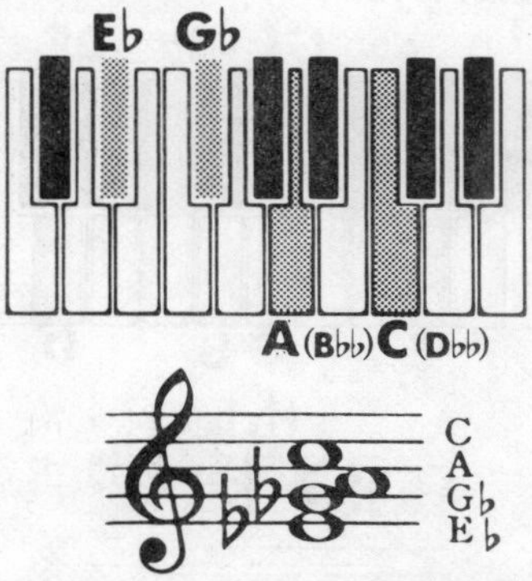

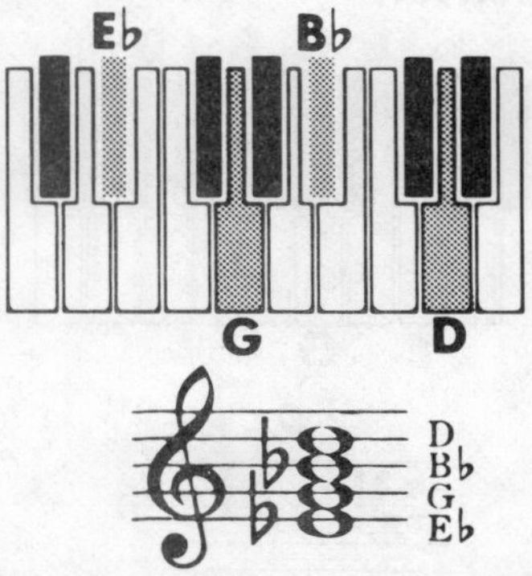

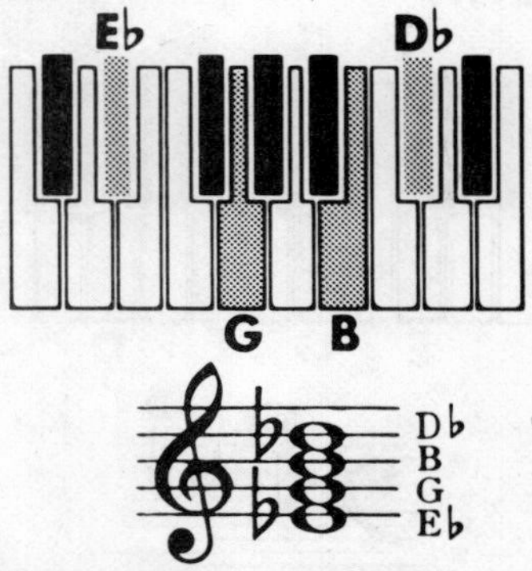

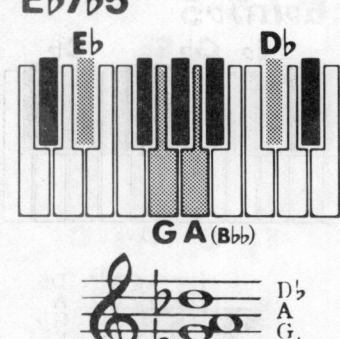
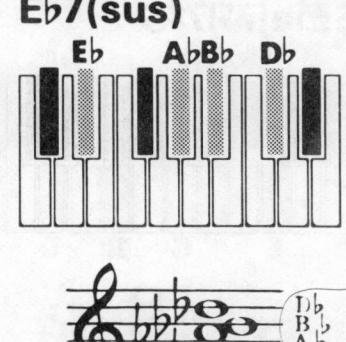
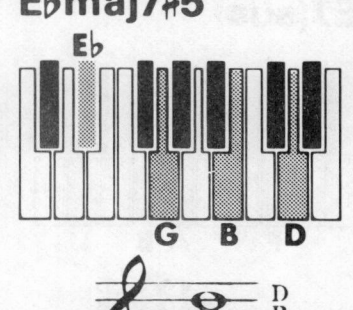
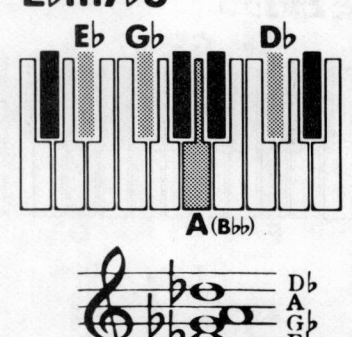

Left Hand Chords On E

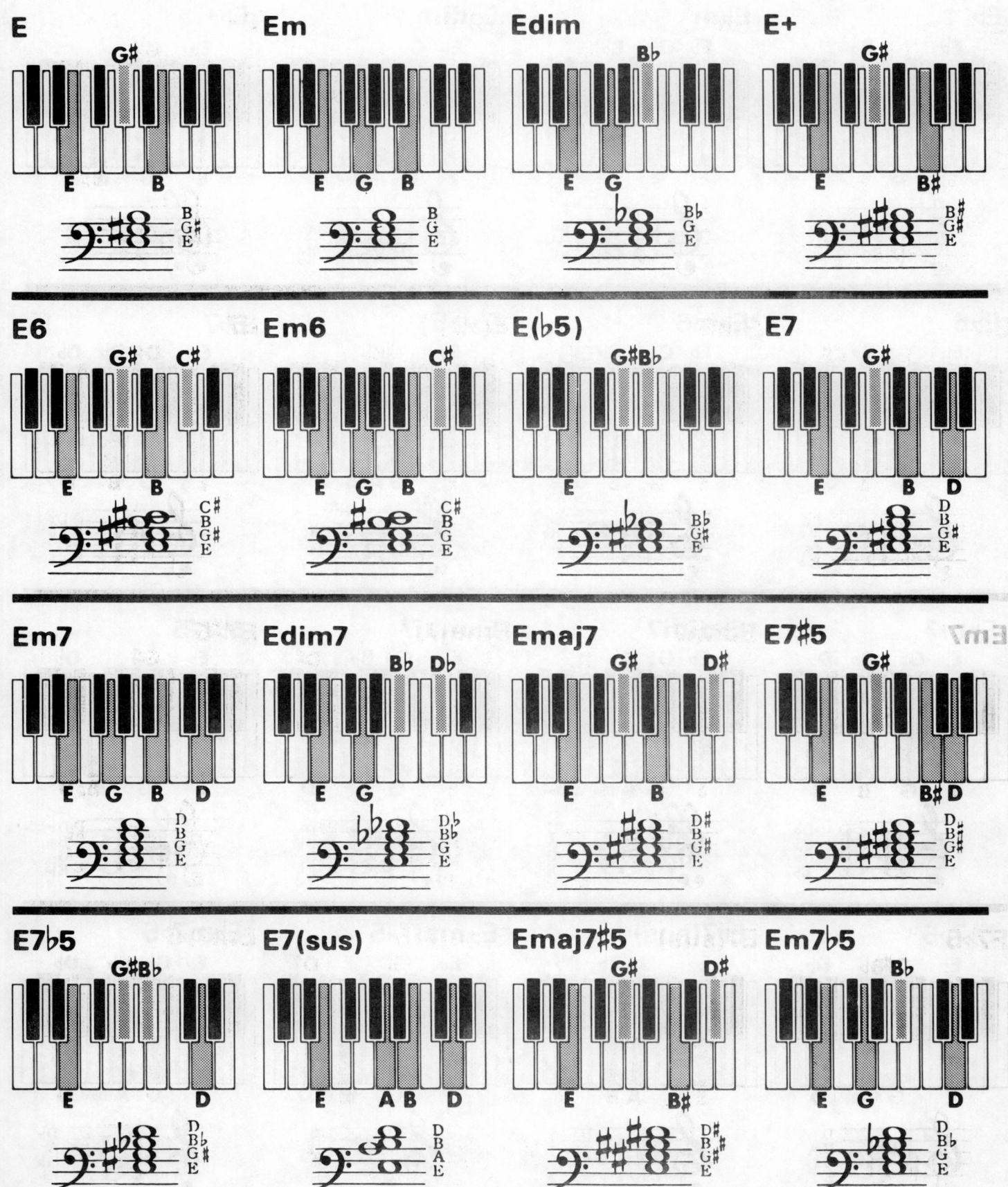

Right Hand Chords On E

E

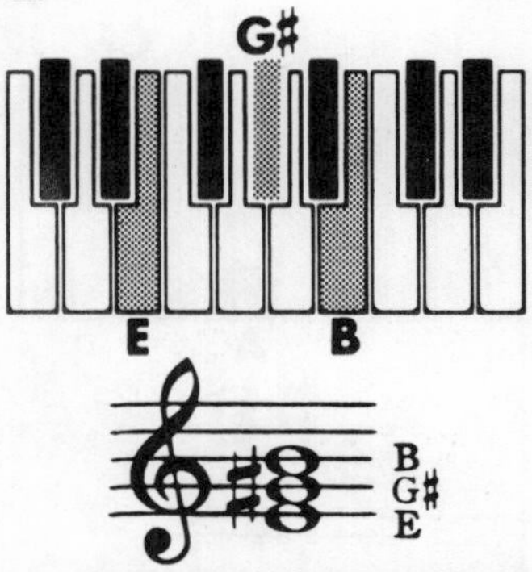

Em

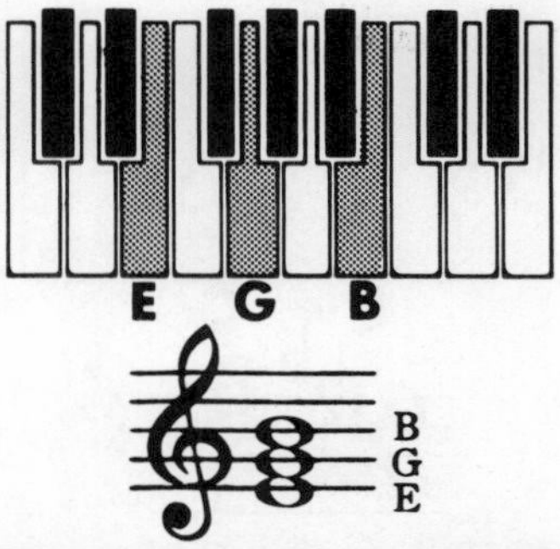

Edim

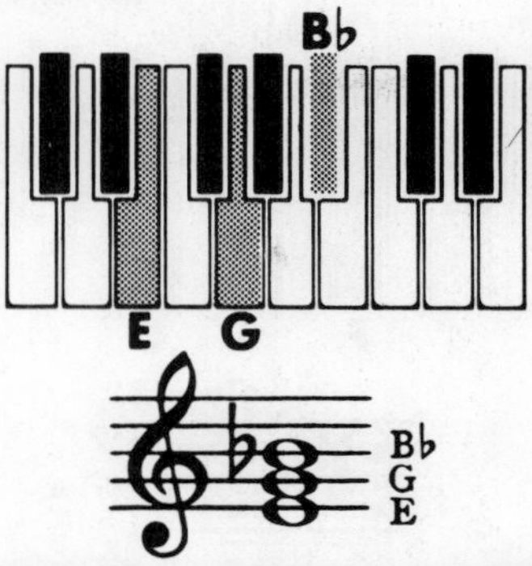

E+

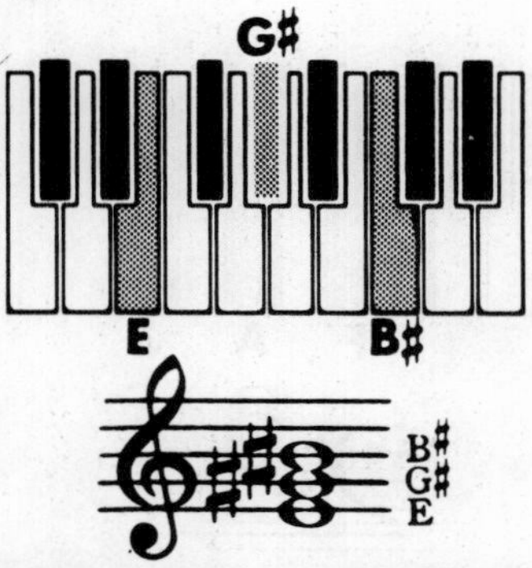

E6

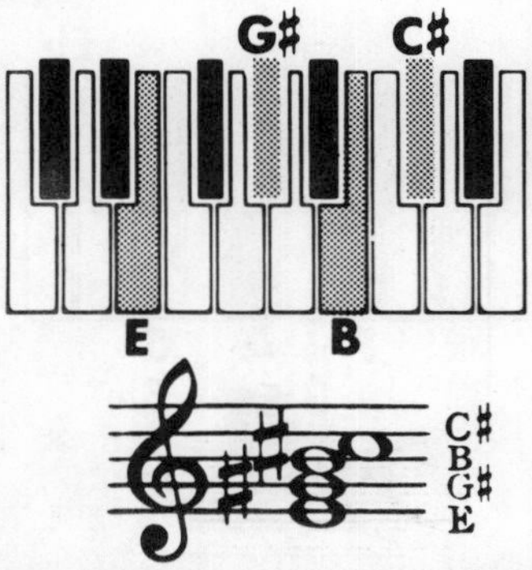

Em6

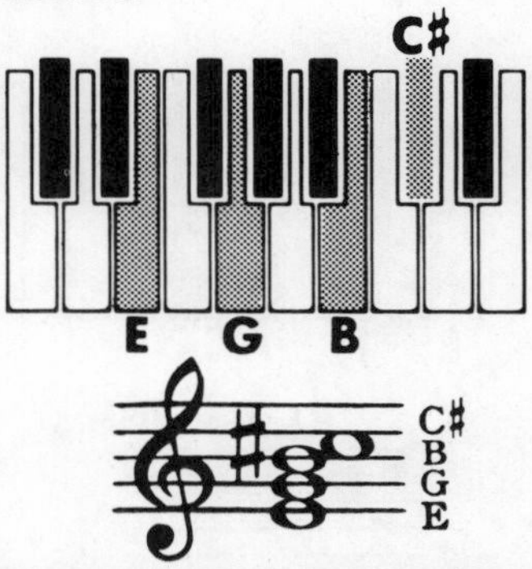

E(♭5)

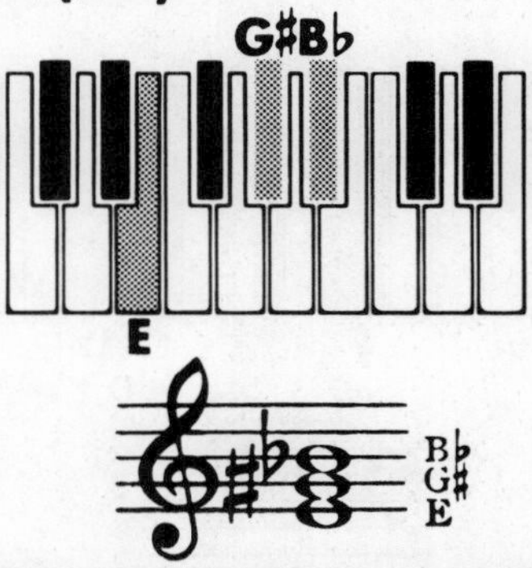

E7

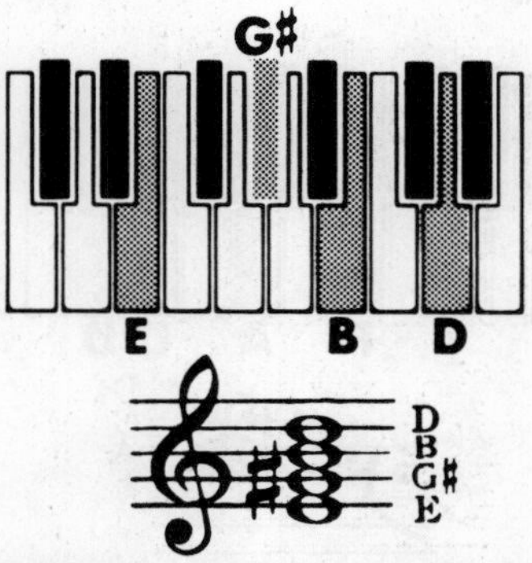

Em7

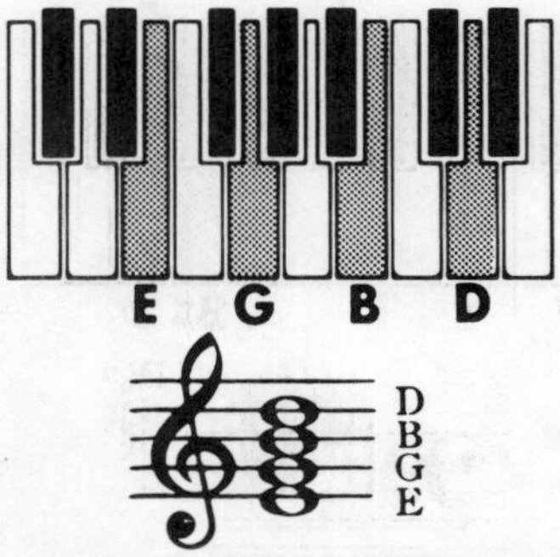

Edim7

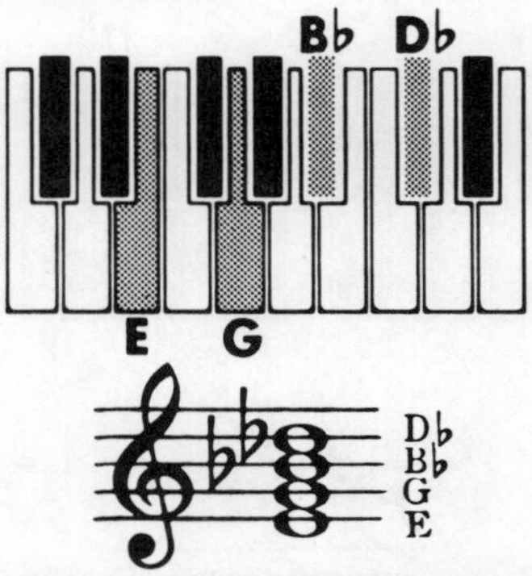

Emaj7

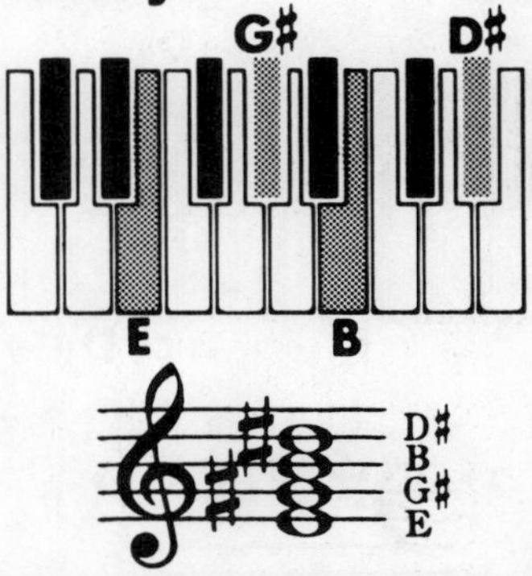

E7#5

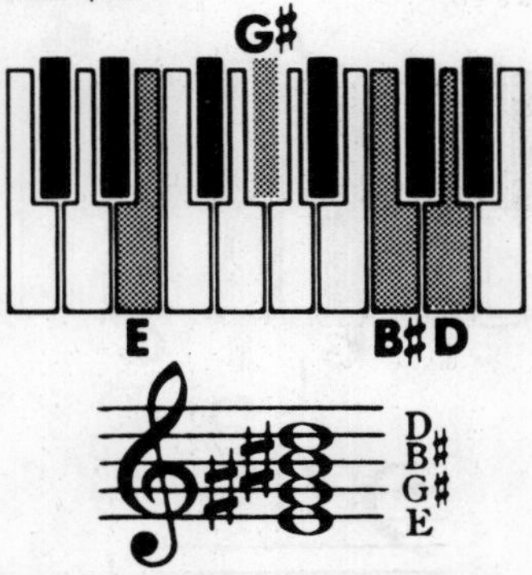

E7♭5

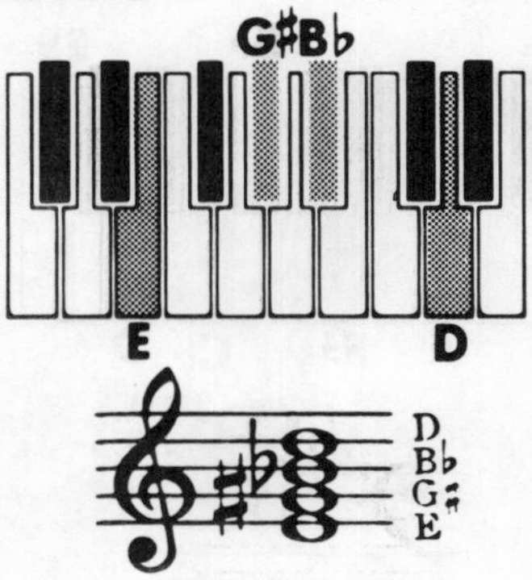

E7(sus)

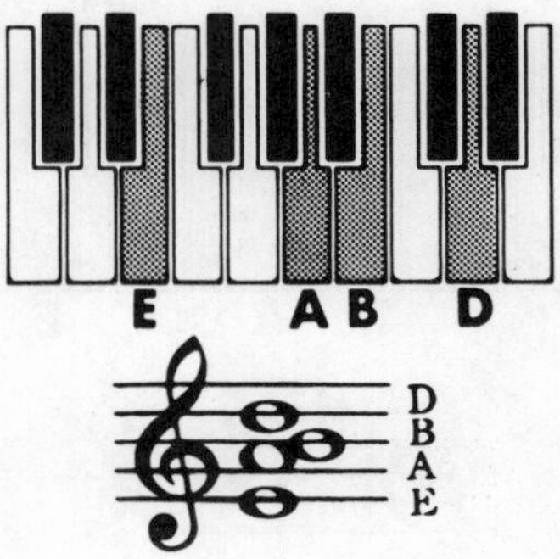

Emaj7#5

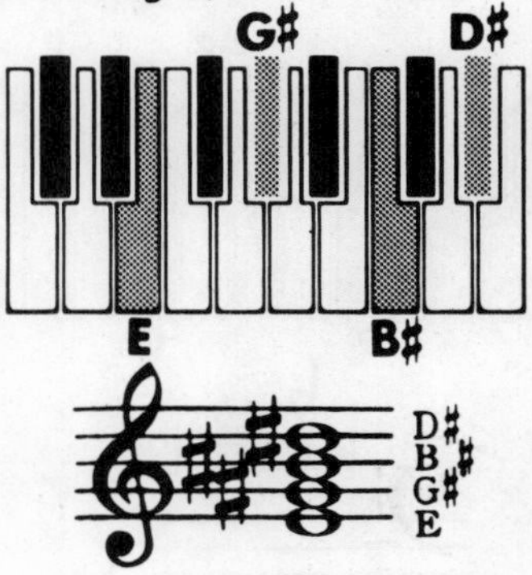

Em7♭5

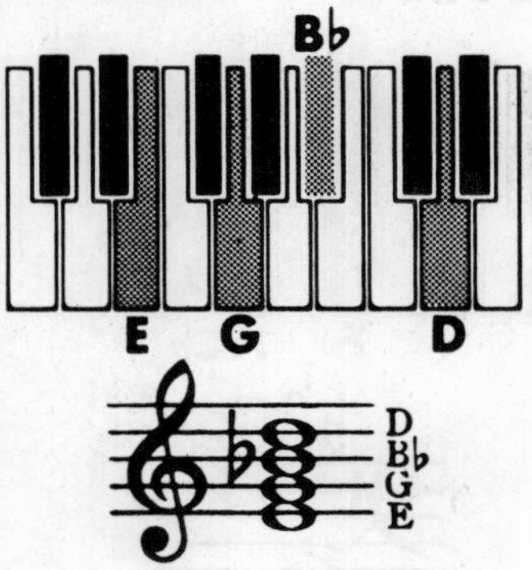

Left Hand Chords On F

𝄢 F

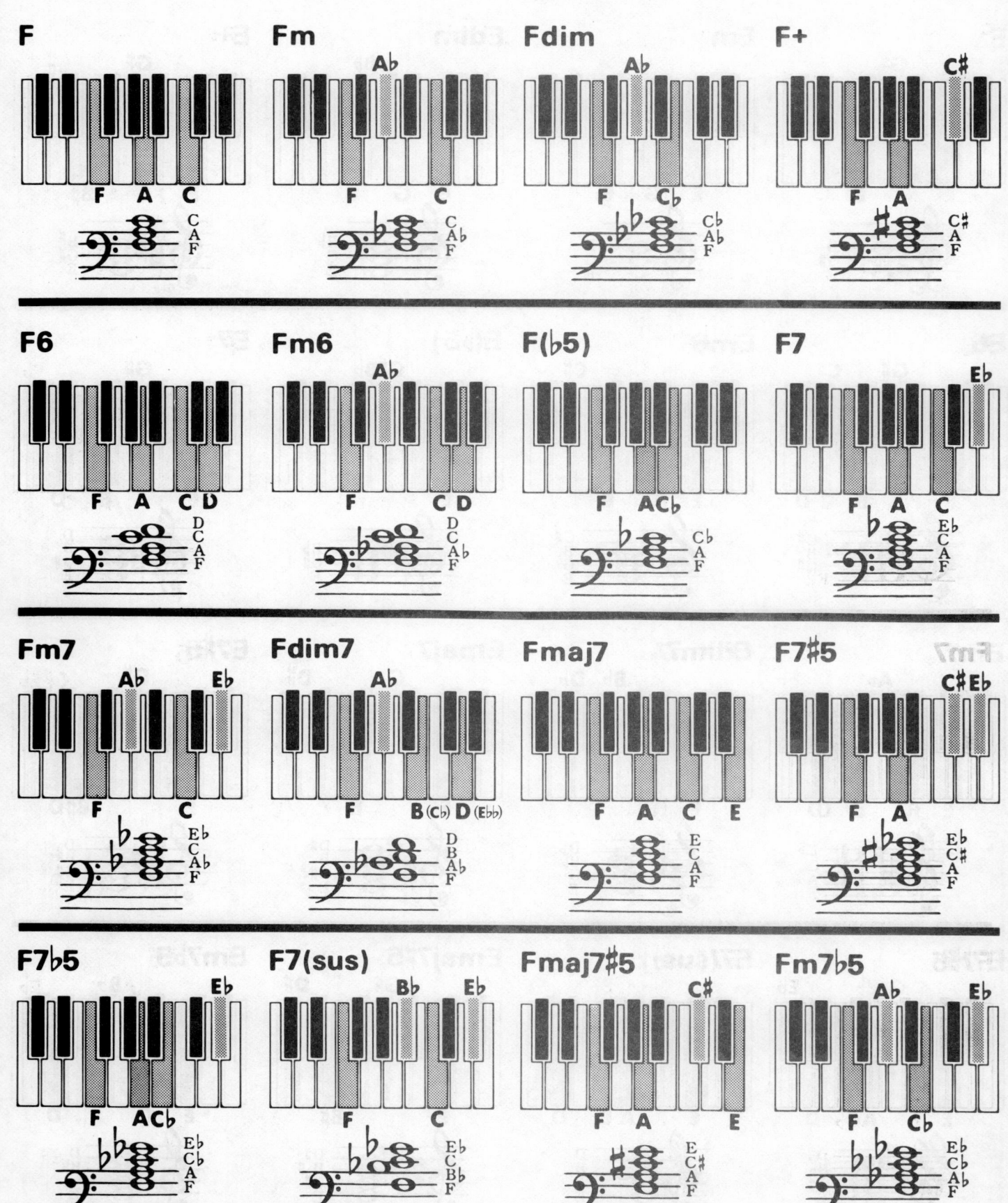

Right Hand Chords On F

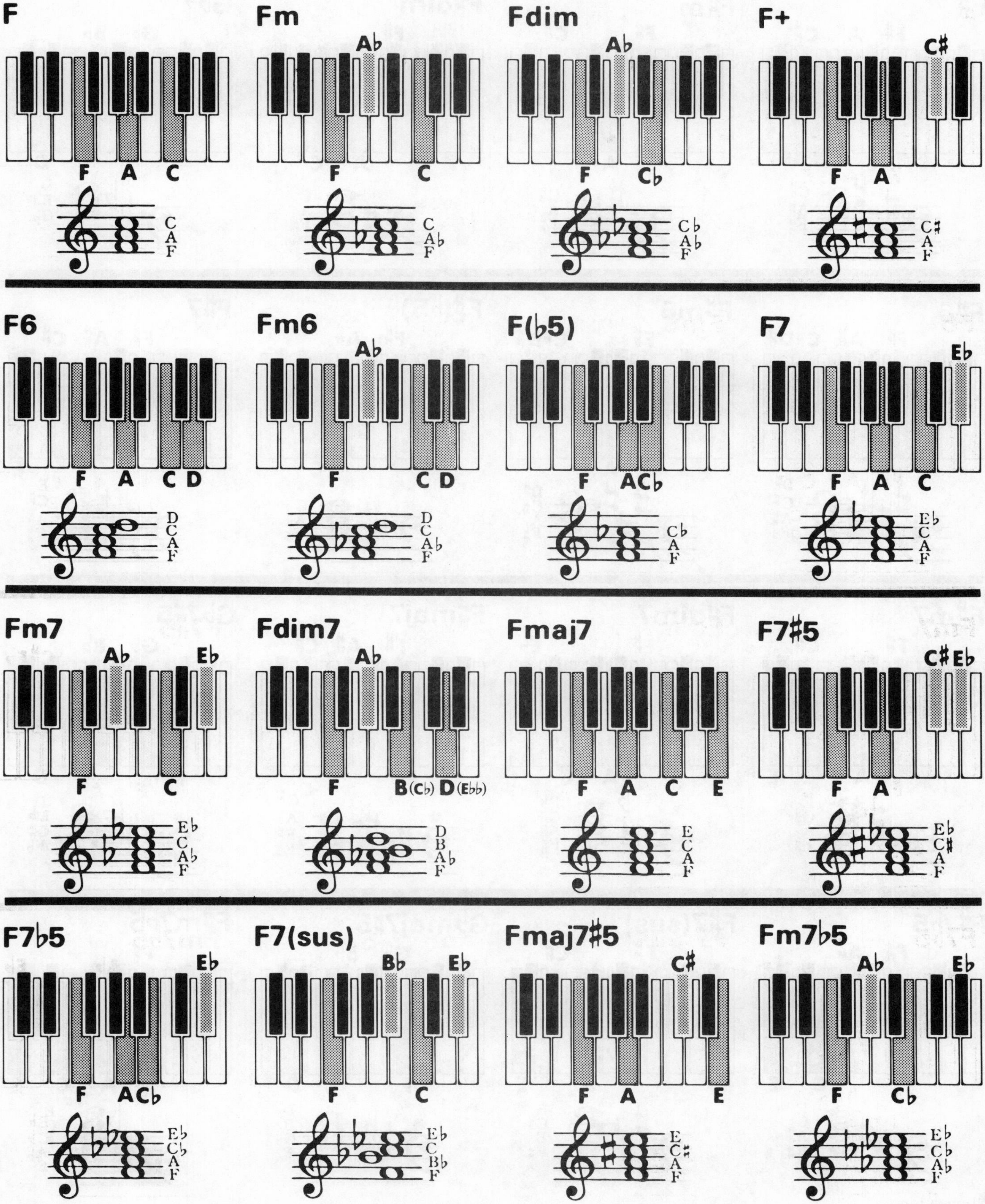

Left Hand Chords On F♯(G♭)

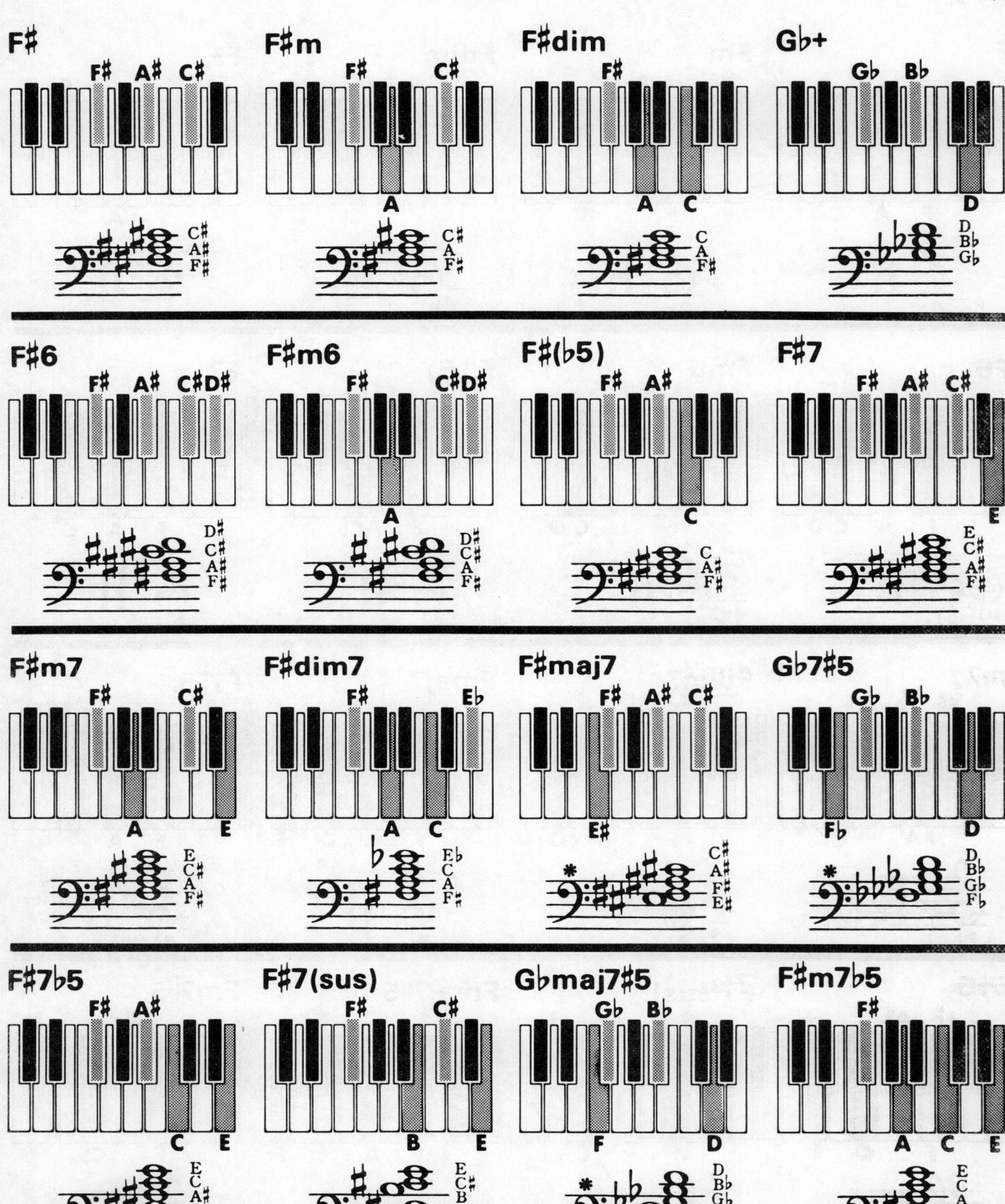

*Inversion

Right Hand Chords On F♯(G♭)

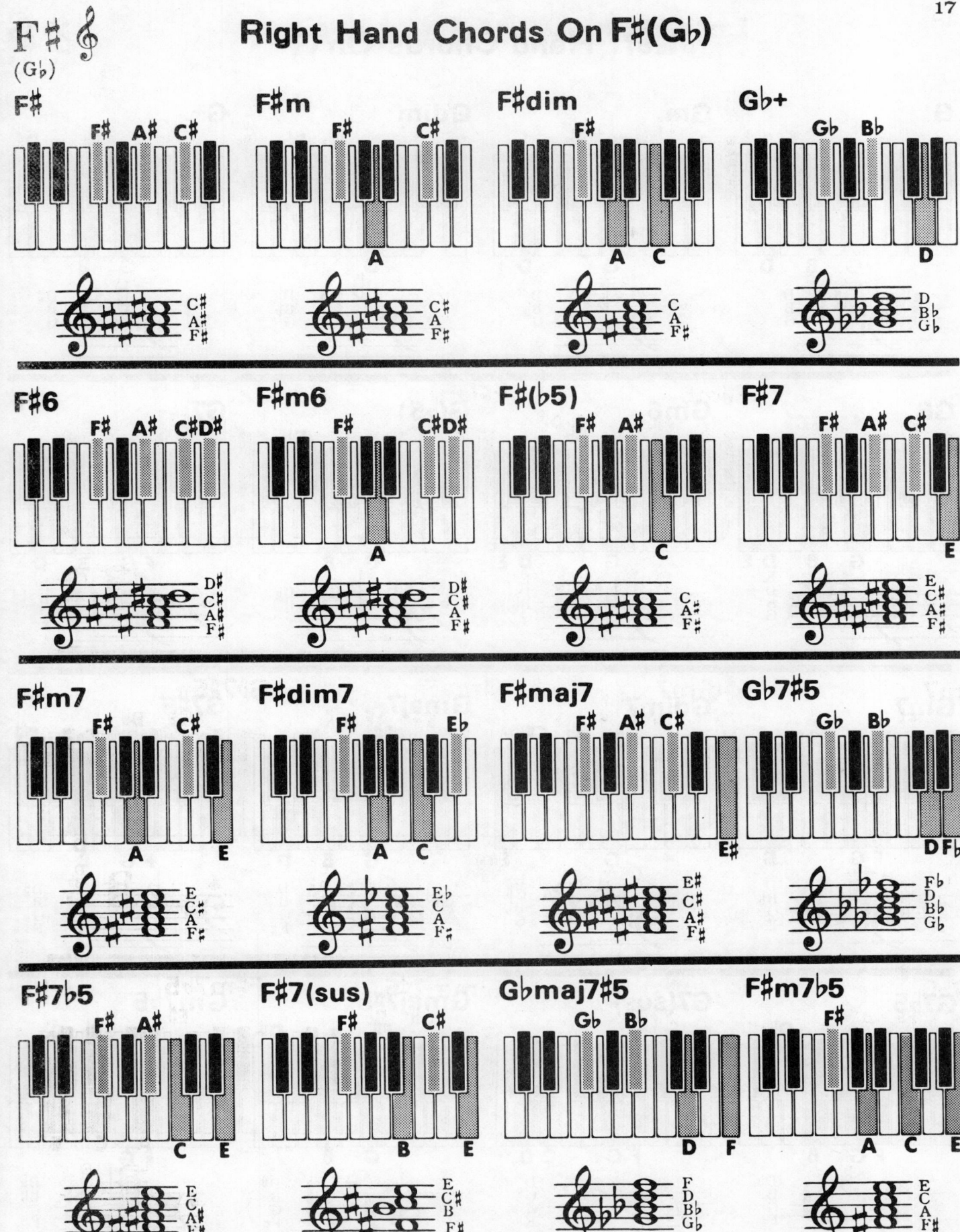

Left Hand Chords On G

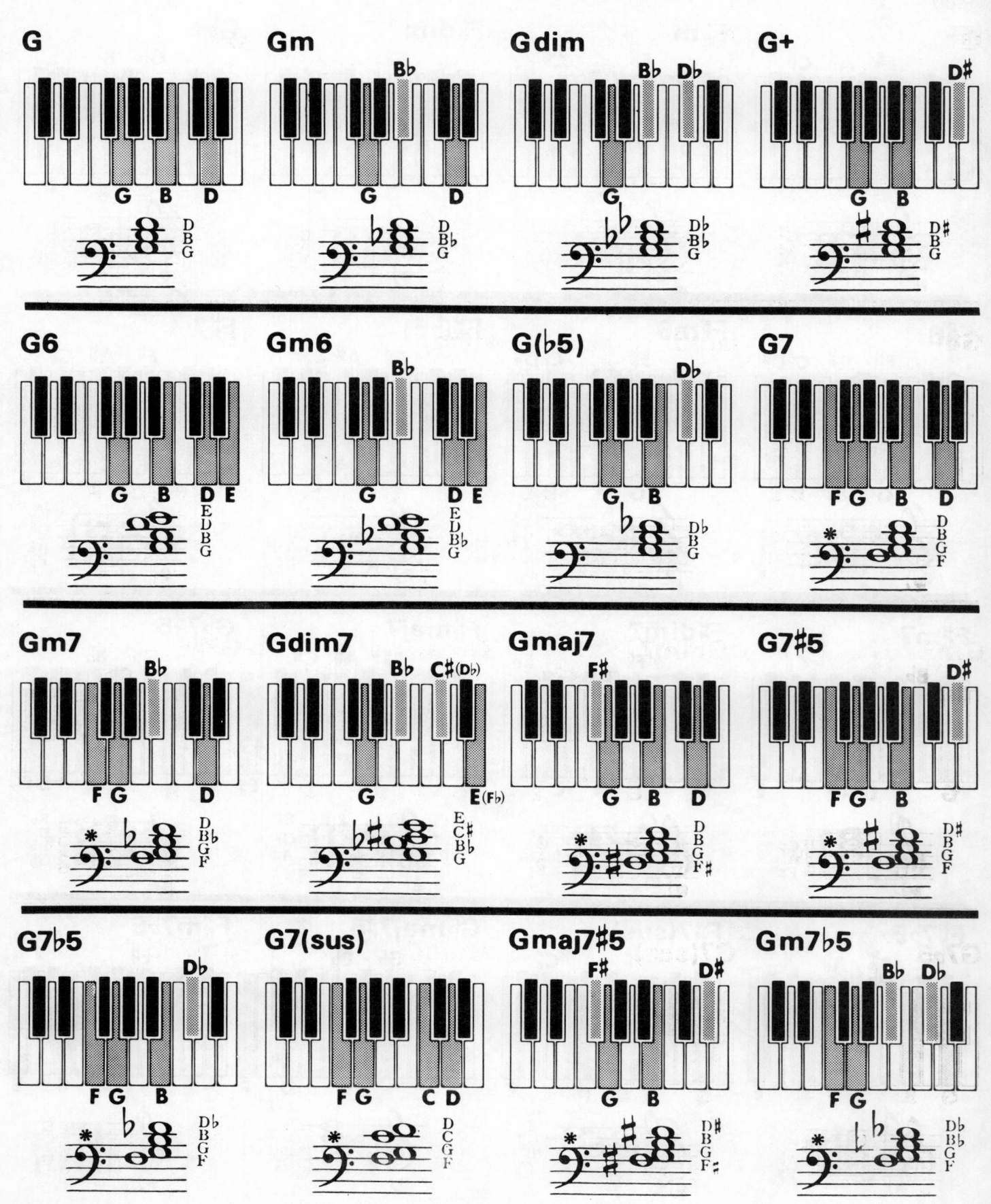

*Inversion

Right Hand Chords On G

G

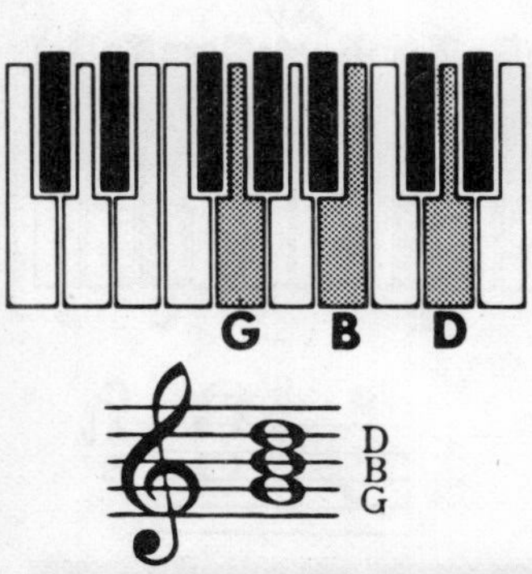

Gm

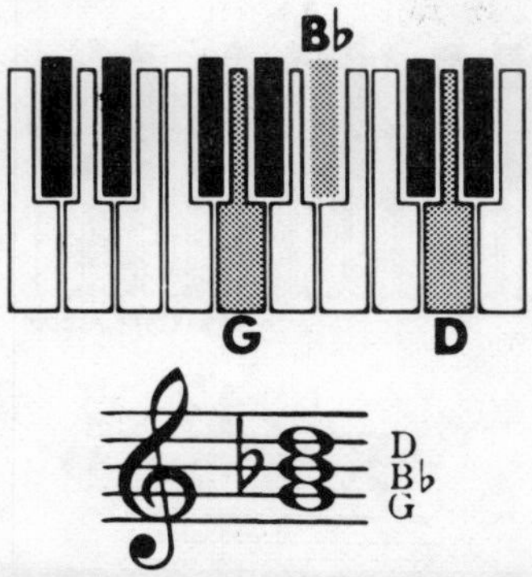

G dim

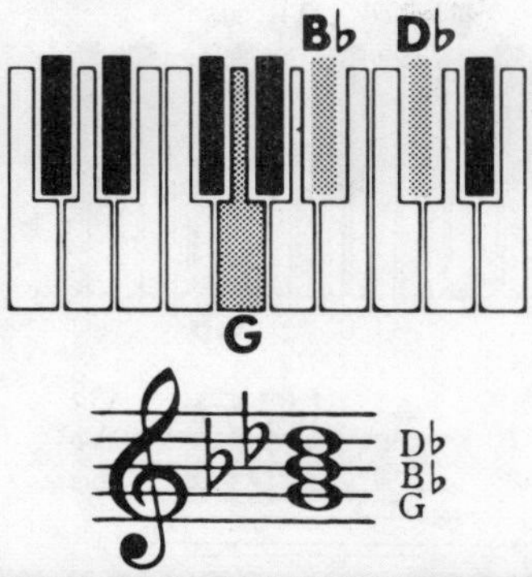

G+

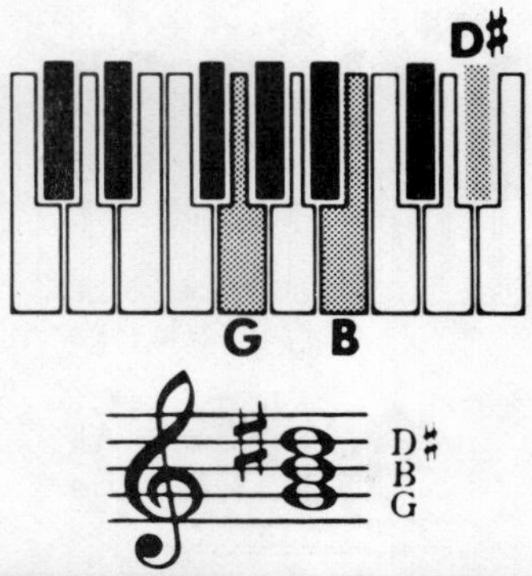

G6

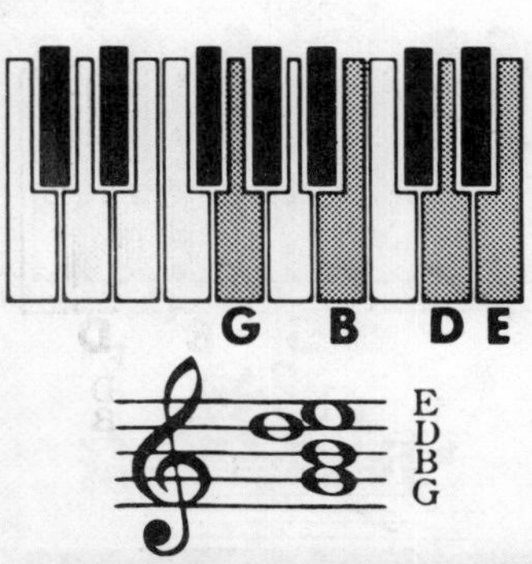

Gm6

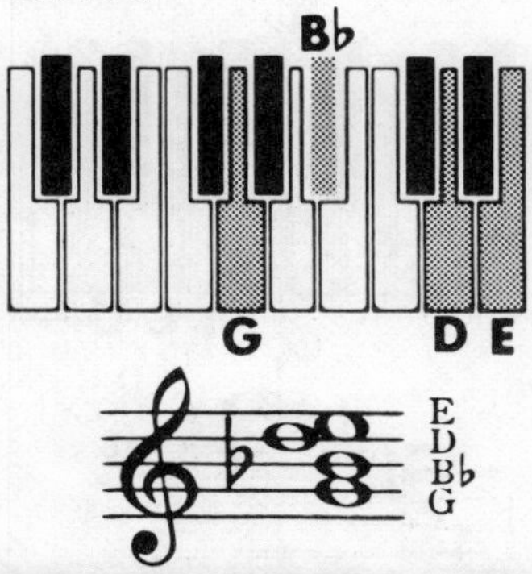

G(♭5)

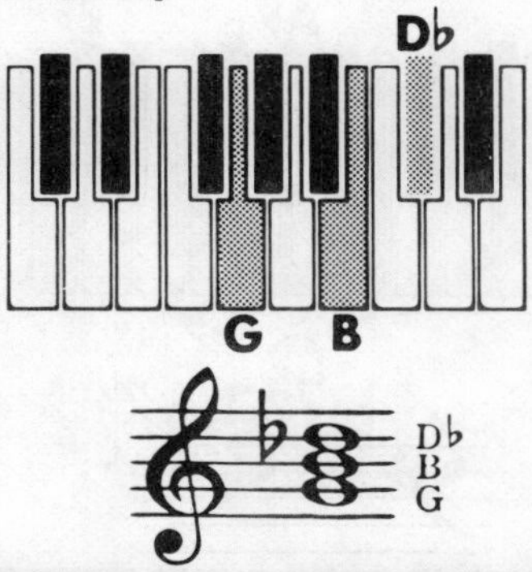

G7

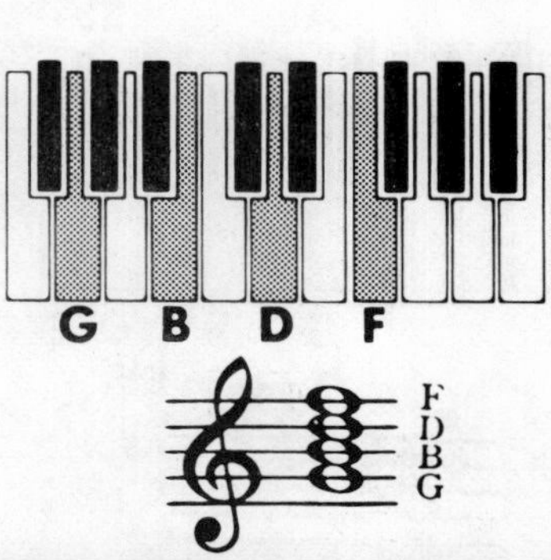

Gm7

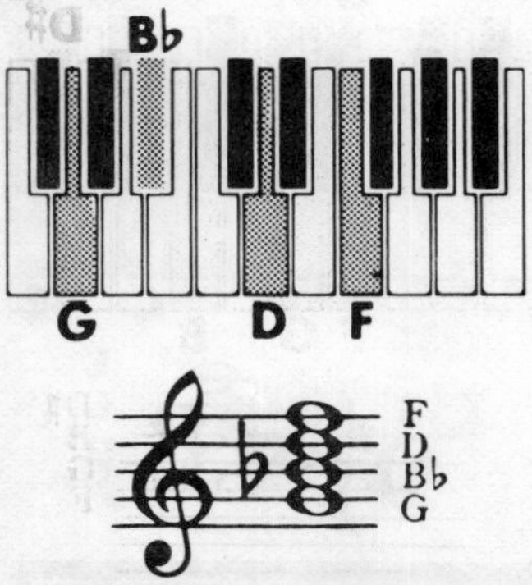

Gdim7

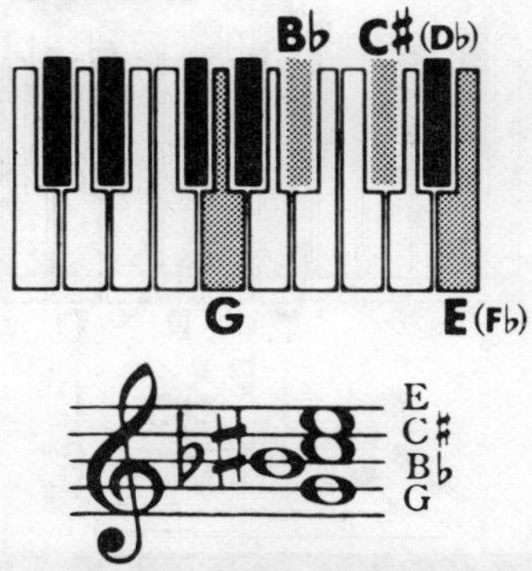

Gmaj7

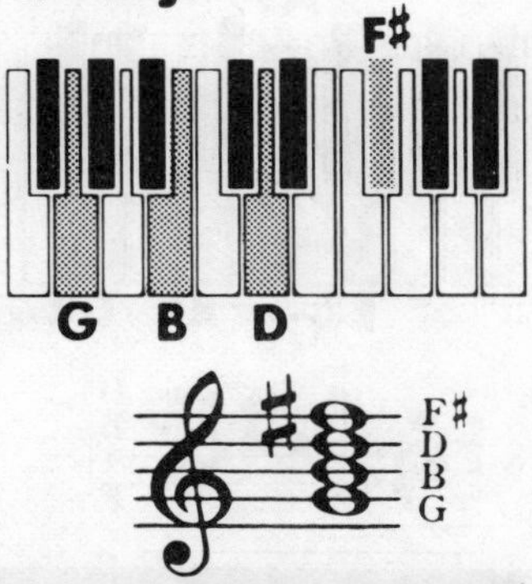

G7♯5

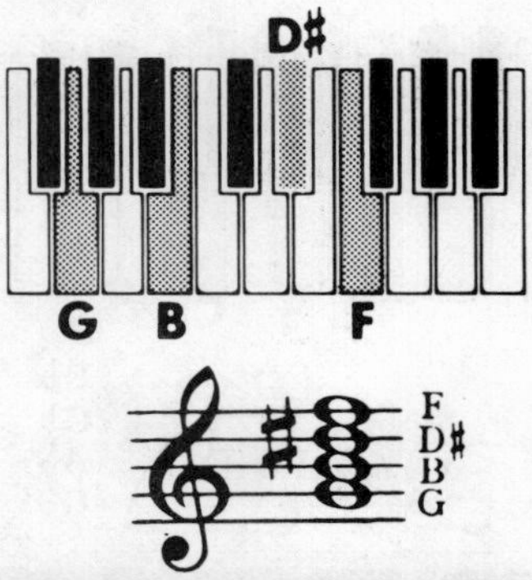

G7♭5

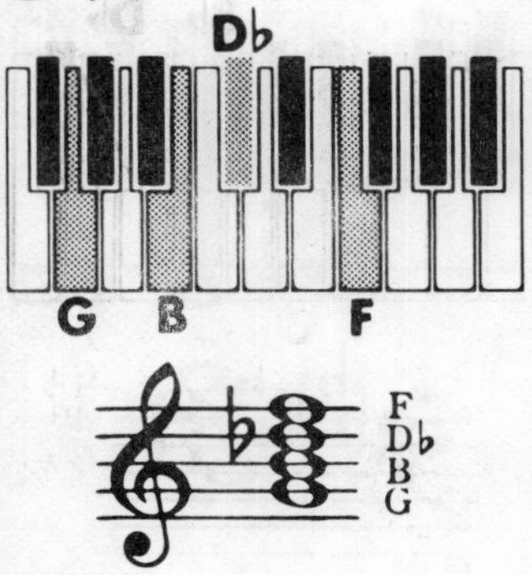

G7(sus)

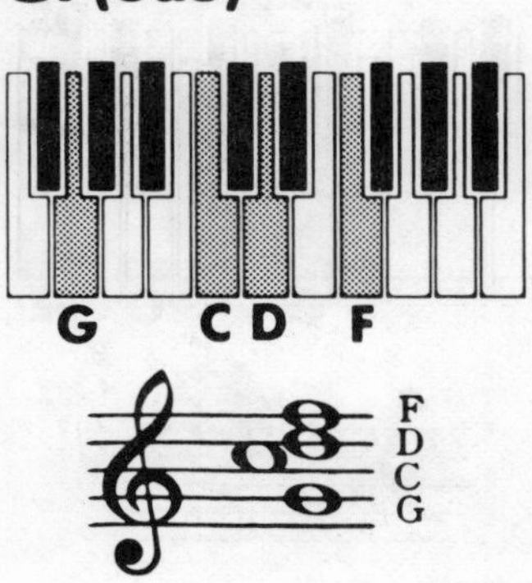

Gmaj7♯5

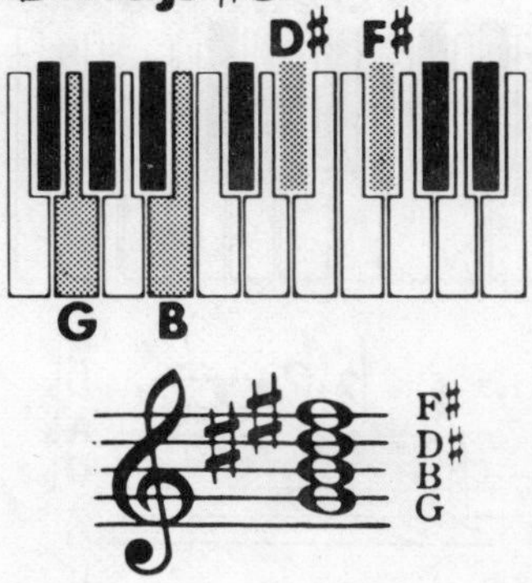

Gm7♭5

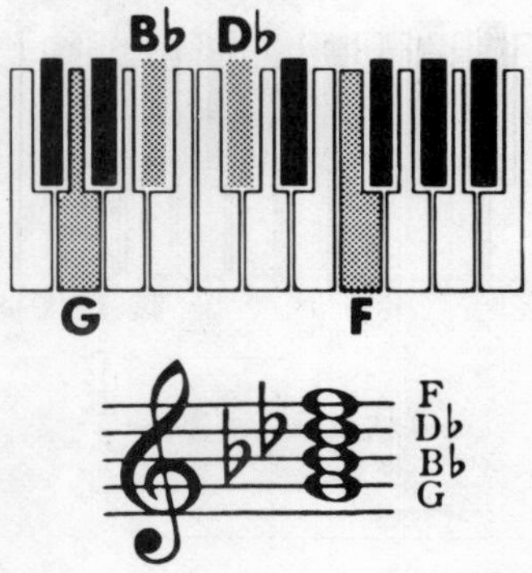

Left Hand Chords On Ab

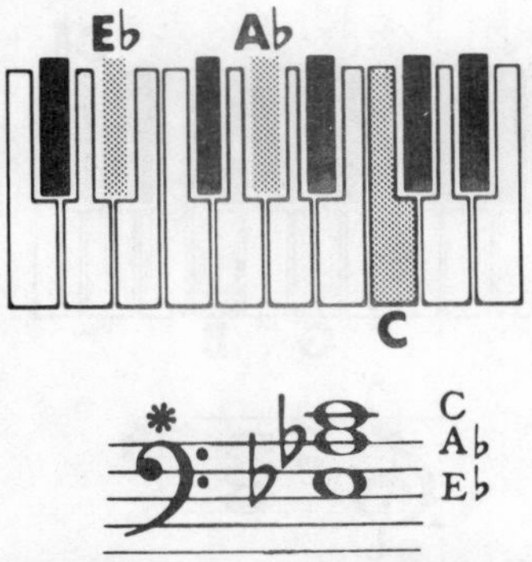

𝄢 Ab

Ab
Eb · Ab
C
C
Ab
Eb

Abm
Eb · Ab
Cb
Cb
Ab
Eb

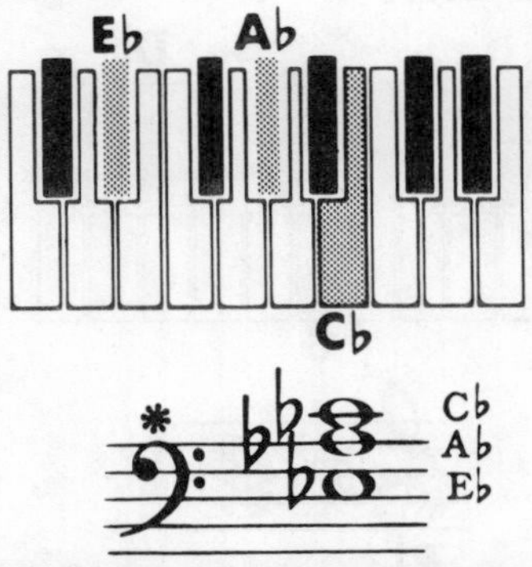

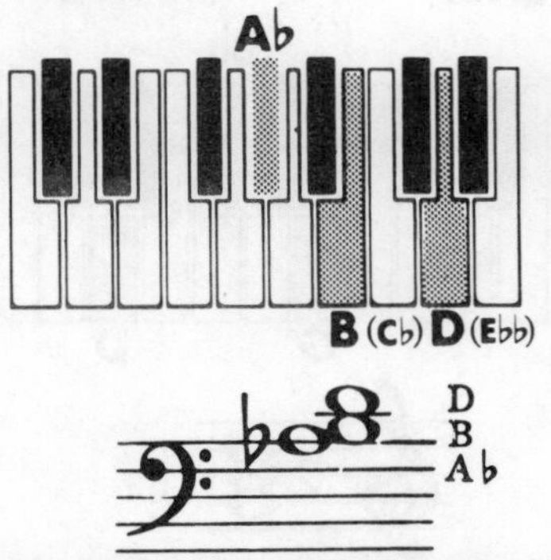

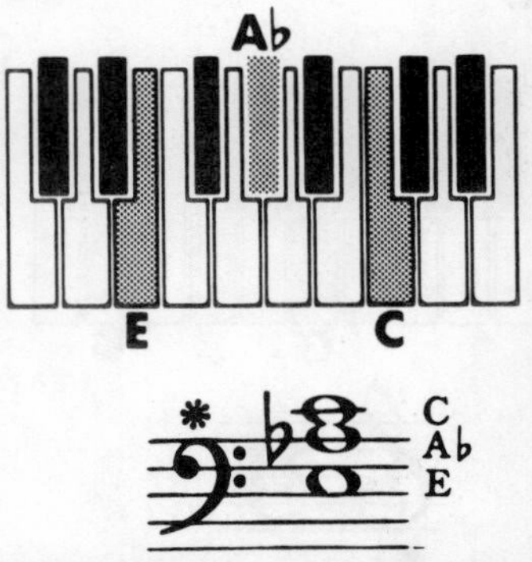

Abdim
Ab
B(Cb) D(Ebb)
D
B
Ab

Ab+
Ab
E · C
C
Ab
E

Ab6
Ab · Eb
F · C
Eb
C
Ab
F

Abm6
Ab · Eb
F · Cb
Eb
Cb
Ab
F

Ab(b5)
Ab
C D(Ebb)
D
C
Ab

Ab7
GbAb · Eb
C
Eb
C
Ab
Gb

Abm7
GbAb · Eb
Cb
Eb
Cb
Ab
Gb

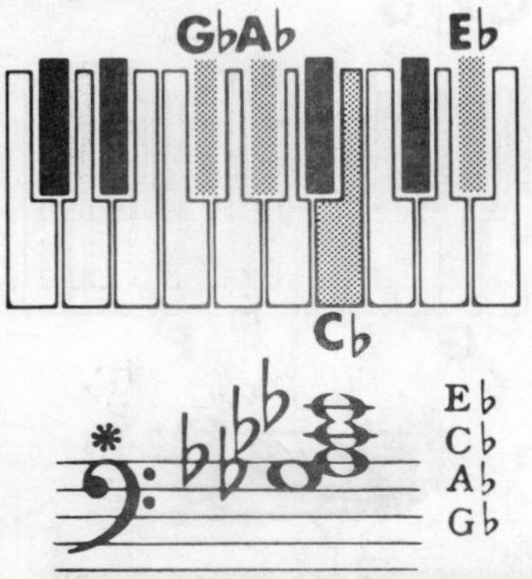

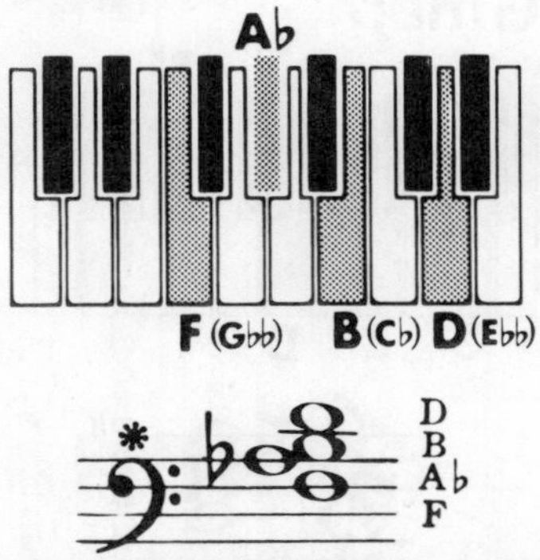

Abdim7
Ab
F(Gbb) B(Cb) D(Ebb)
D
B
A
F

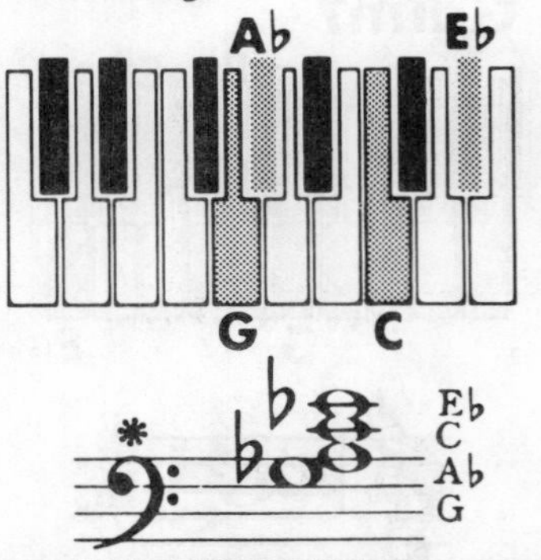

Abmaj7
Ab · Eb
G · C
Eb
C
Ab
G

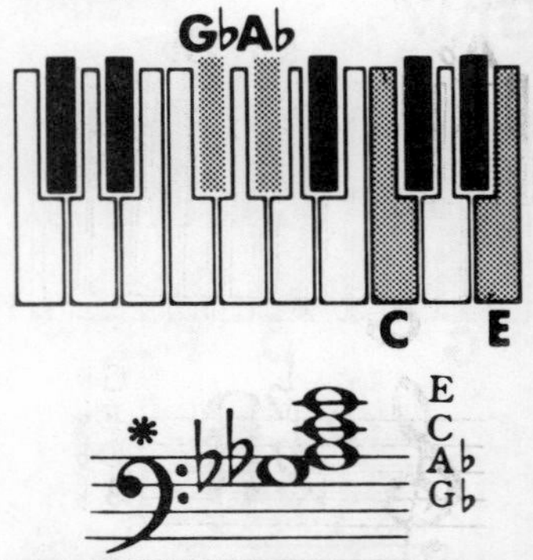

Ab7#5
GbAb
C E
E
C
Ab
Gb

Ab7b5
GbAb
C D(Ebb)
D
C
Ab
Gb

Ab7(sus)
GbAb · DbEb
Eb
Db
Ab
Gb

Abmaj7#5
Ab
G C E
E
C
A
G

Abm7b5
GbAb
Cb D(Ebb)
D
Cb
Ab
Gb

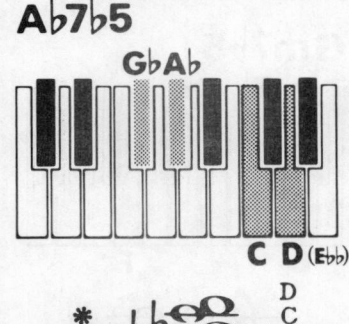
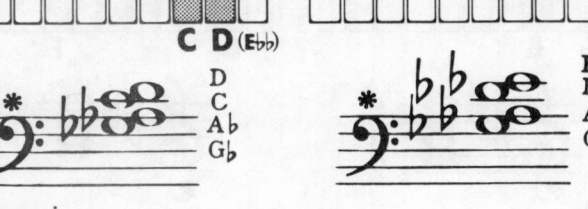
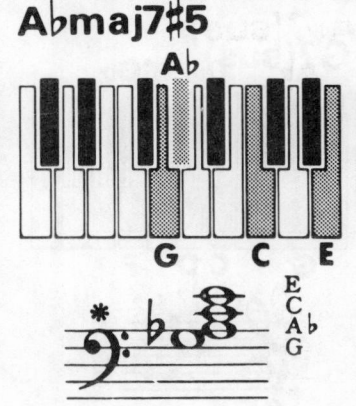
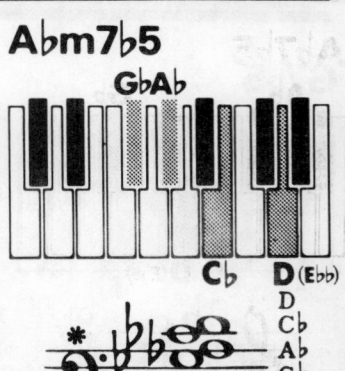

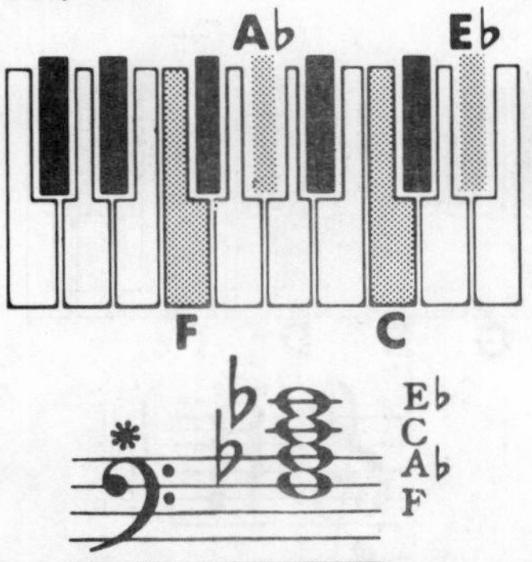

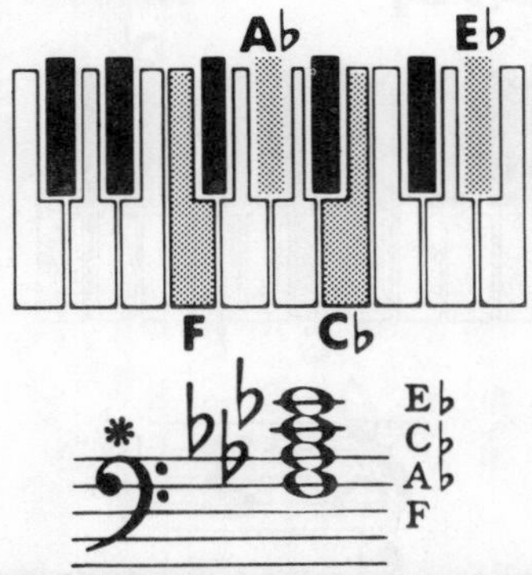

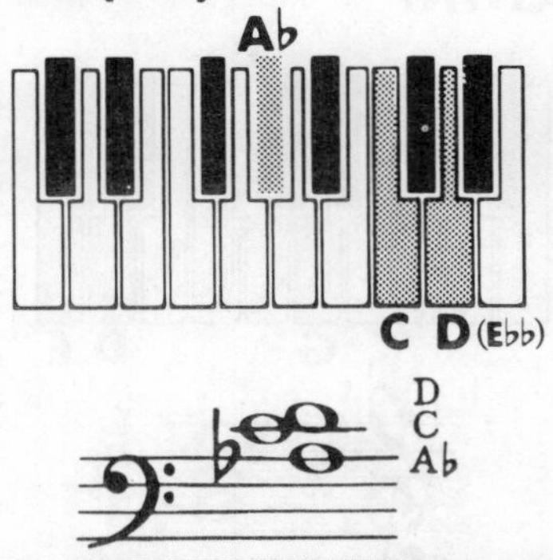

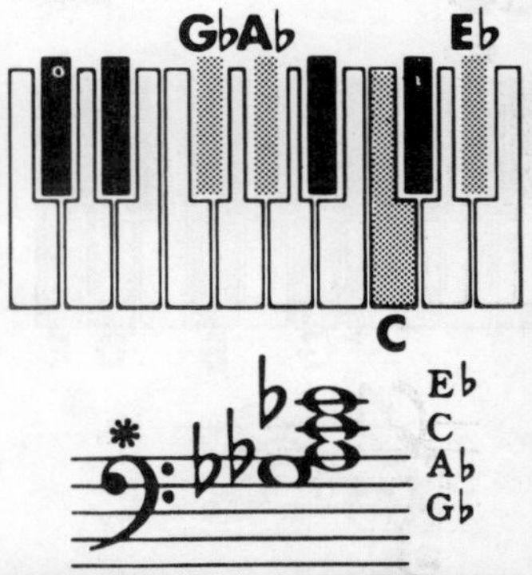

*Inversion

Ab   **Abm**   **Abdim**   **Ab+**

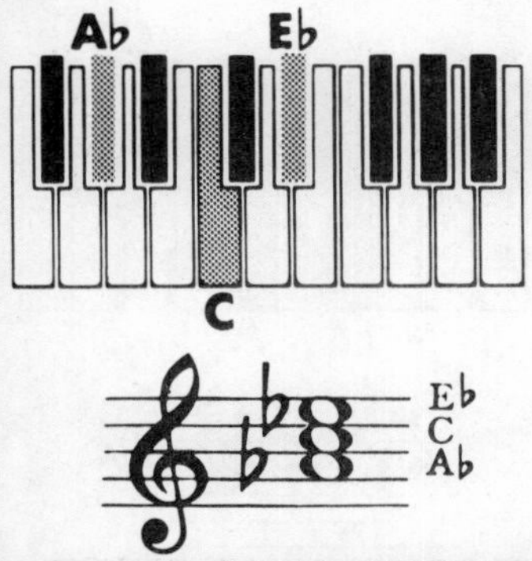

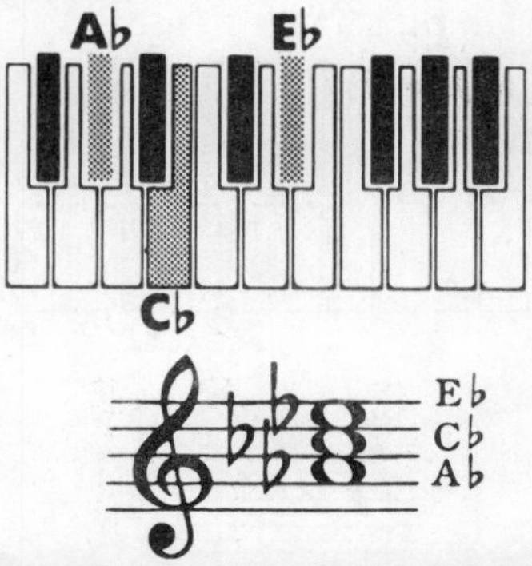

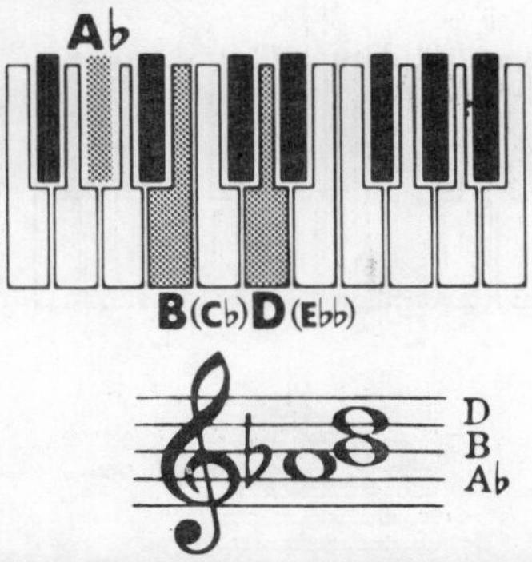

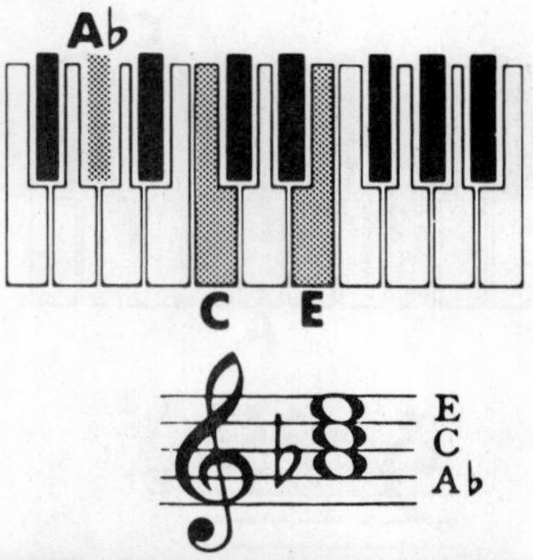

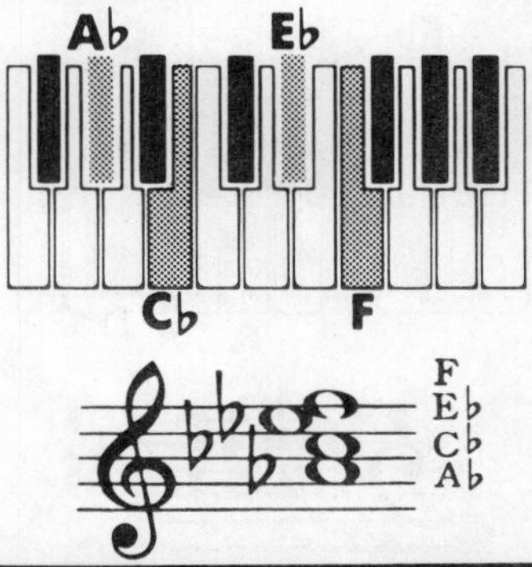

Ab6   **Abm6**   **Ab(b5)**   **Ab7**

Abm7   **Abdim7**   **Abmaj7**   **Ab7#5**

Ab7b5   **Ab7(sus)**   **Abmaj7#5**   **Abm7b5**

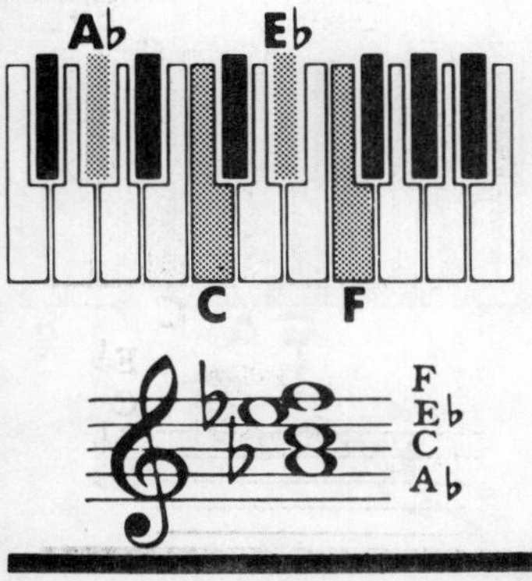

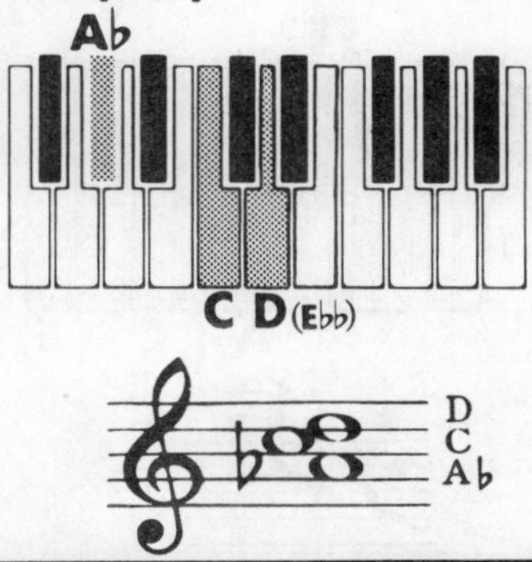

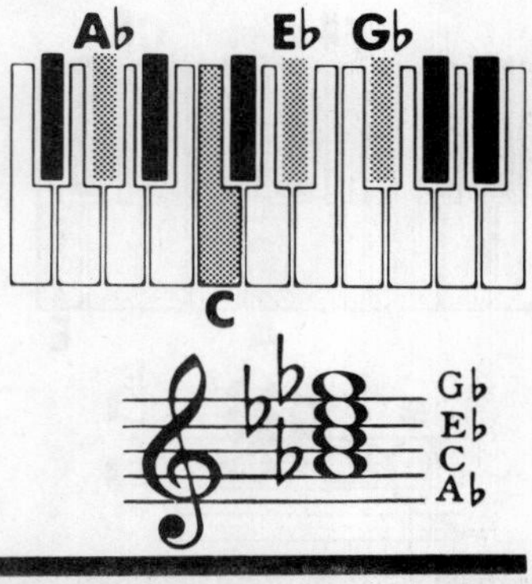

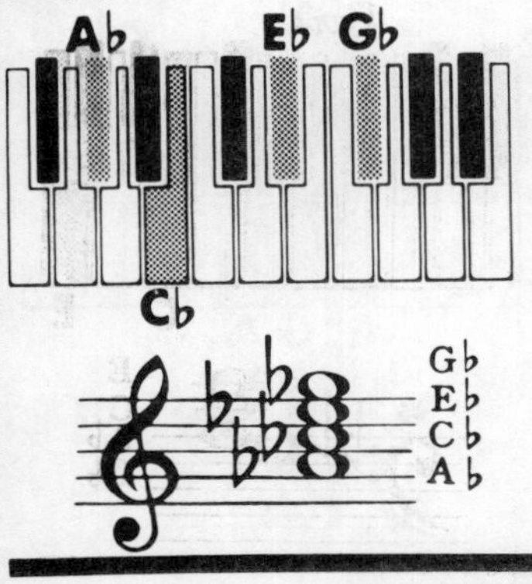

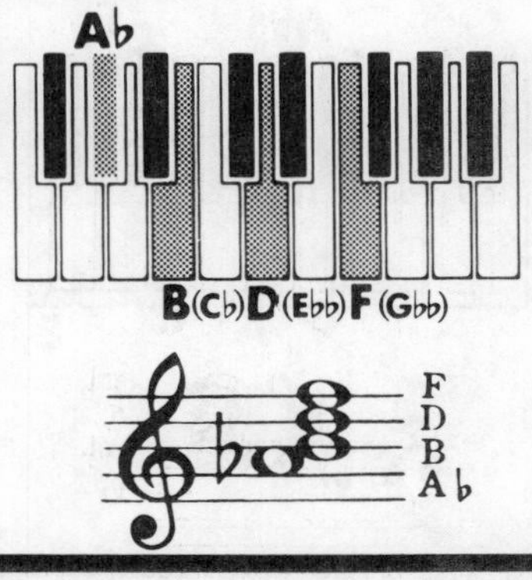

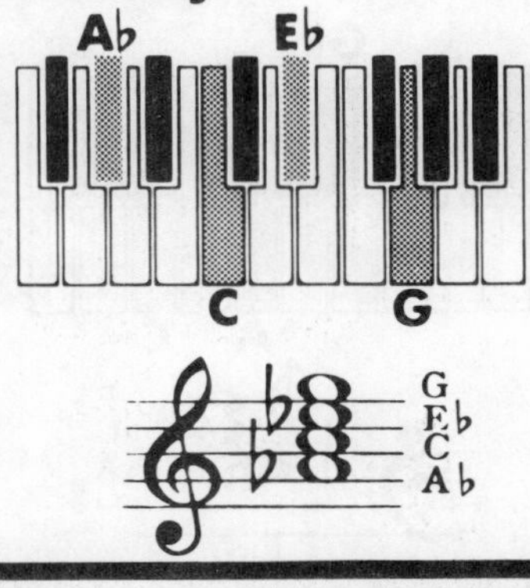

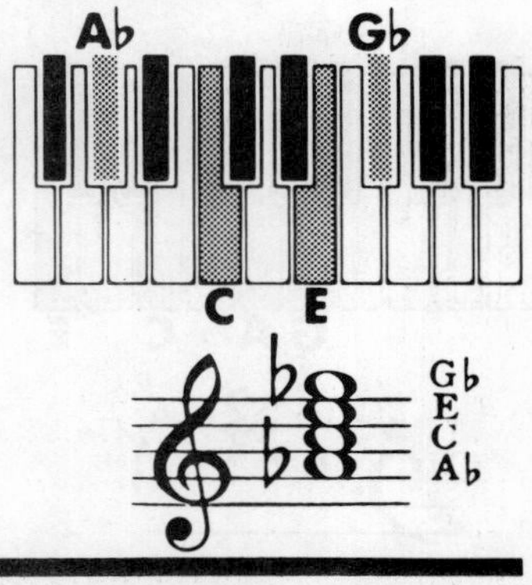

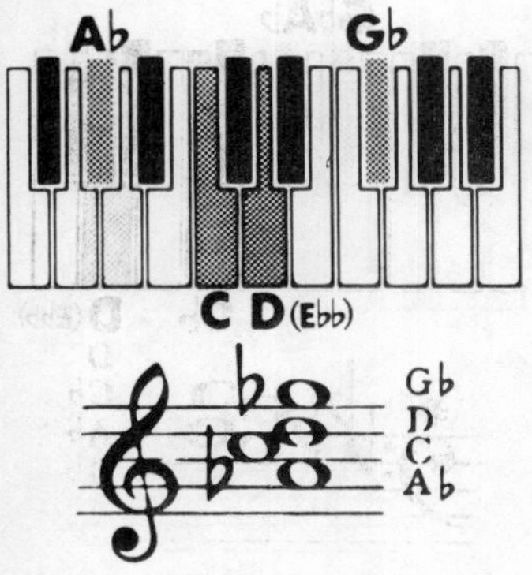

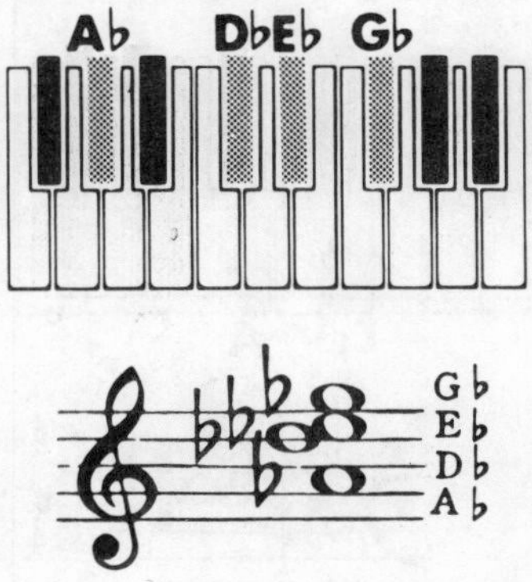

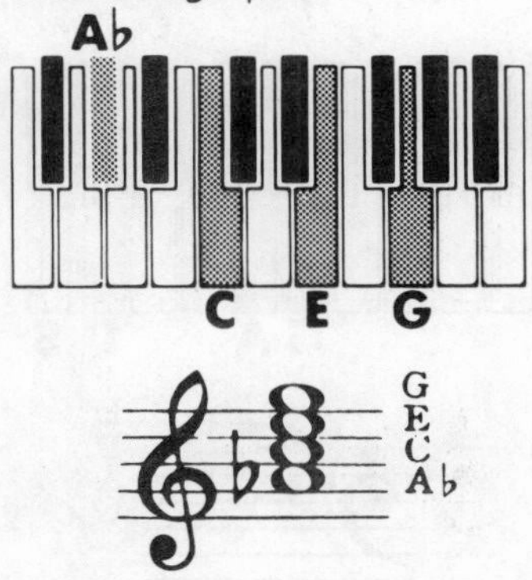

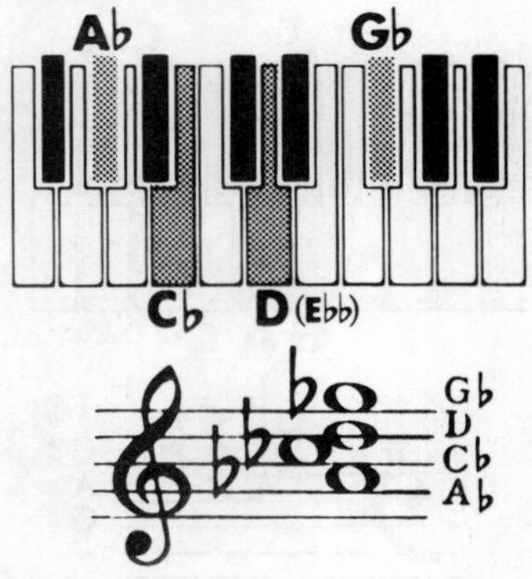

Left Hand Chords On A

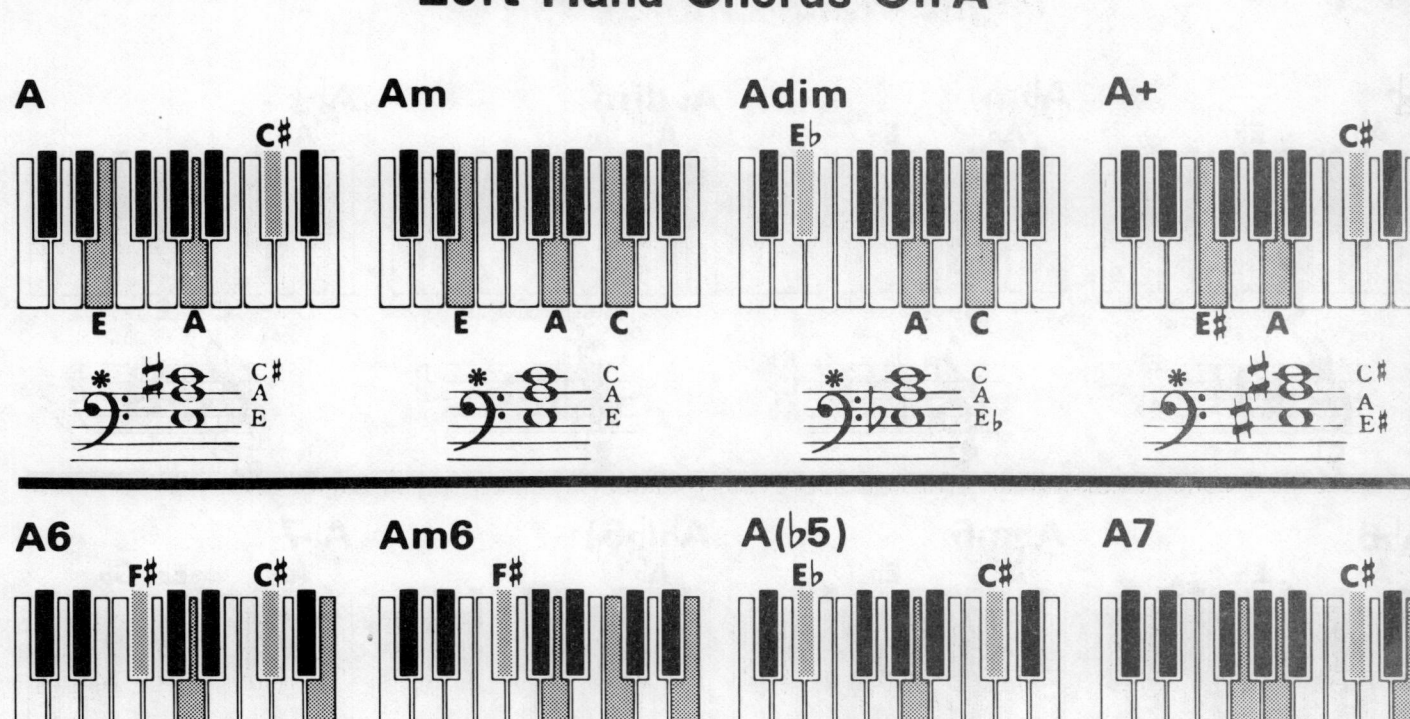

A	Am	Adim	A+
A6	Am6	A(♭5)	A7
Am7	Adim7	Amaj7	A7#5
A7♭5	A7(sus)	Amaj7#5	Am7♭5

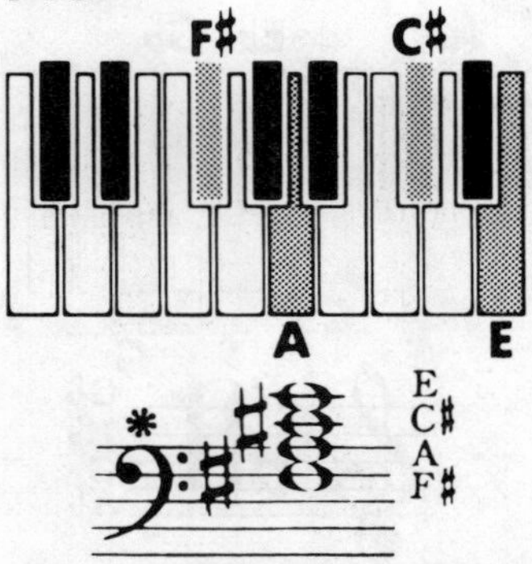

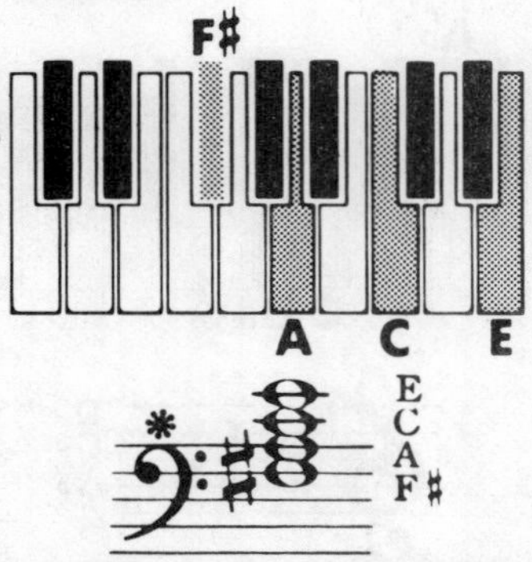

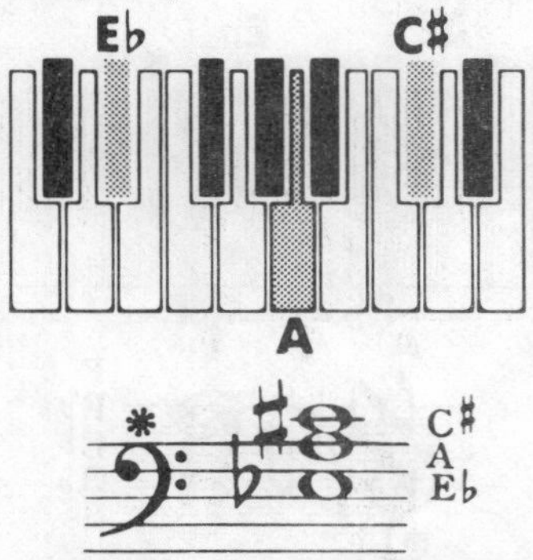

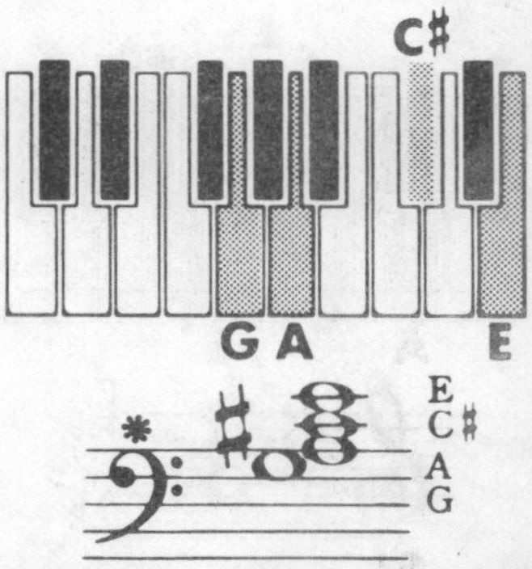

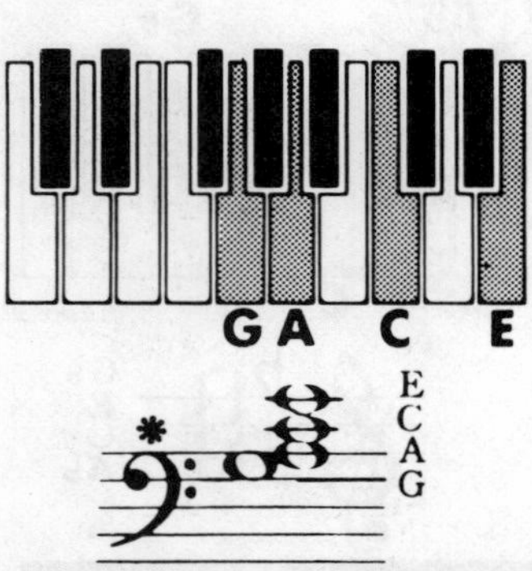

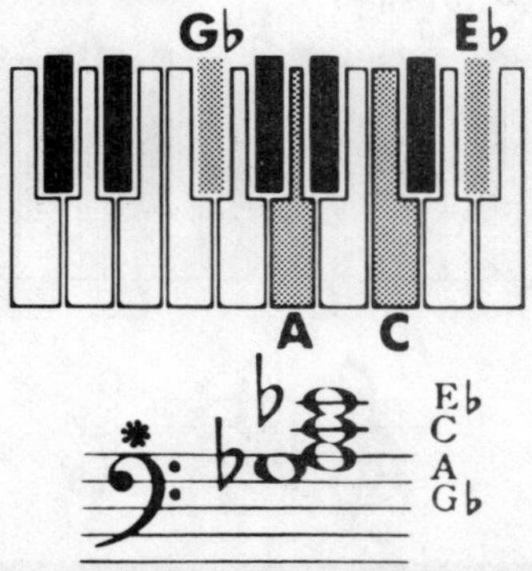

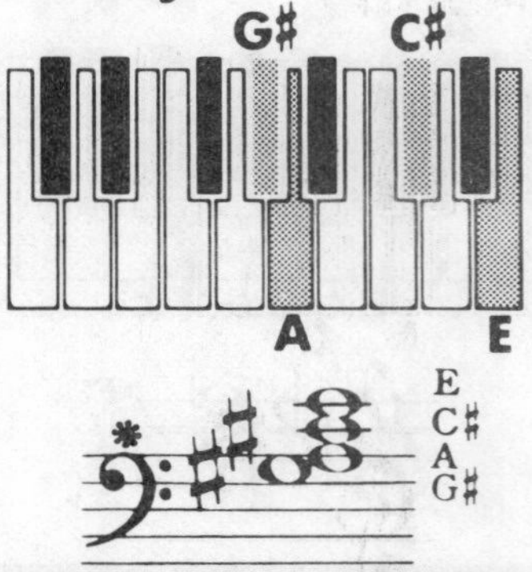

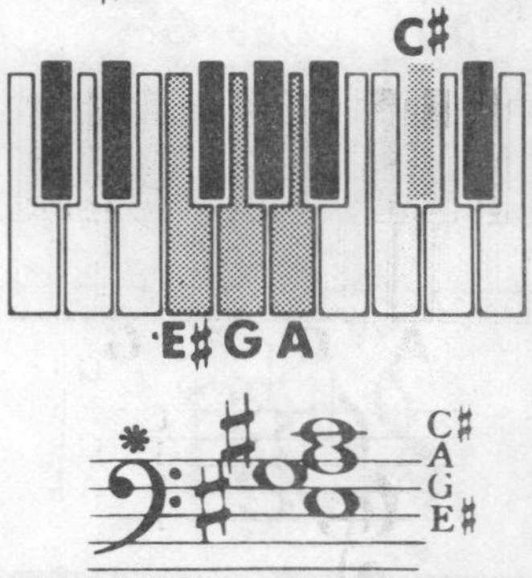

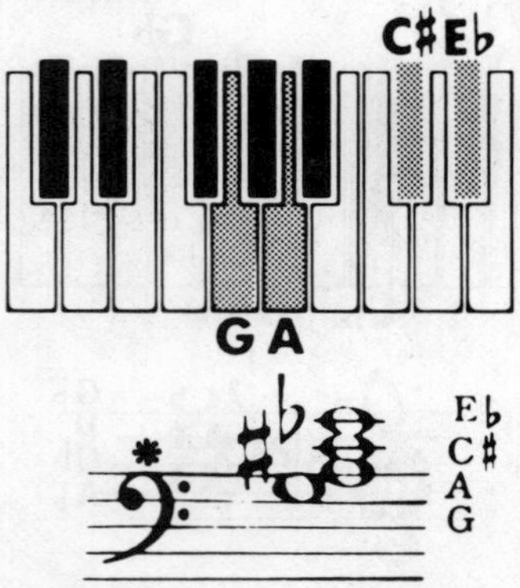

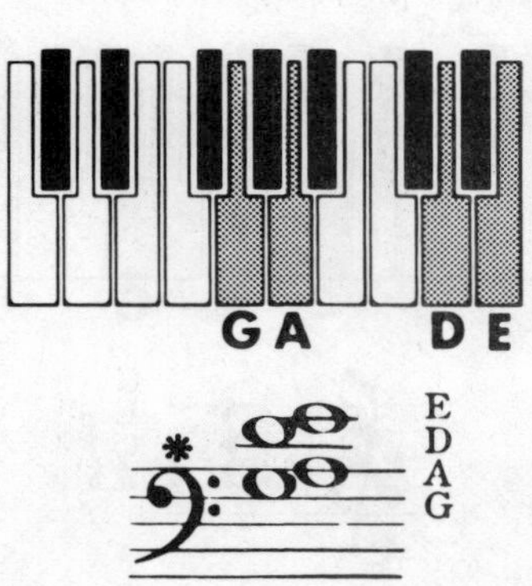

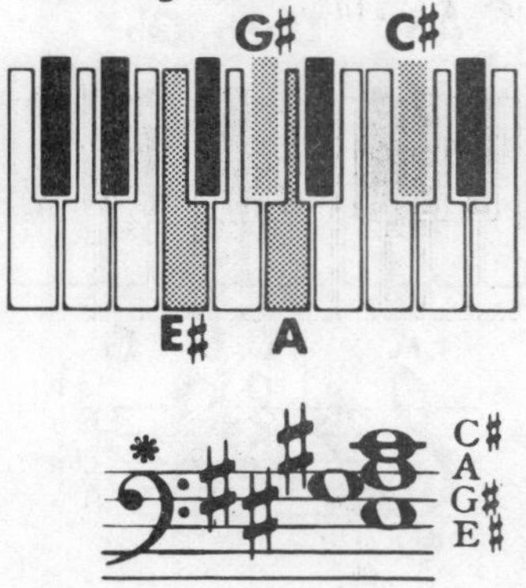

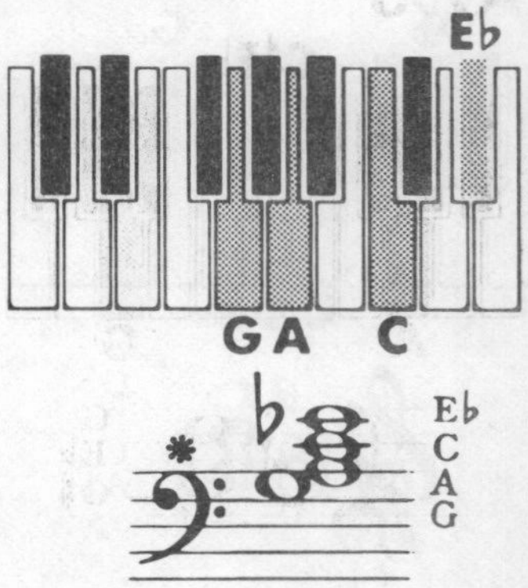

＊ Inversion

Right Hand Chords On A

A

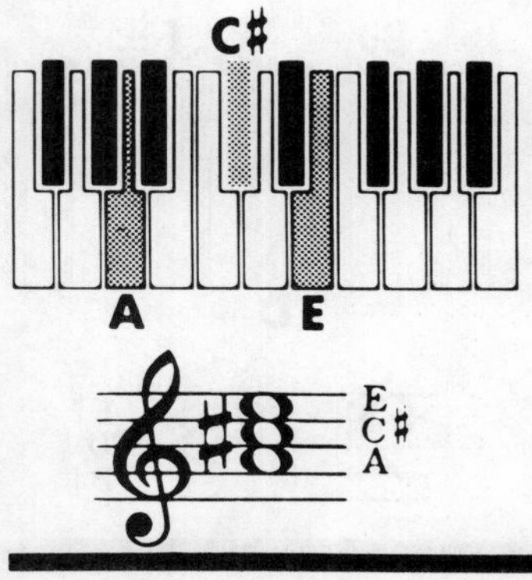

Am

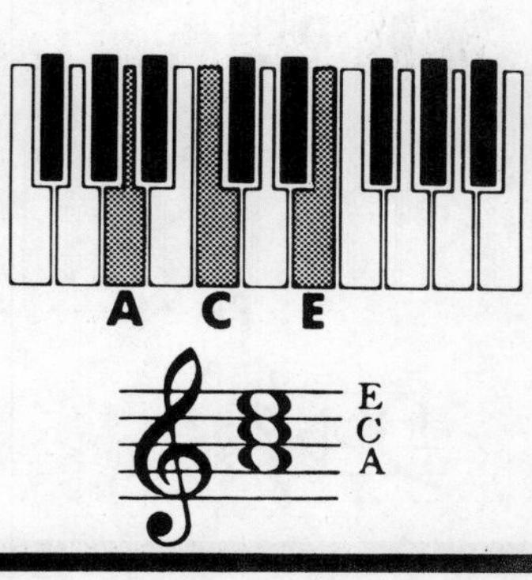

Adim

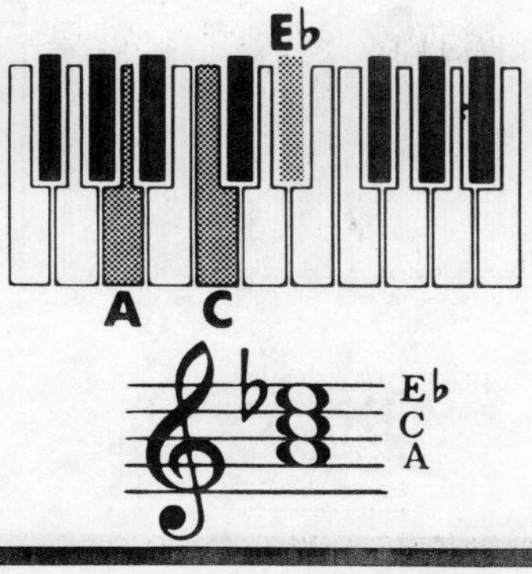

A+

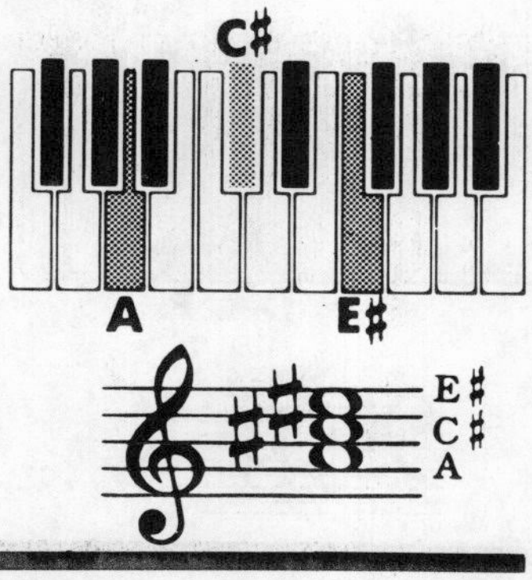

A6

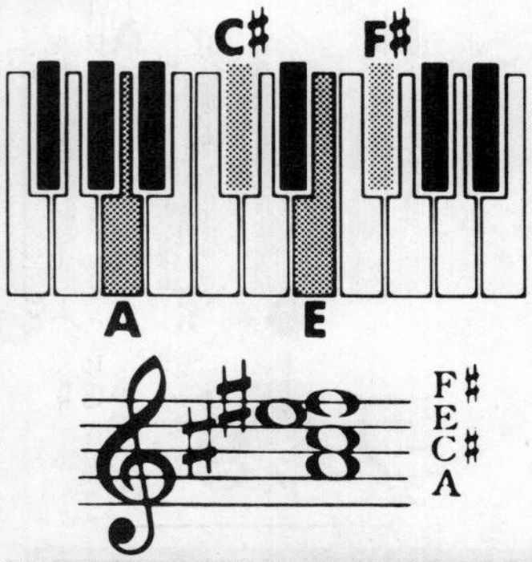

Am6

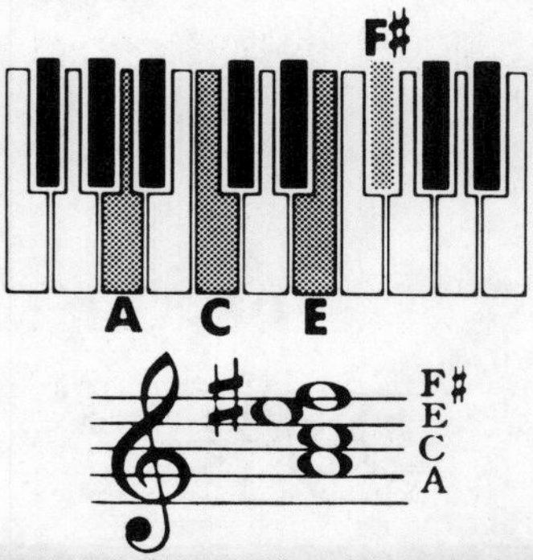

A(♭5)

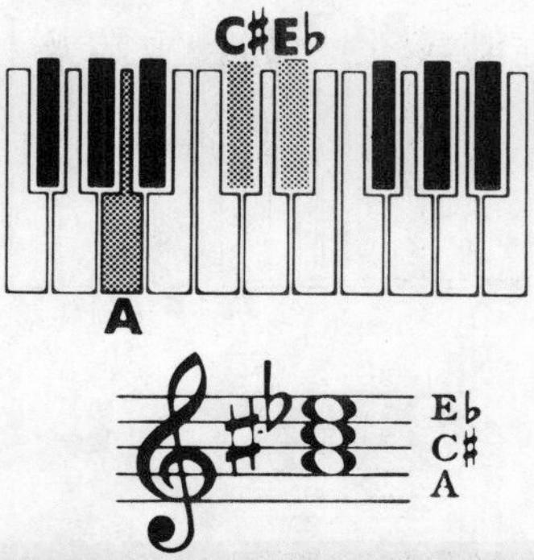

A7

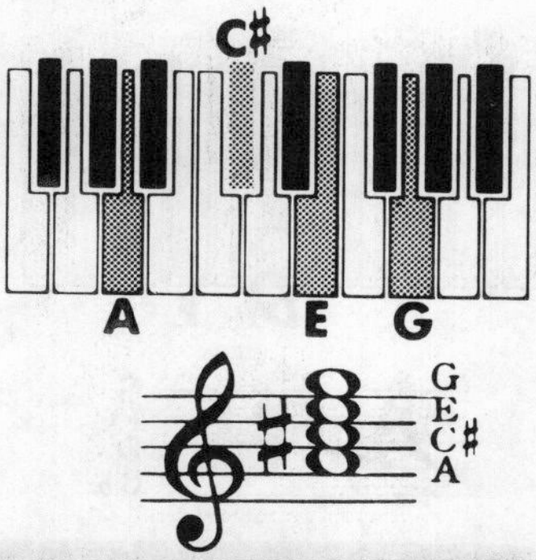

Am7

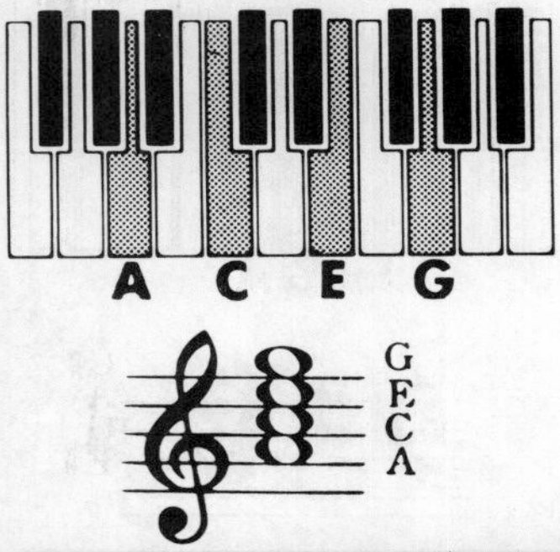

Adim7

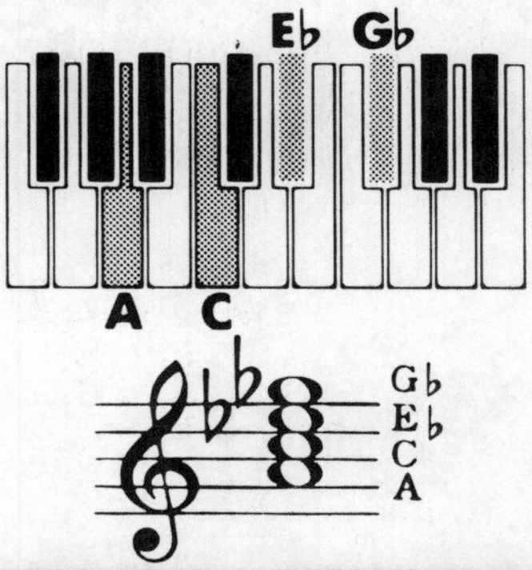

Amaj7

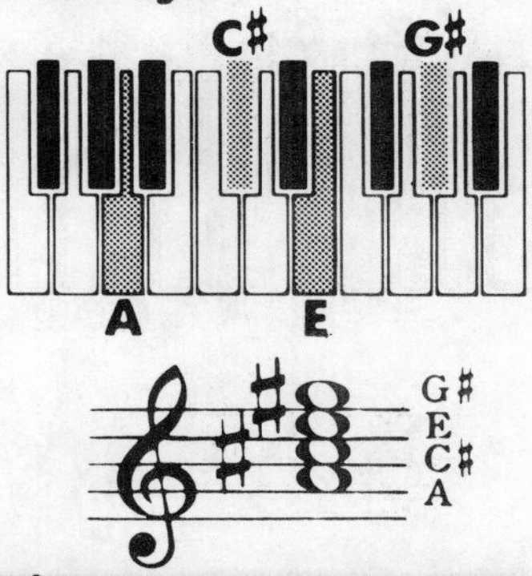

A7♯5

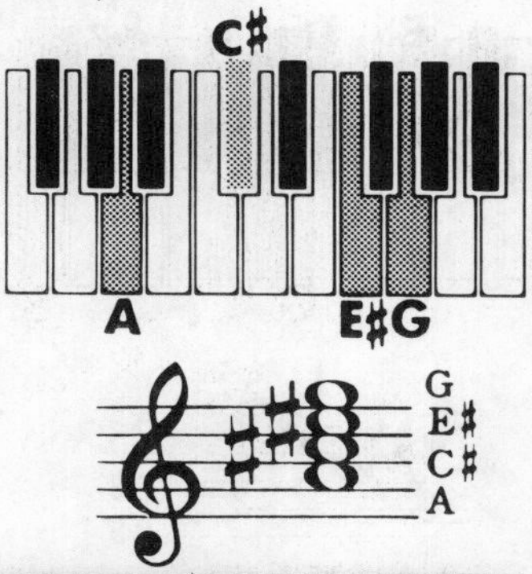

A7♭5

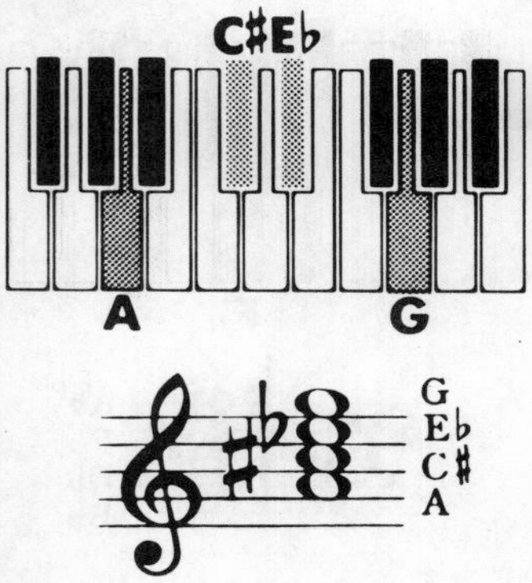

A7(sus)

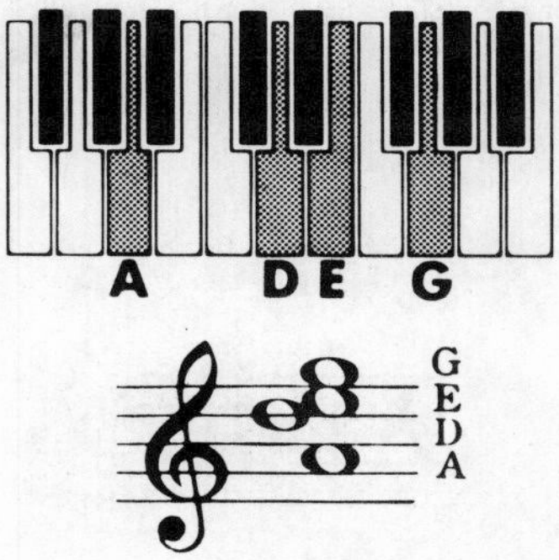

Amaj7♯5

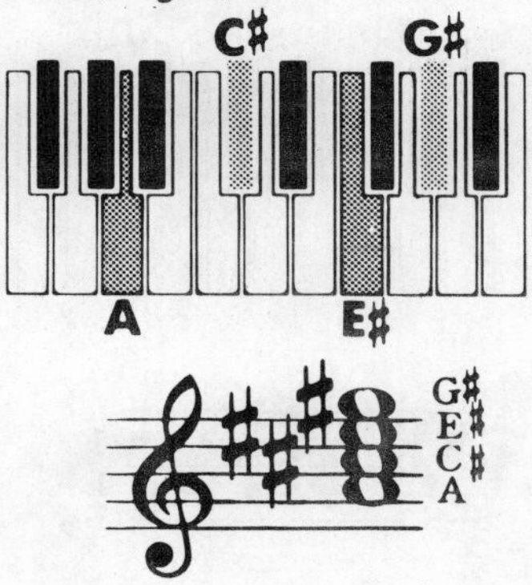

Am7♭5

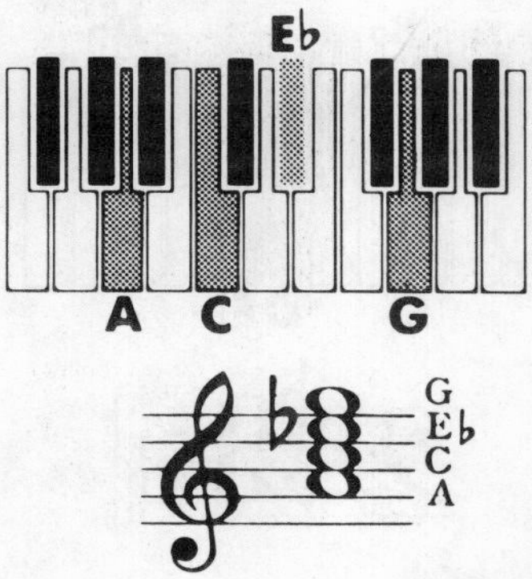

Left Hand Chords On B♭

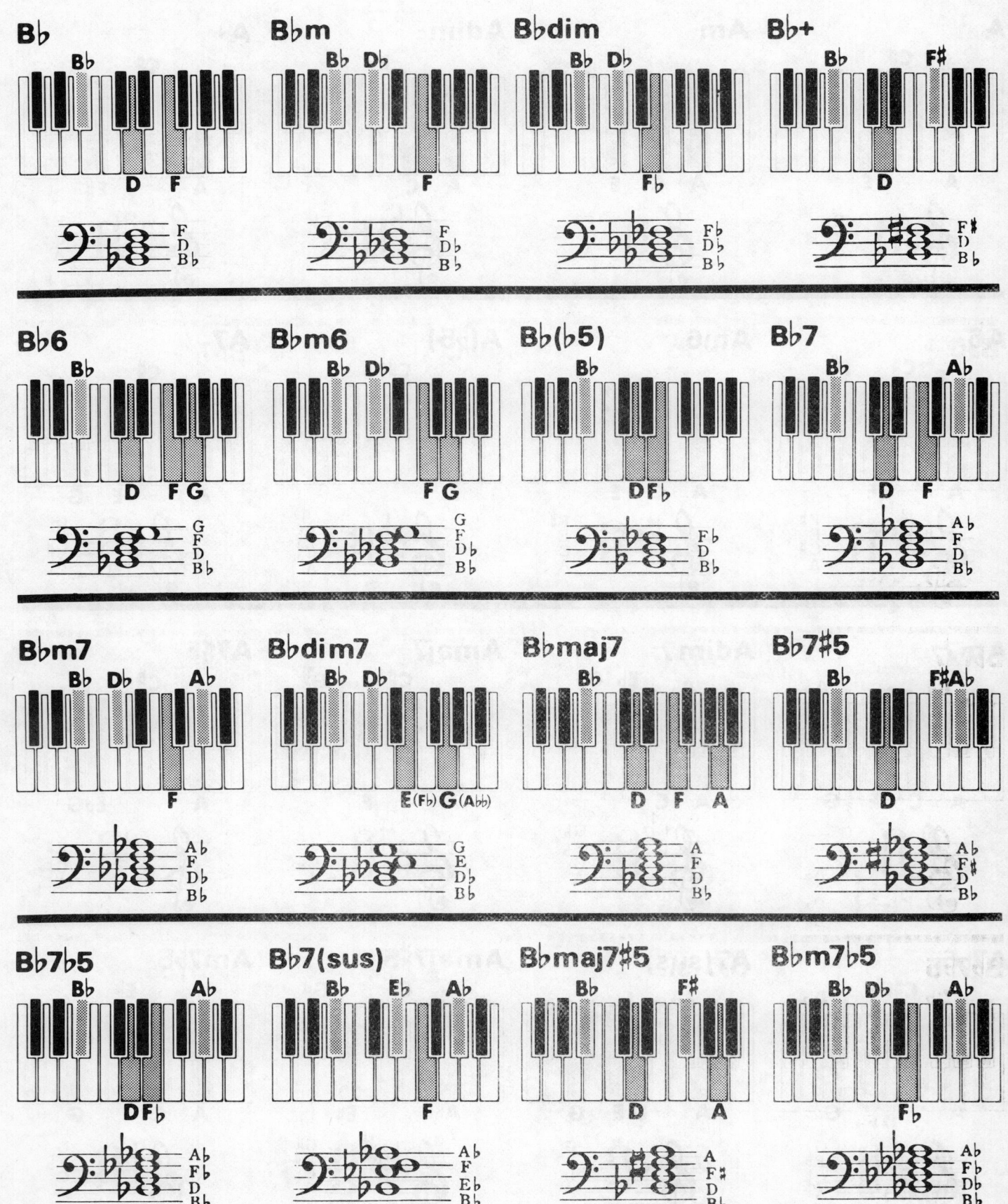

Right Hand Chords On B♭

B♭ 𝄞

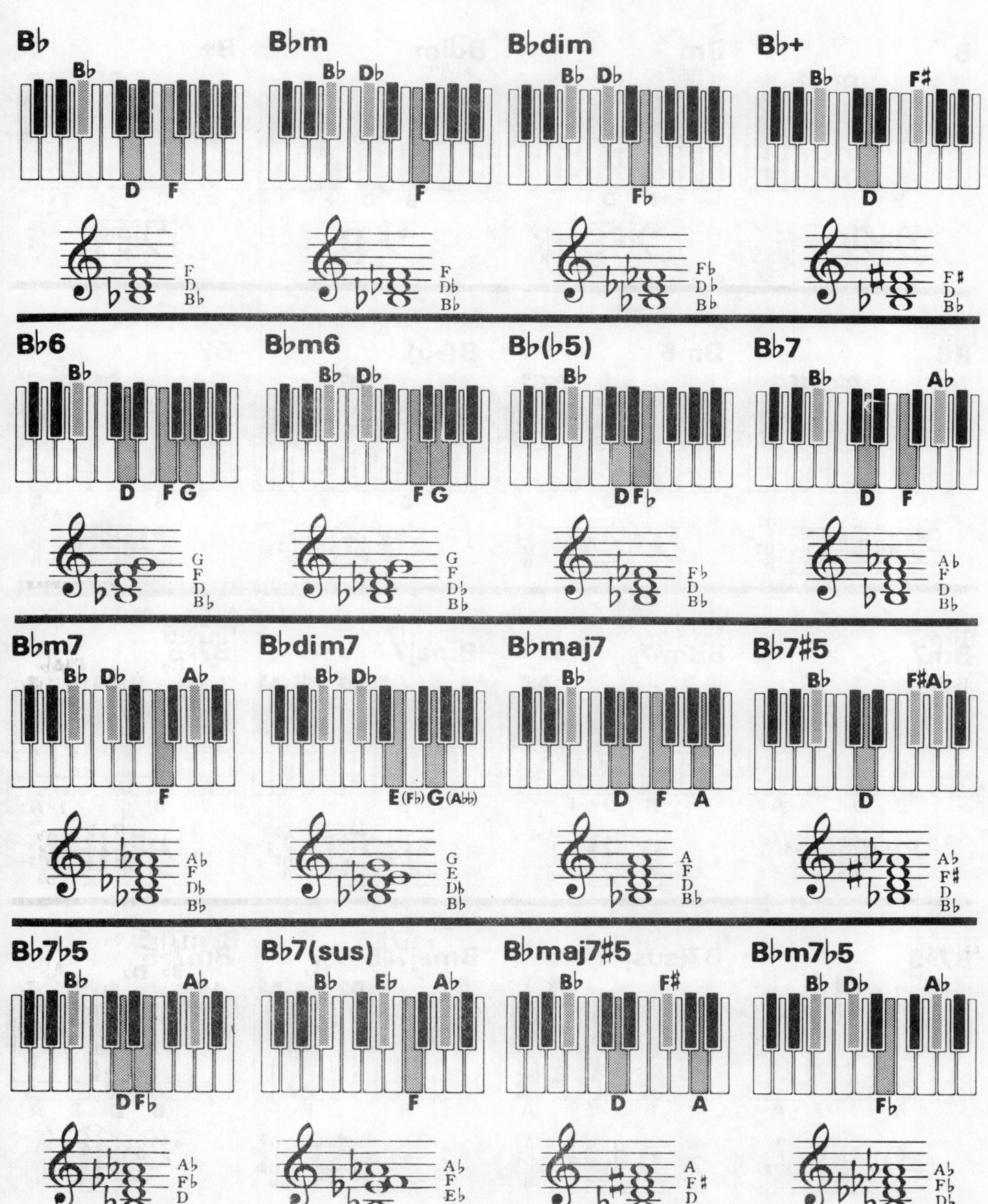

Left Hand Chords On B

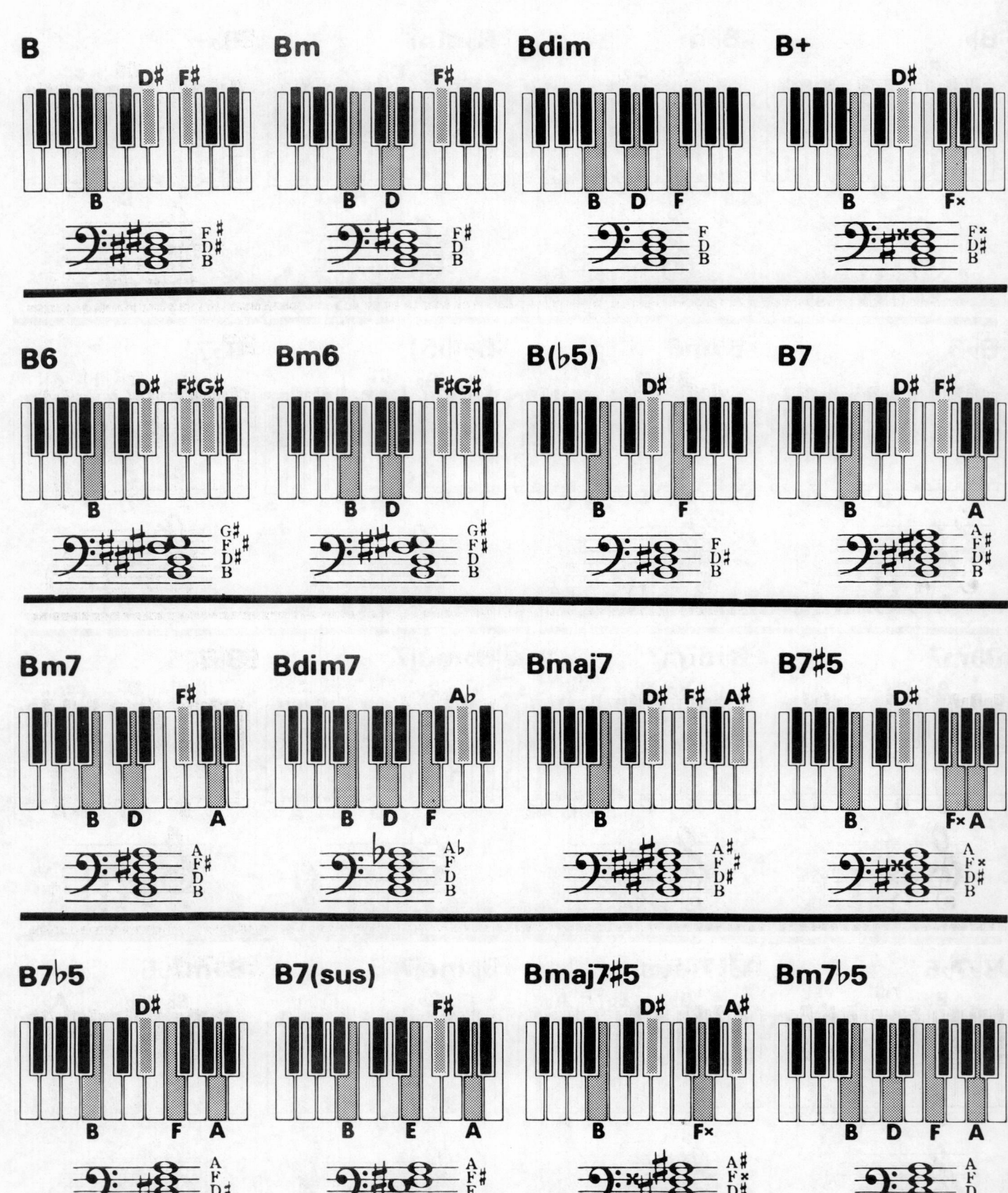

B  Right Hand Chords On B

B

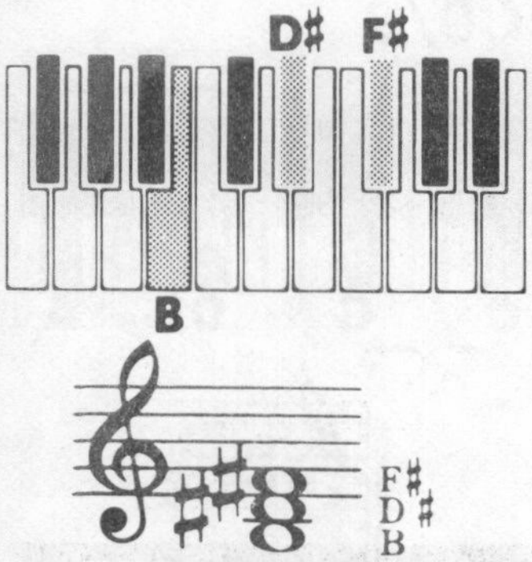

Bm

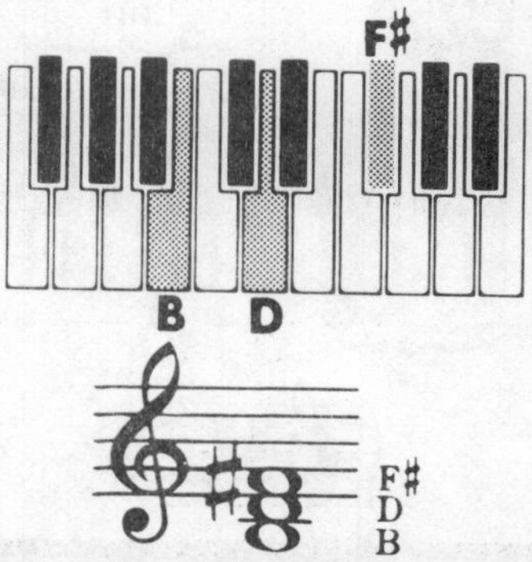

Bdim

B+

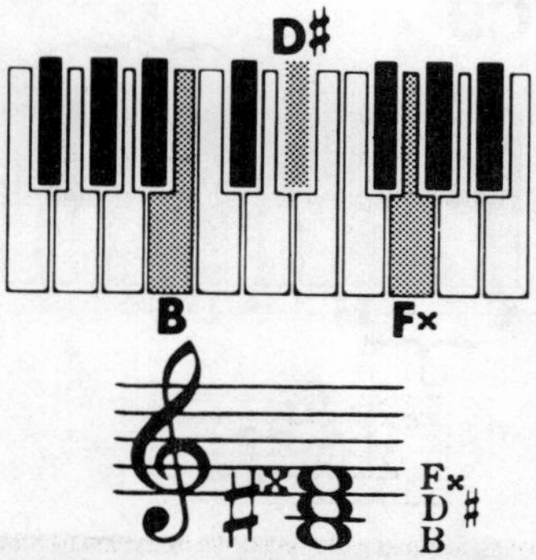

B6

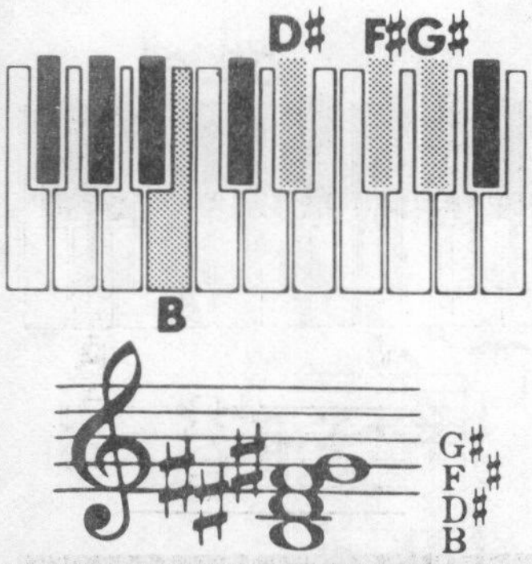

Bm6

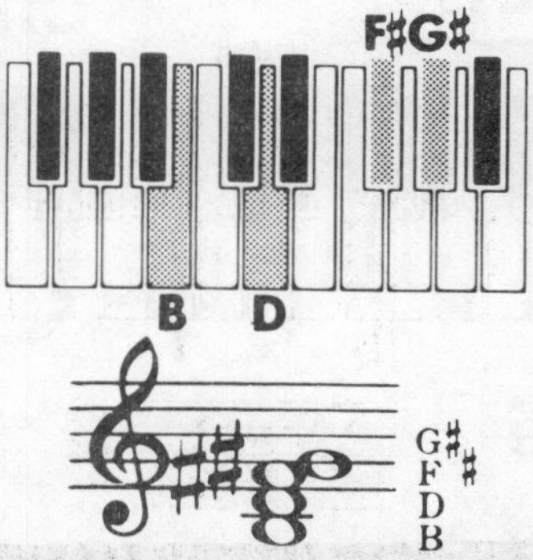

B(♭5)

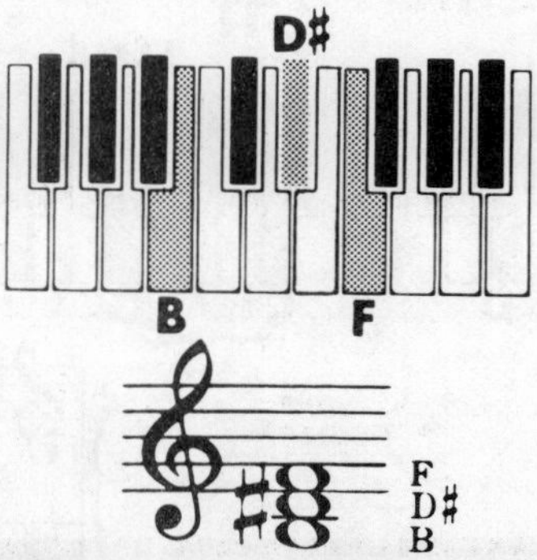

B7

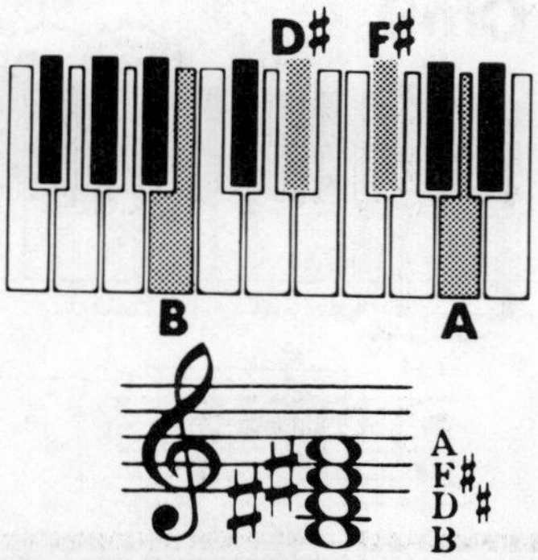

Bm7

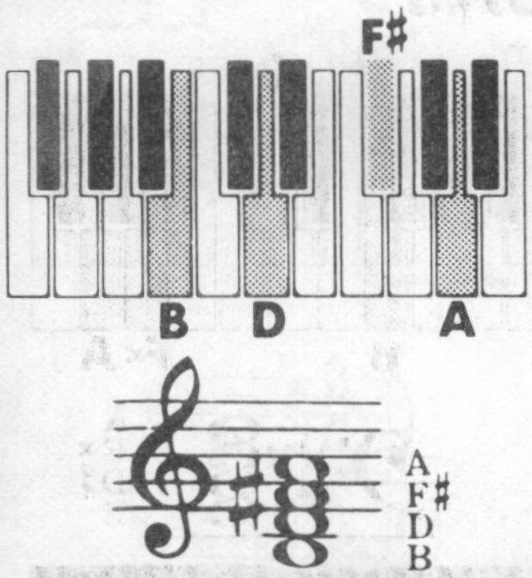

Bdim7

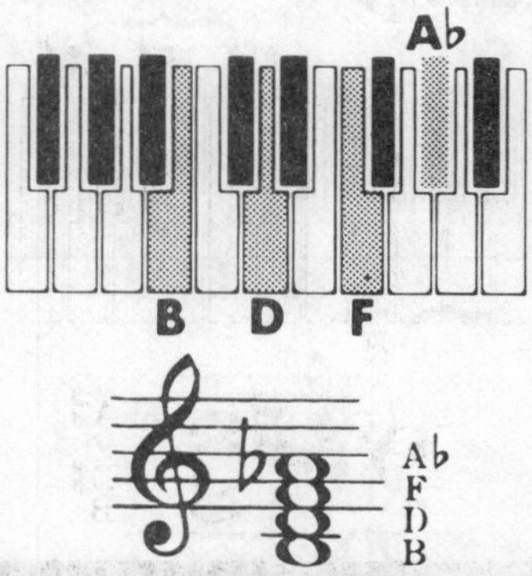

Bmaj7

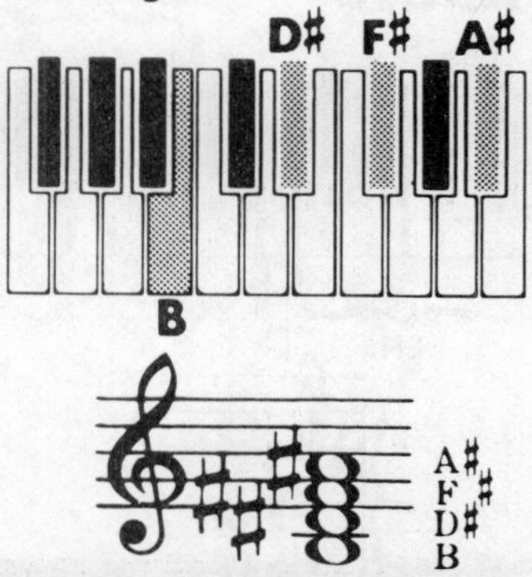

B7♯5

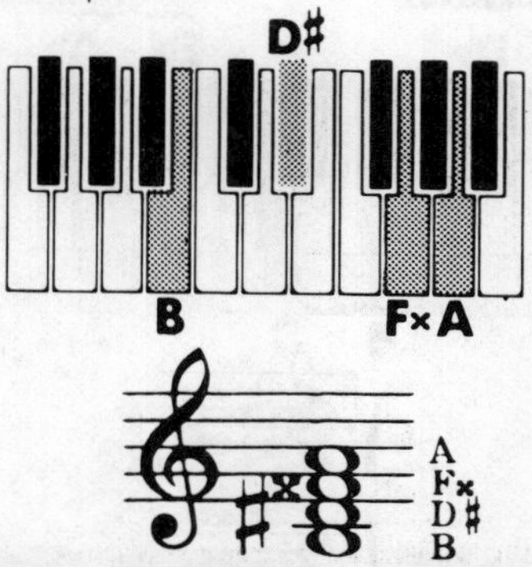

B7♭5

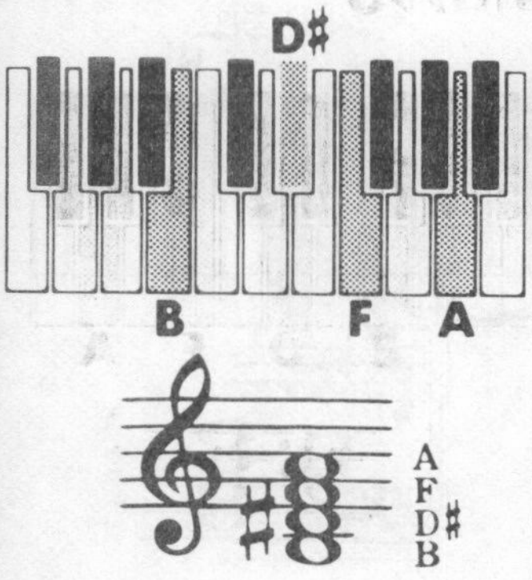

B7(sus)

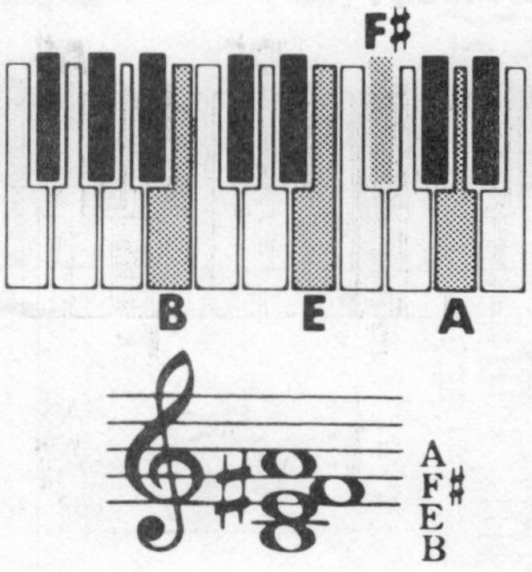

Bmaj7♯5

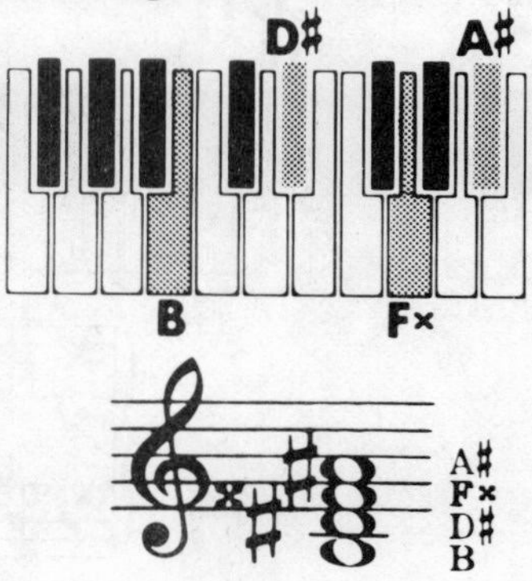

Bm7♭5

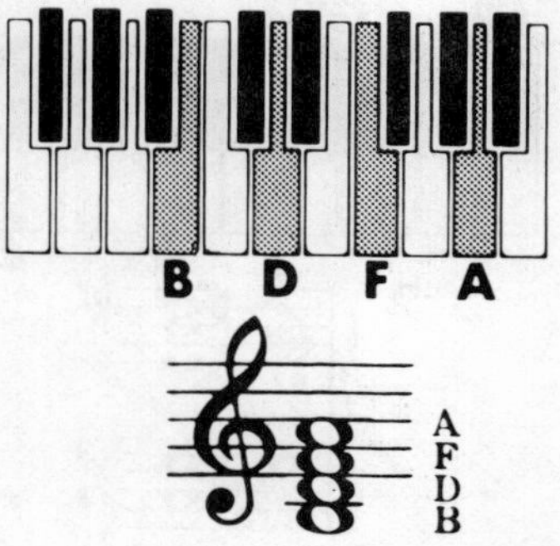

Chords For Both Hands

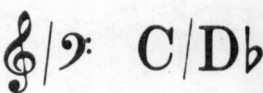

C9

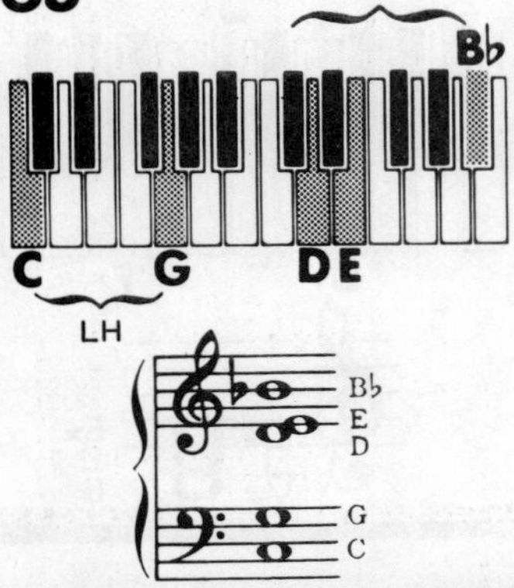

C9#5

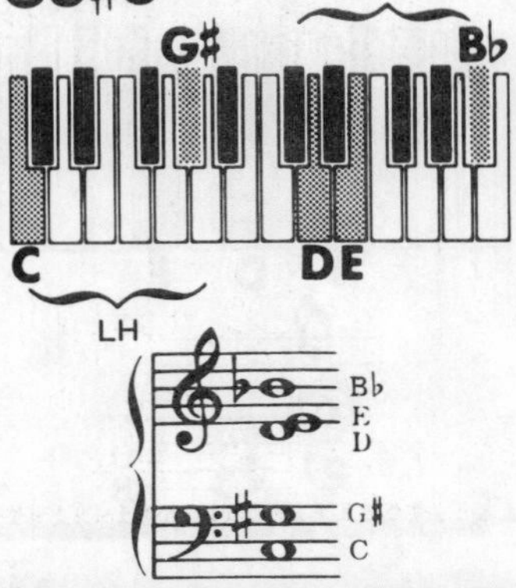

C7♭9

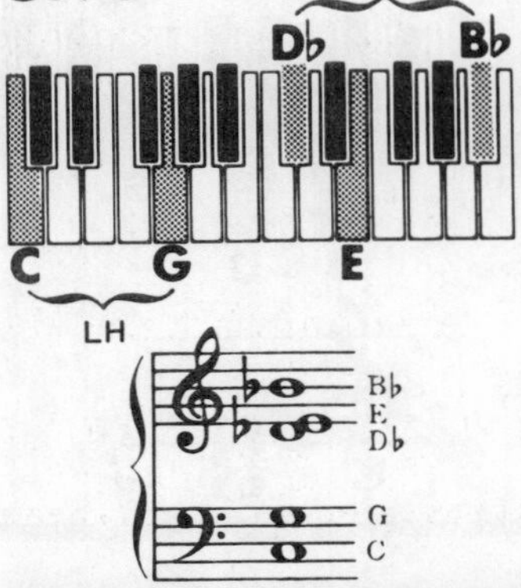

C6/9

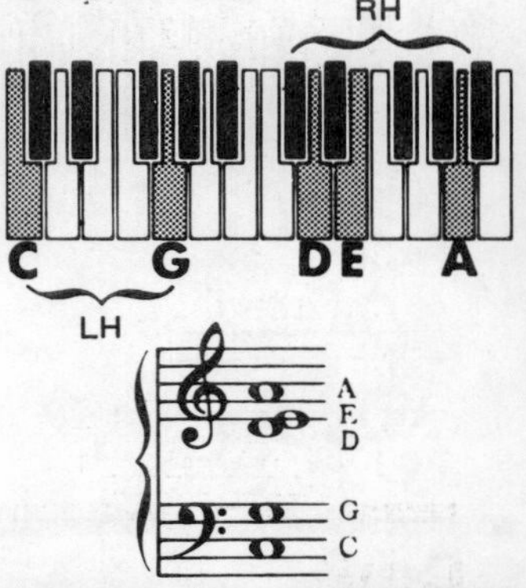

Cm9

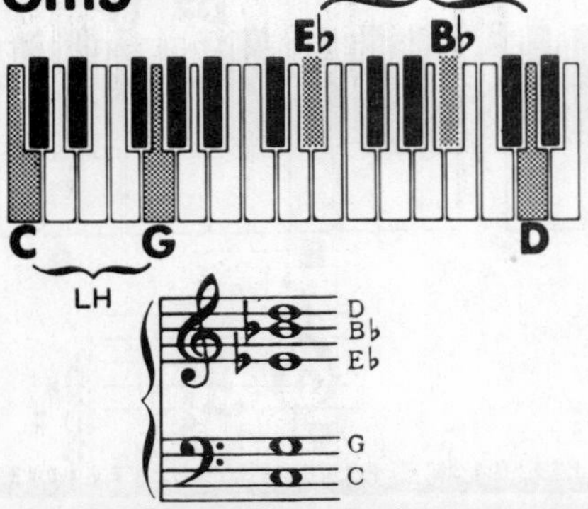

C11

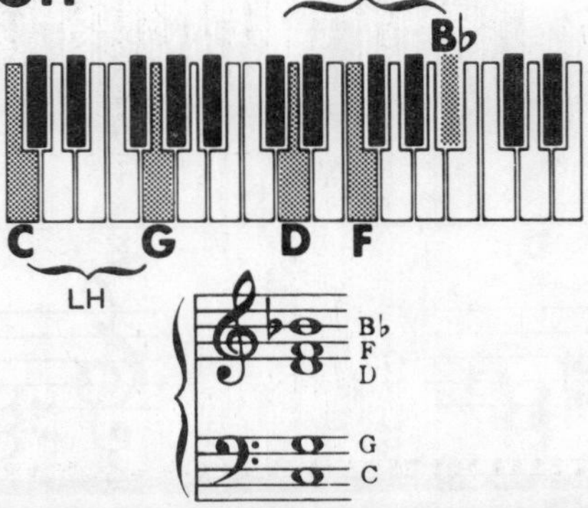

C13

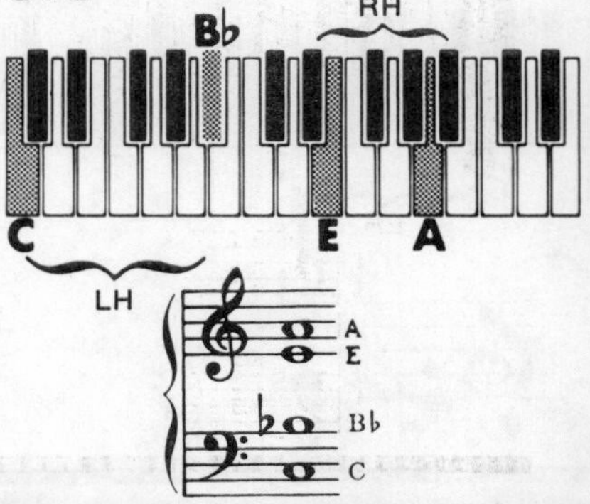

D♭9

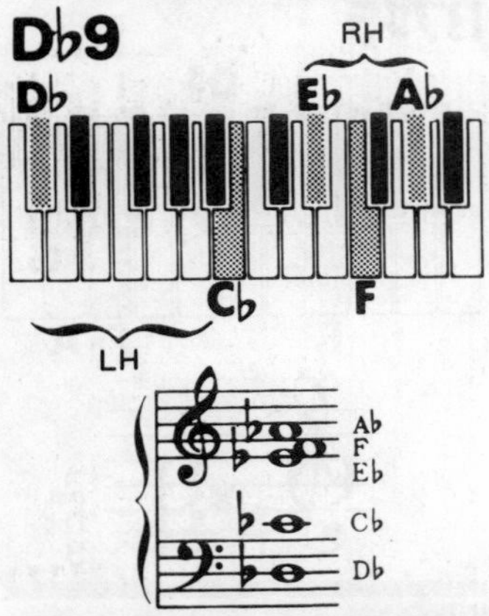

D♭9#5

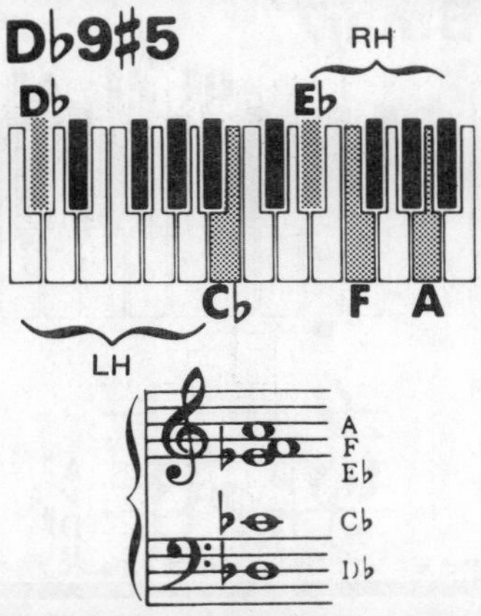

D♭7♭9

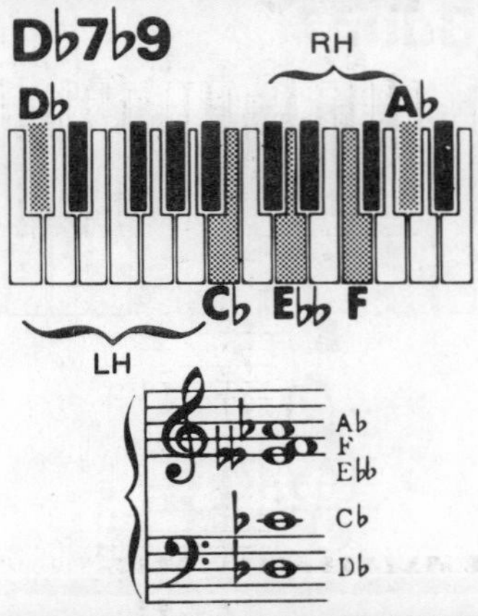

D♭6/9

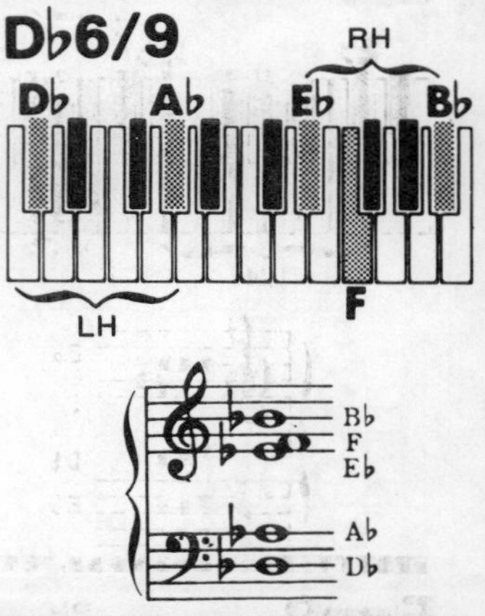

C#m9

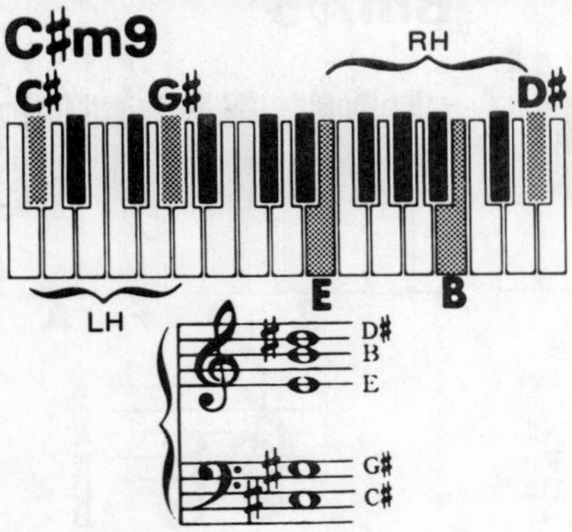

D♭11

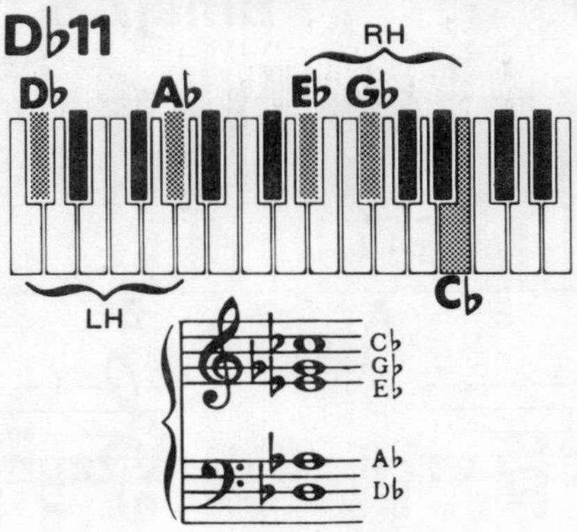

D♭13

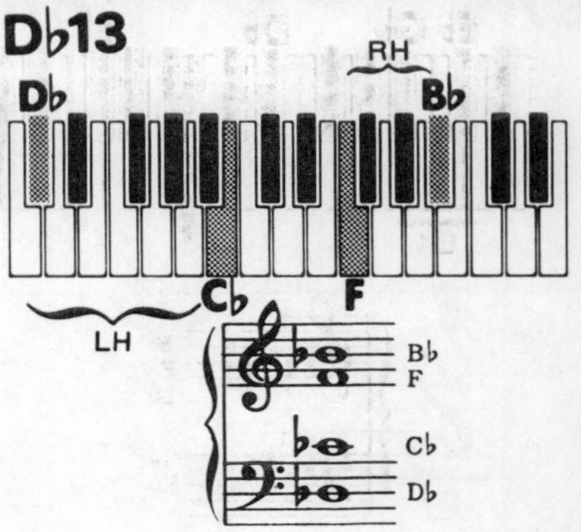

Chords For Both Hands

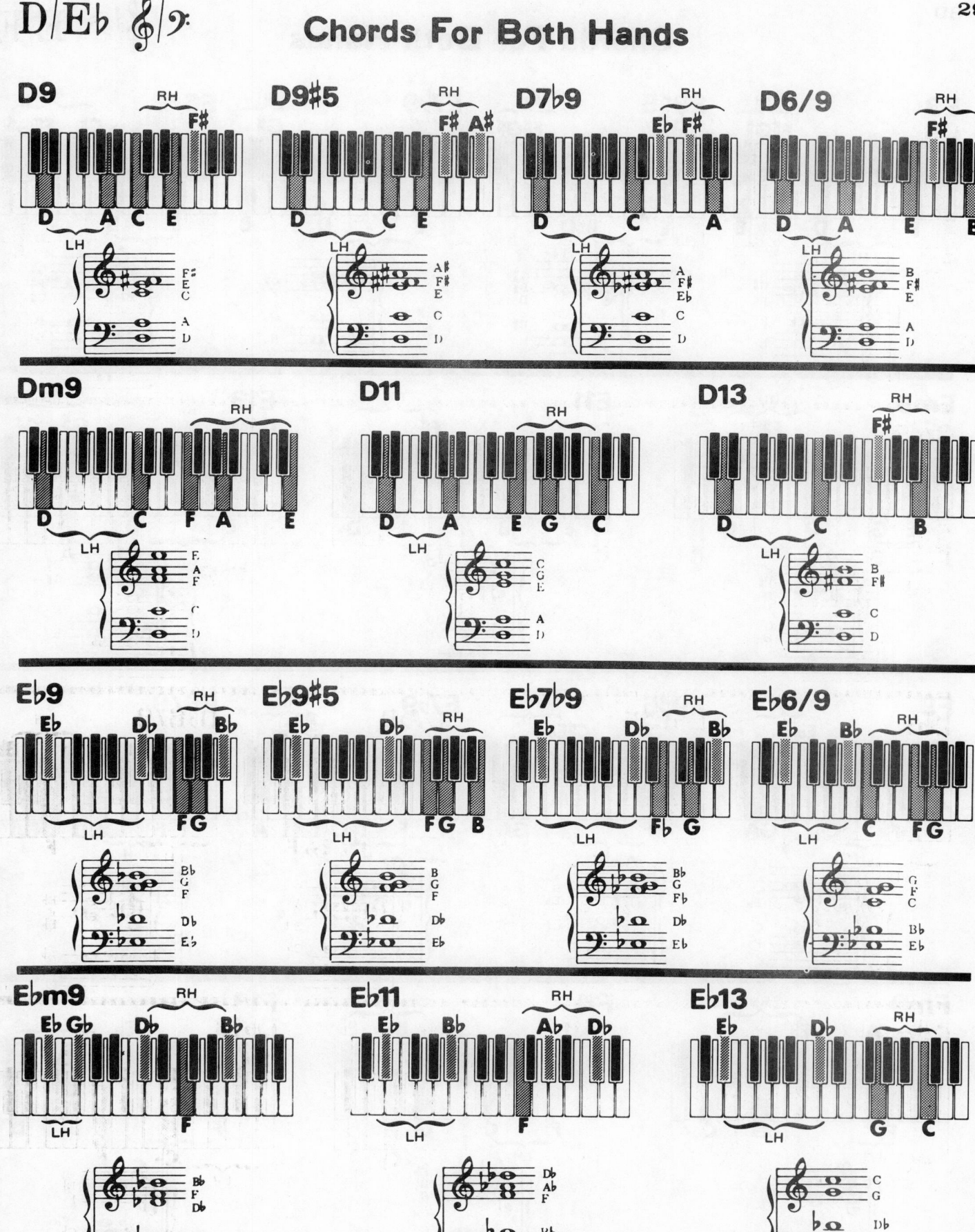

Chords For Both Hands

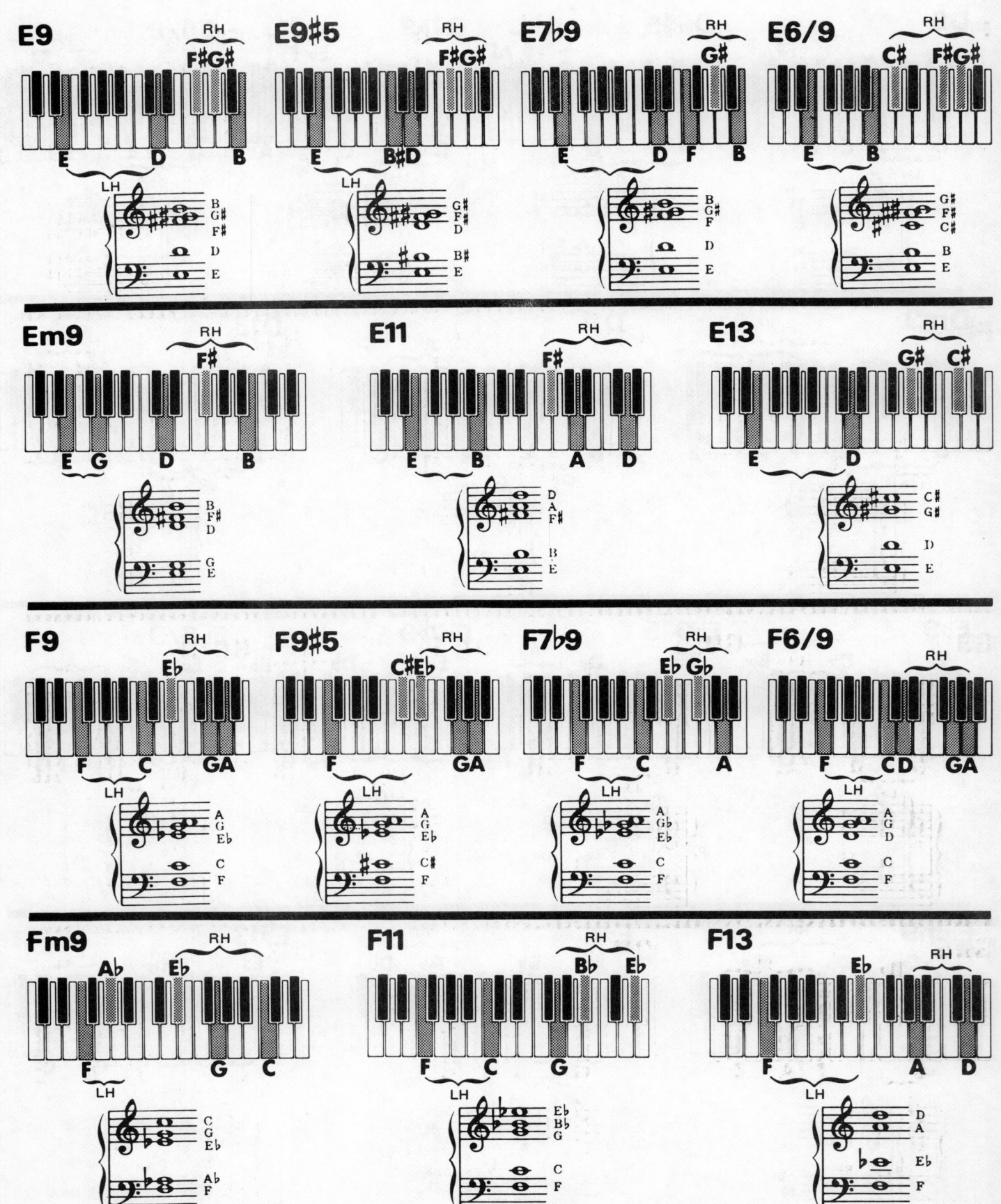

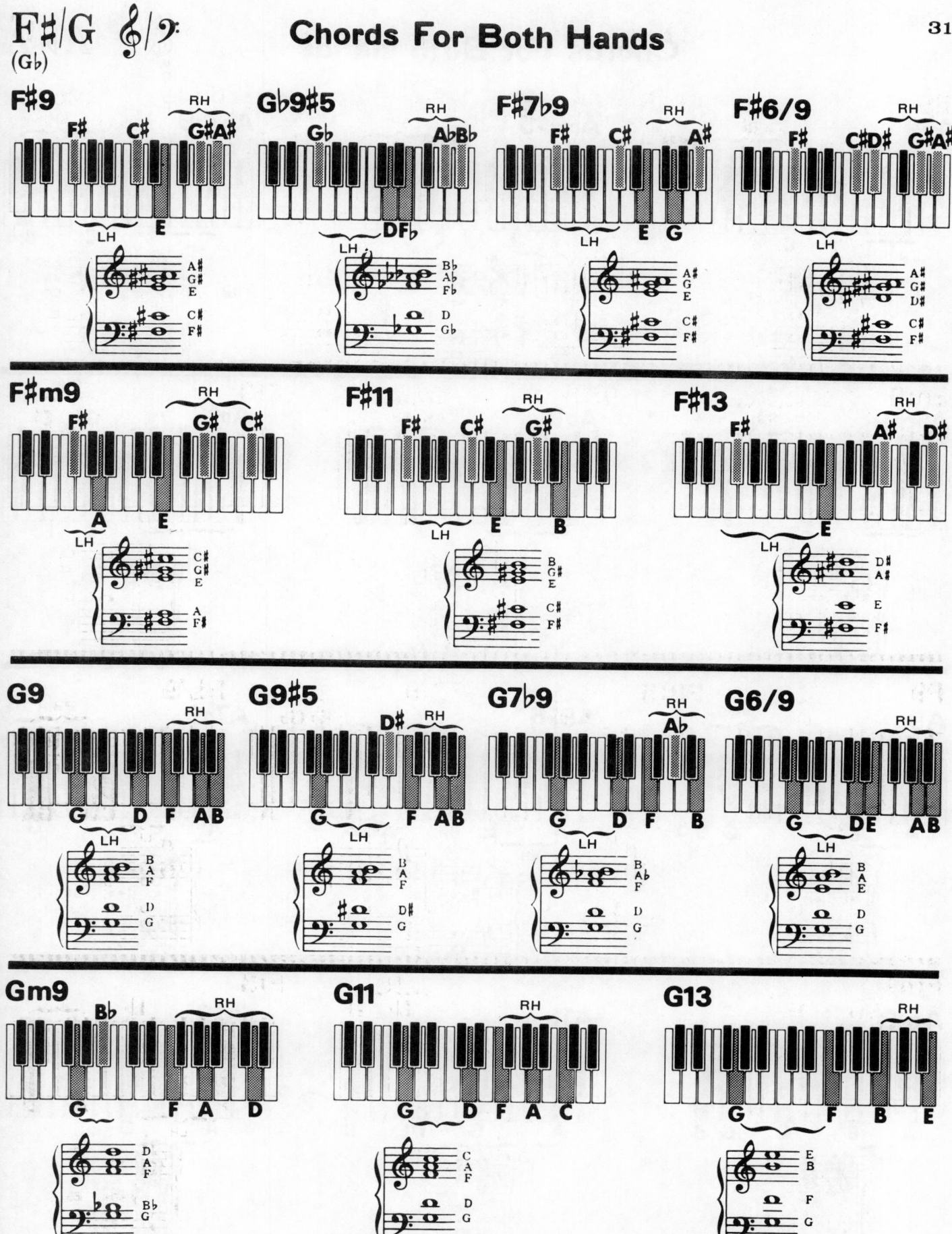

F♯/G (G♭) 𝄞/𝄢: Chords For Both Hands

Chords For Both Hands

ϕ/9: Ab/A

Ab9

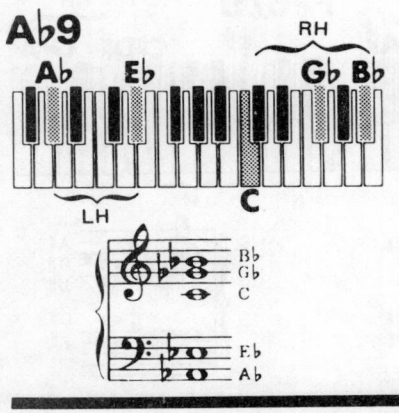

Ab9#5

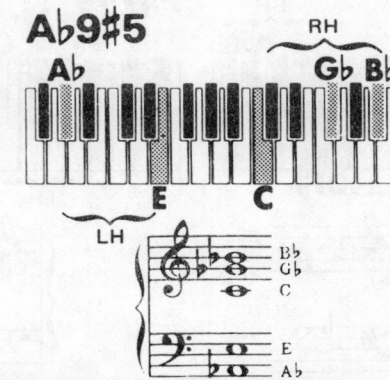

Ab7b9

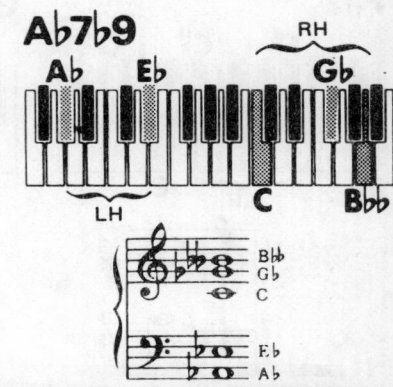

Abm9

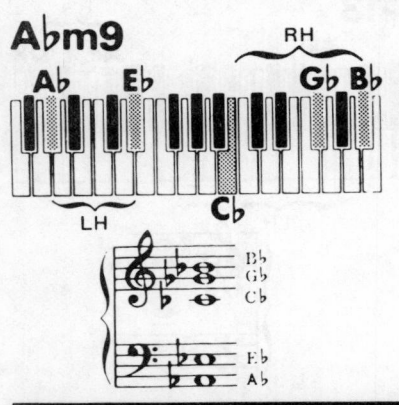

Ab11

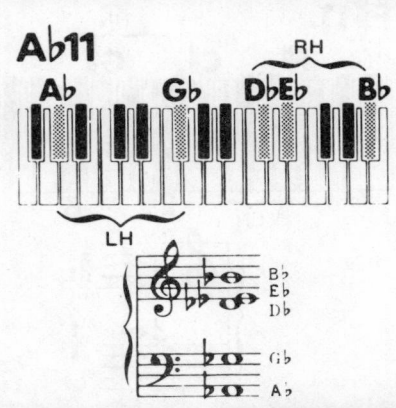

Ab13

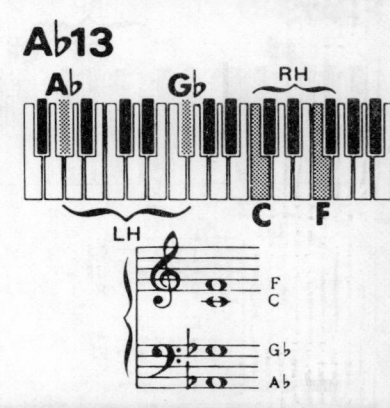

A9

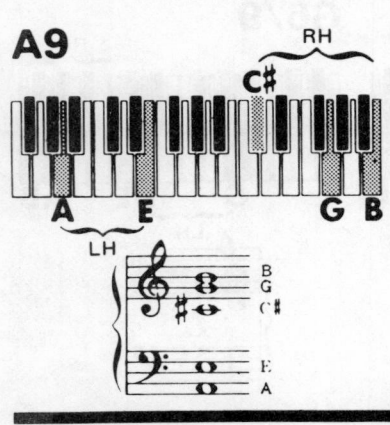

A9#5

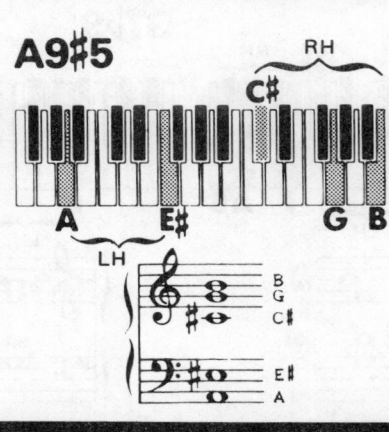

A7b9

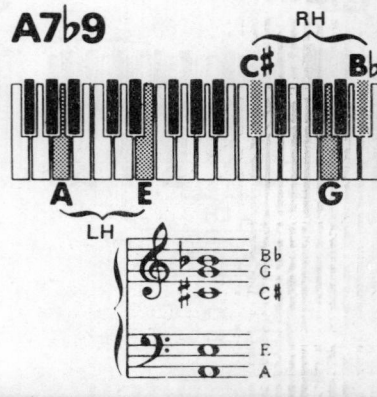

Am9

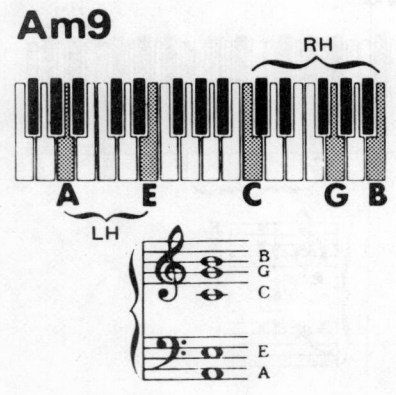

A11

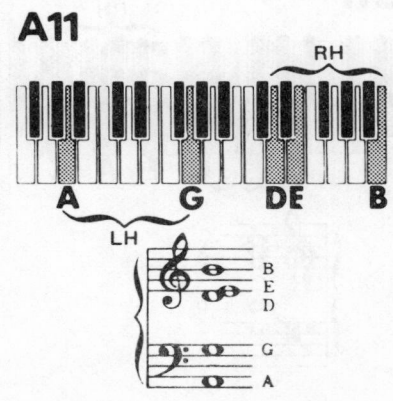

A13

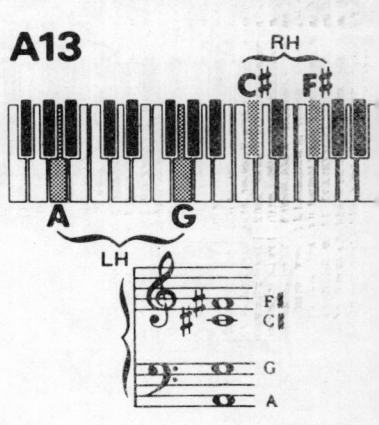

B♭/B 𝄞/𝄢   Chords For Both Hands

B♭9
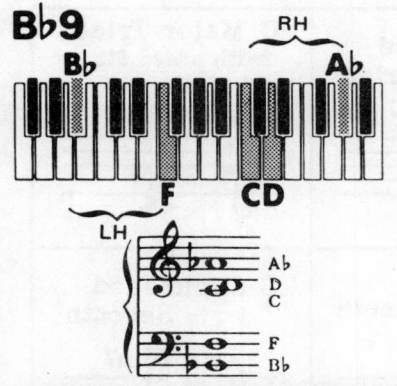

B♭9#5
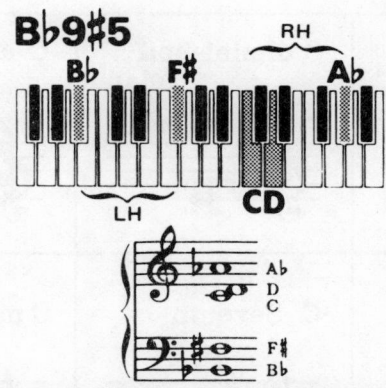

B♭7♭9
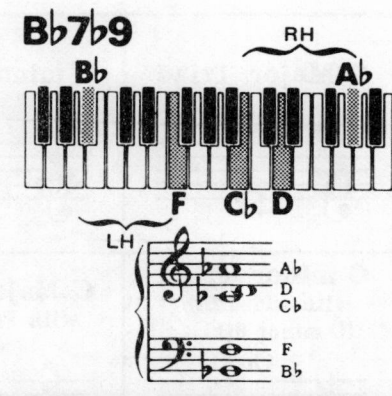

B♭m9
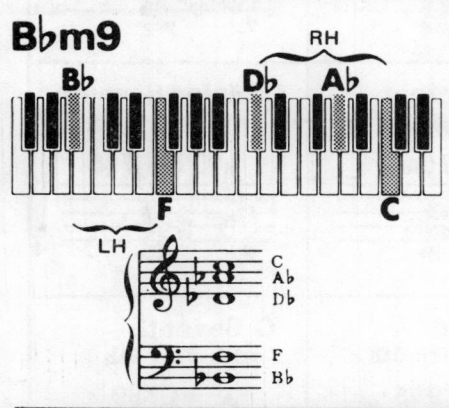

B♭11
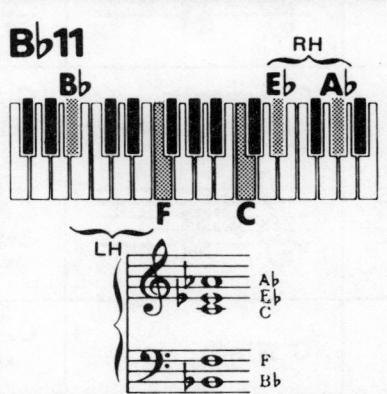

B♭13
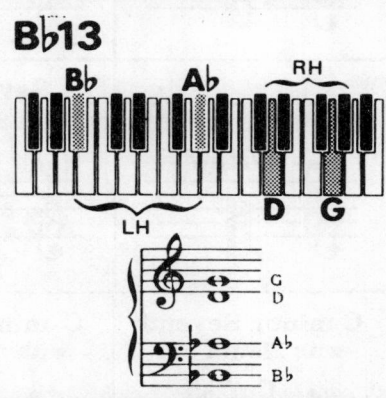

B9
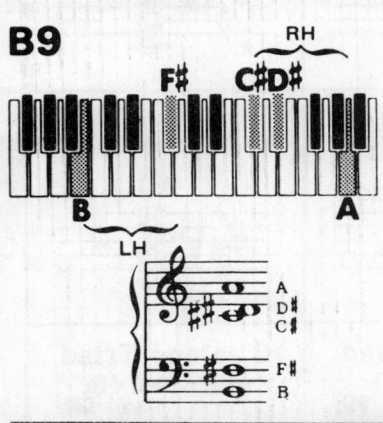

B9#5
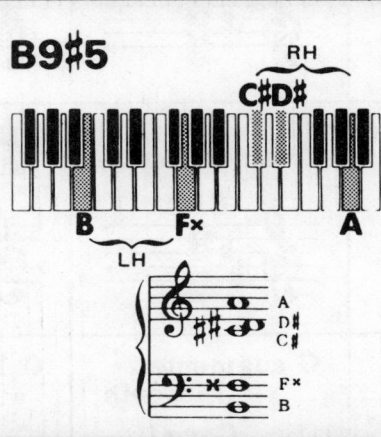

B7♭9
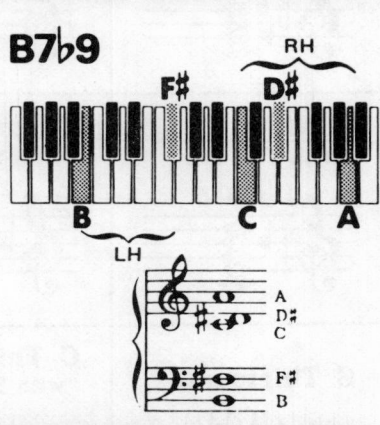

Bm9
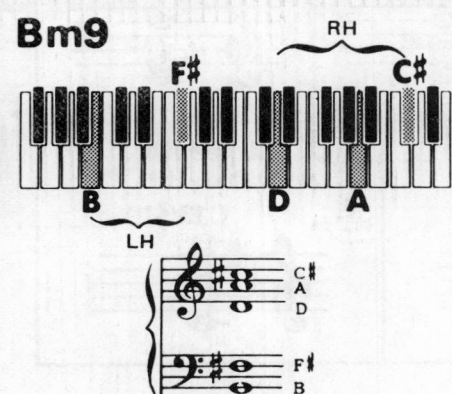

B11
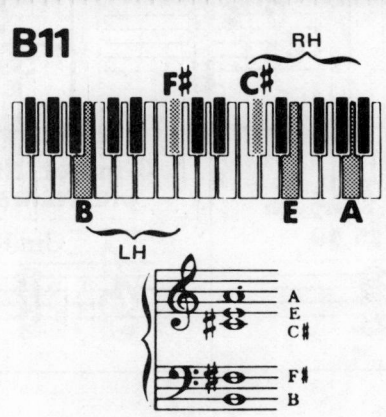

B13
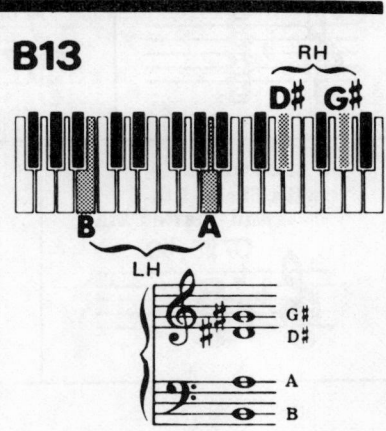

TABLE OF COMPLETE CHORD TYPES (on C)

VISUAL CHORDS

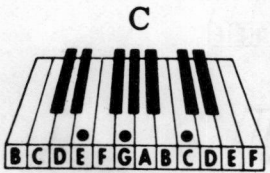 C

 G7

 F

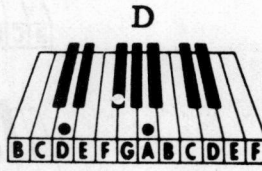 D

 F#dim

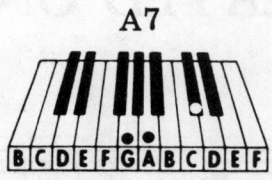 A7

 D7

 Ab7

ALLEY CAT
(Omkring Et Flygel)

By FRANK BJORN

Moderately Slow

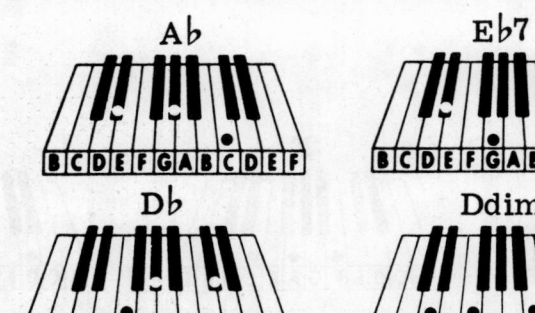

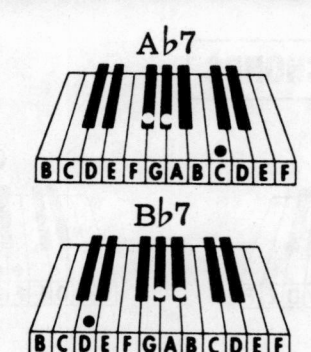

THE BAND PLAYED ON

Words by JOHN F. PALMER
Music by CHARLES B. WARD
1895

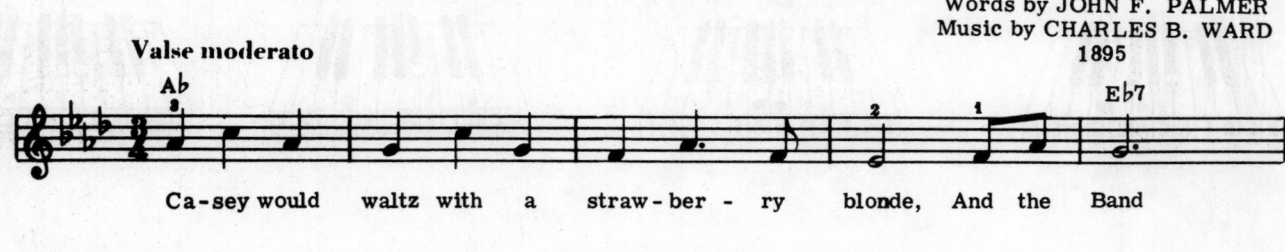

Ca-sey would waltz with a straw-ber-ry blonde, And the Band

played on, _____ He'd glide 'cross the floor with the

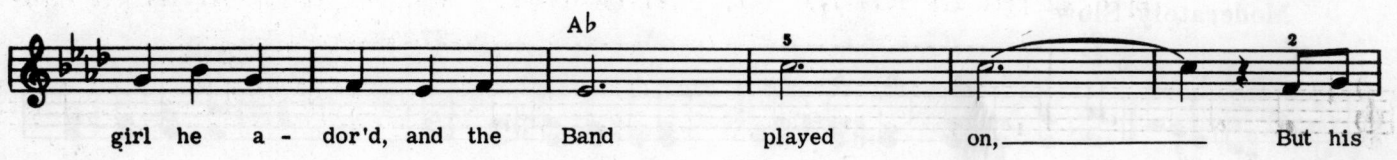

girl he a-dor'd, and the Band played on, _____ But his

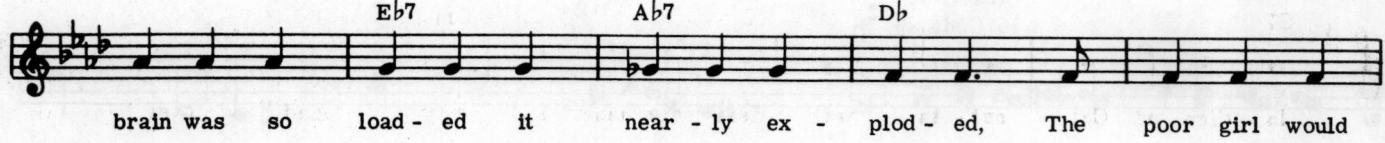

brain was so load-ed it near-ly ex-plod-ed, The poor girl would

shake with a-larm. _____ He'd ne'er leave the girl with the

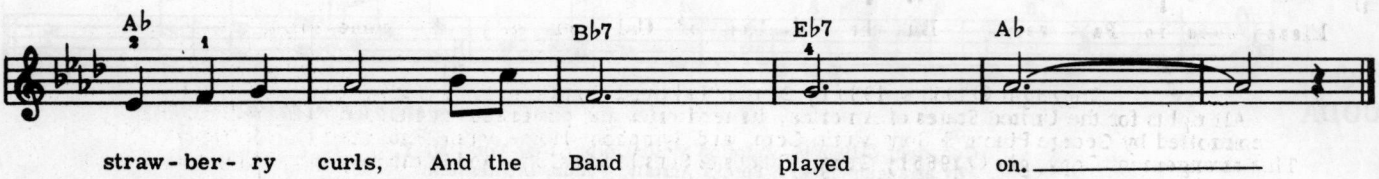

straw-ber-ry curls, And the Band played on. _____

G
D7
G7
C
Cm
A7
Am
BCDEFGABCDEF

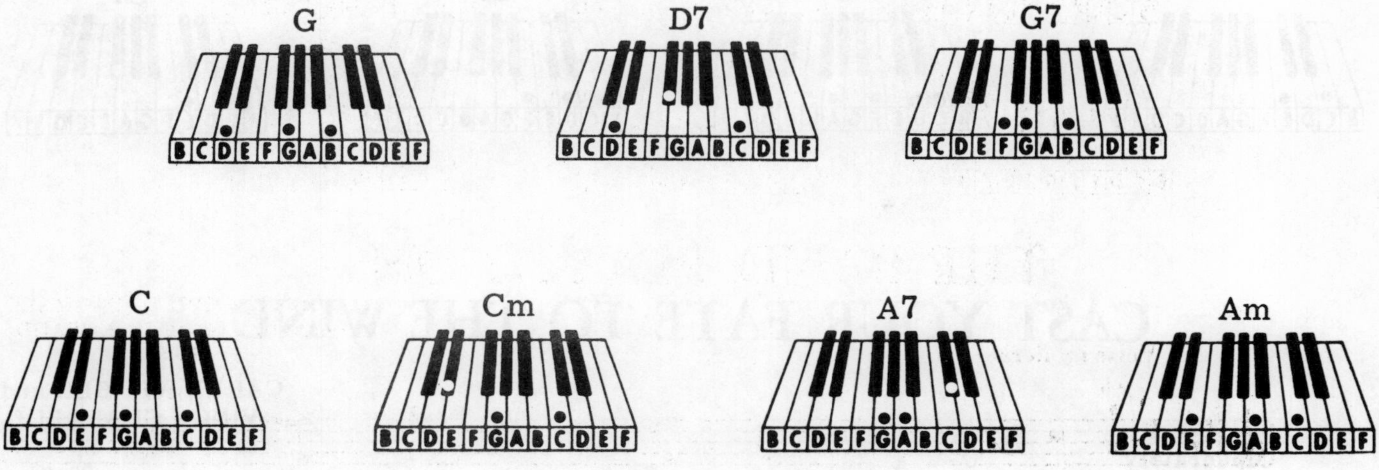

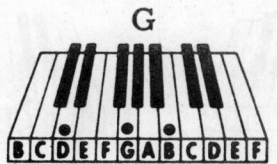

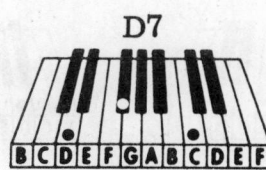

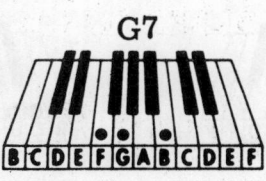

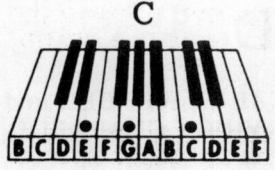

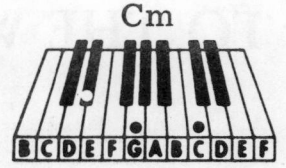

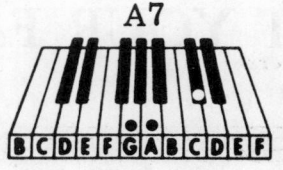

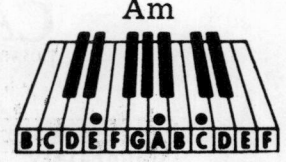

CALCUTTA

By
LEE POCKRISS
PAUL J. VANCE
and HEINO GAZE

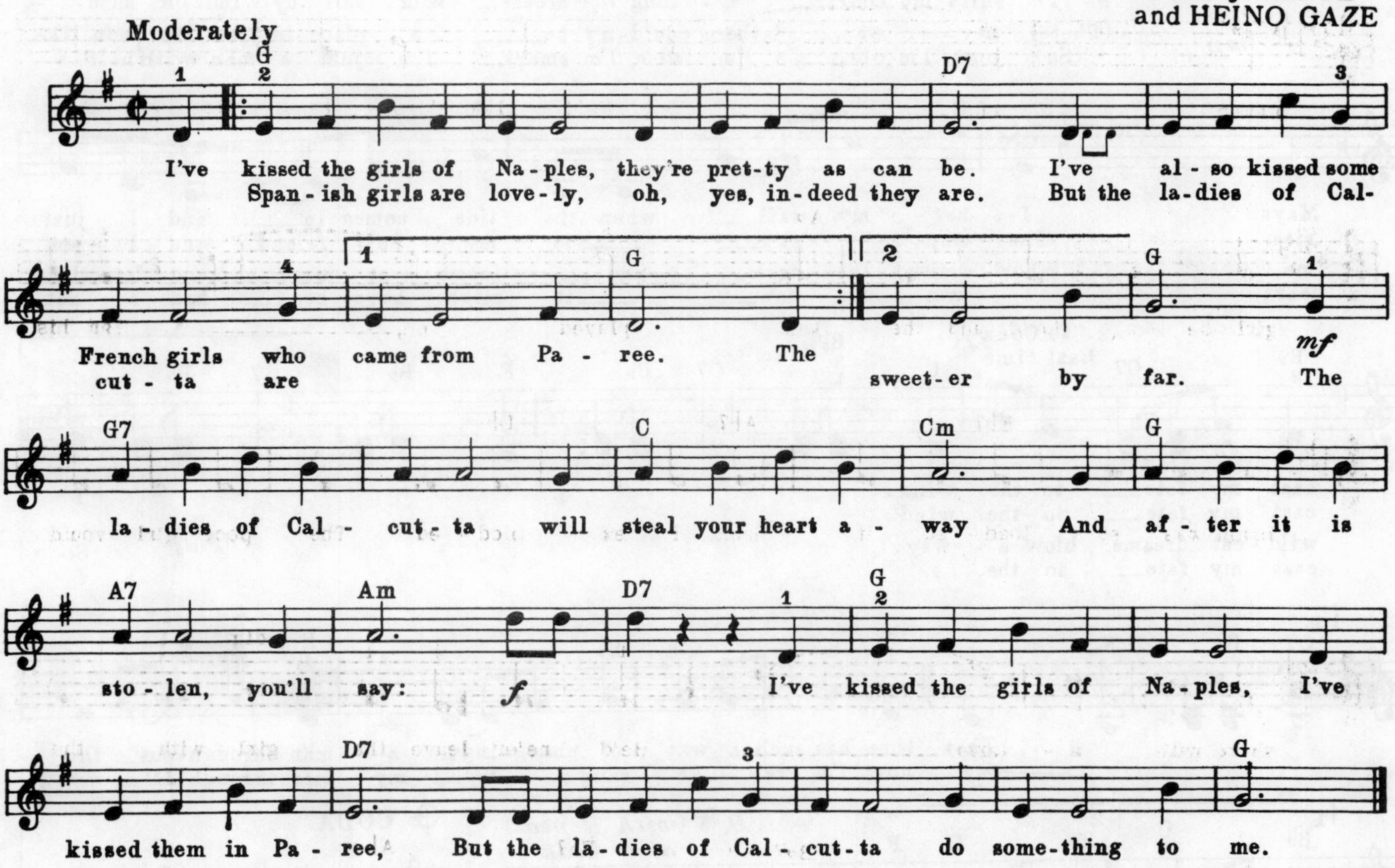

Moderately
I've kissed the girls of Na-ples, they're pret-ty as can be. I've al-so kissed some French girls who came from Pa-ree. The
Span-ish girls are love-ly, oh, yes, in-deed they are. But the la-dies of Cal-cut-ta are sweet-er by far.
mf
The la-dies of Cal-cut-ta will steal your heart a-way And af-ter it is sto-len, you'll say:
f
I've kissed the girls of Na-ples, I've kissed them in Pa-ree, But the la-dies of Cal-cut-ta do some-thing to me.

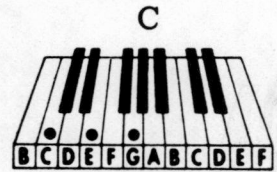
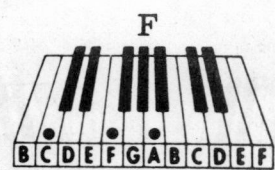
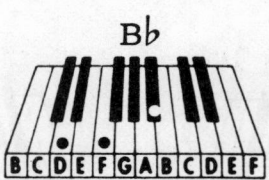
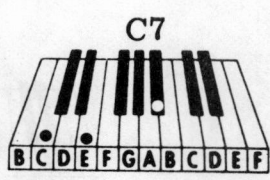

C   F   Bb   C7

CAST YOUR FATE TO THE WIND

By
CAREL WERBER and
VINCE GUARALDI

Moderately

mp

A month of nights,— A year of days,— Oc - to - bers drift-ing in - to
(I) shift my course— a - long the breeze,— won't sail up-wind on mem - o -
(There) nev - er was, there could-n't be a place in time for men like
(So) now I'm old,— I'm wise, I'm smart,— I'm just a man with half a

Mays. I set my sail— when the tide comes in— and I just
ries. The emp - ty sky— — is my best friend— and I just
me, Who'd drink the dark— and— laugh at day— and let their
heart. I won - der how— —it might have been— had I not

to Coda
Last time

cast my fate— to the wind.
cast my fate— to the wind.
wild - est dreams— blow a - way.
cast my fate— to the

I
So

mf

That time has such a way of chang-ing— a man through-out— the
now I'm re - ar - rang - ing— my life through all— my

1. 2.
years,— And tears— a - lone. *mp* There

D. %. (with Repeat)
al ⊕ Coda

⊕ CODA

wind. *poco rit.*

C
F
E♭dim
Dm7
Fm
G7
B C D E F G A B C D E F

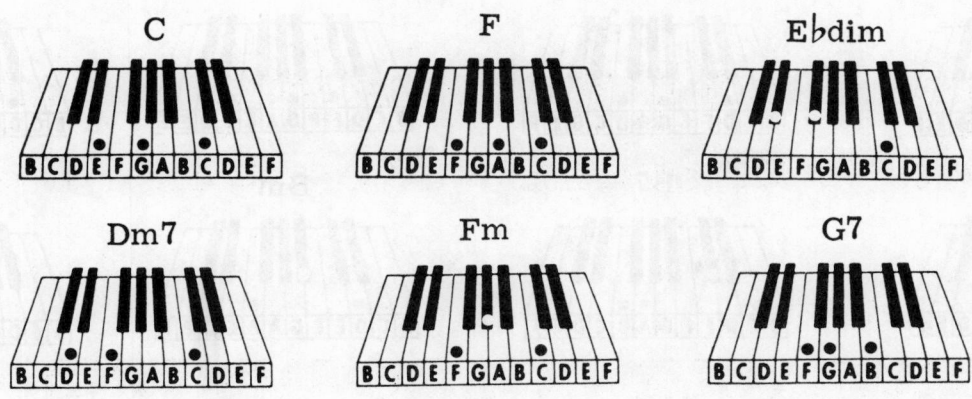

FASCINATION

By
BILL HANSEN and
F. D. MARCHETTI

The little run-up in eighth-notes, that precedes each phrase must be fingered very carefully, as marked, if smoothness is to be achieved.

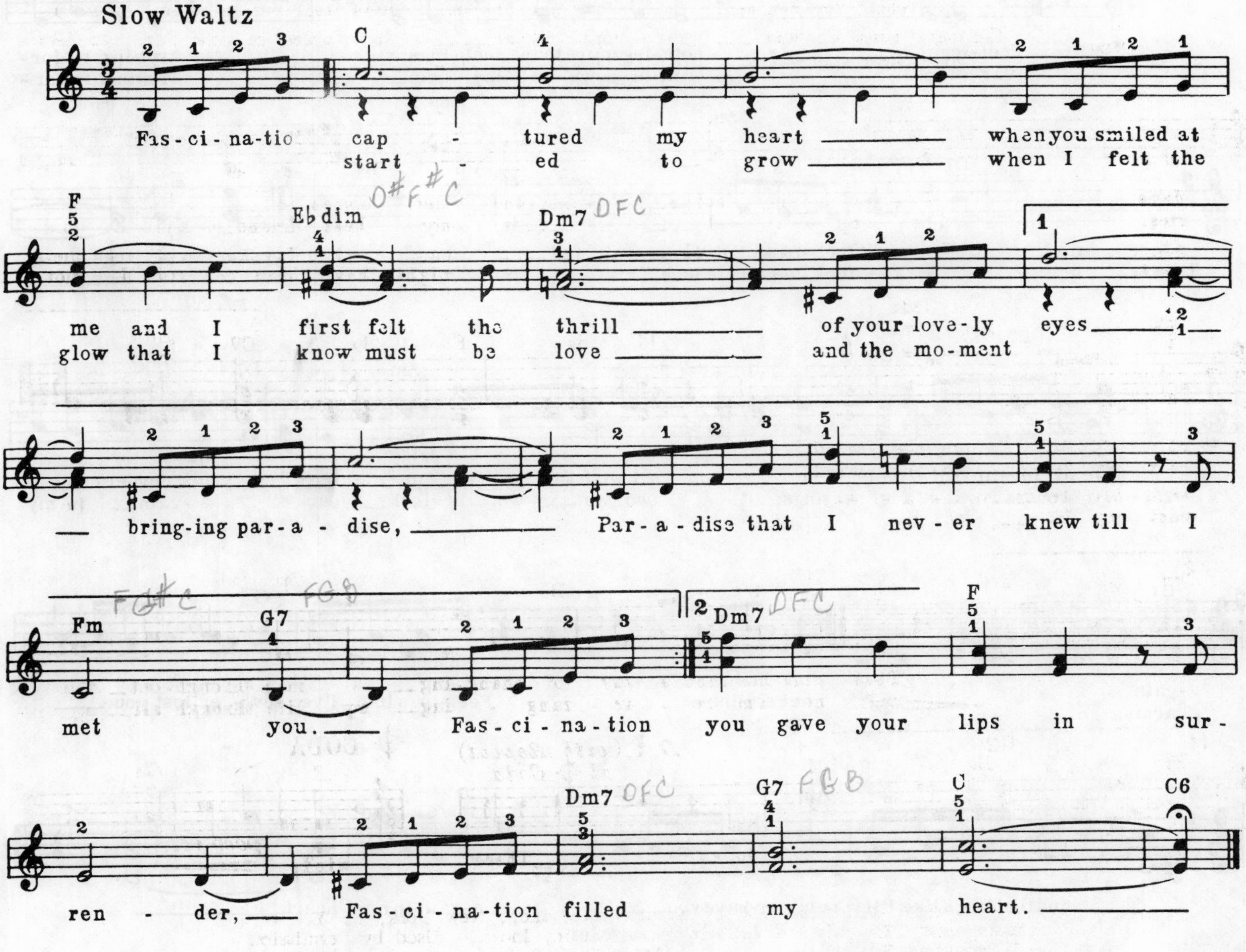

Slow Waltz
Fas-ci-na-tion cap - tured my heart ——— when you smiled at
start - ed to grow ——— when I felt the
me and I first felt the thrill ——— of your love-ly eyes ———
glow that I know must be love ——— and the mo-ment
— bring-ing par-a-dise, ——— Par-a-dise that I nev-er knew till I
met you. ——— Fas-ci-na-tion you gave your lips in sur-
ren - der, ——— Fas-ci-na-tion filled my heart. ———
C
F
E♭dim
Dm7
Fm
G7
C6

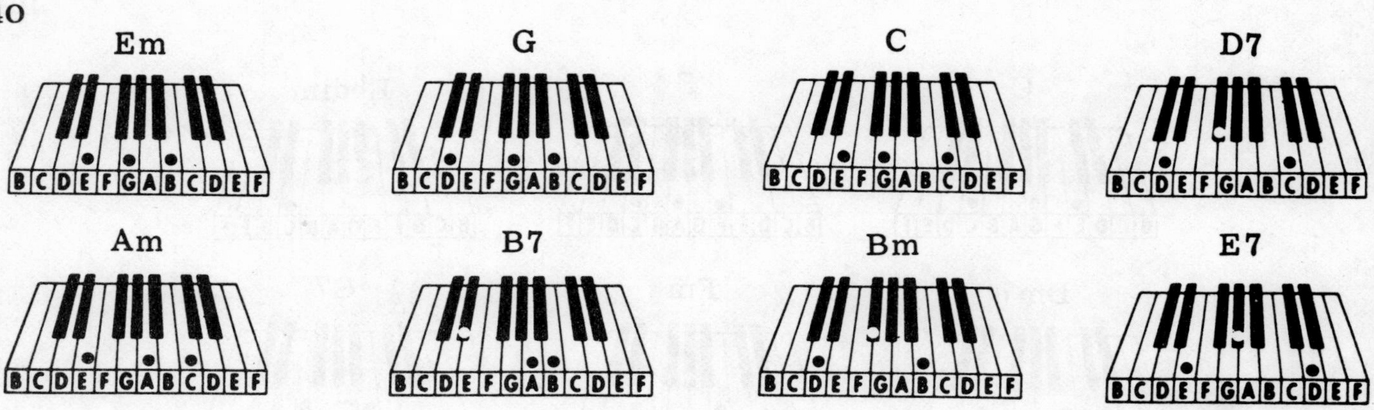

Em  G 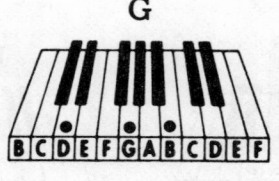 C 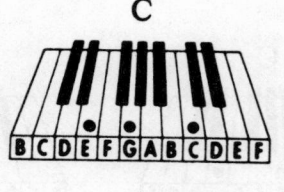 D7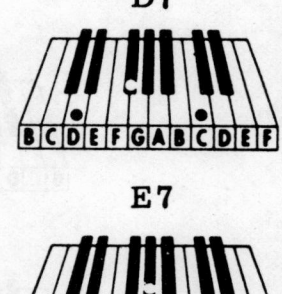

Am B7 Bm E7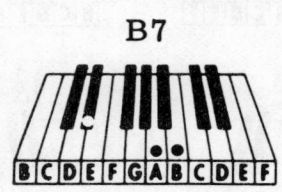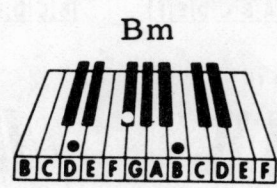

FEELINGS

Words and Music by
MORRIS ALBERT

Moderately

Em   *EGB*

Feel-ings,—   noth-ing more than feel-ings,—   try-ing to for-
Tear-drops.—   roll-ing down on my face,—   try-ing to for-
mp

C   D7   *3*   G   Am *EAC* B7 *D#AD* C

-get my   feel-ings of love.   Feel - ings,—
-get my   feel-ings of love.   Feel - ings,—
mf

Am   D7 *D#B*   Bm   E7 *EG#*   Am   D7

— for all my life I'll feel it,   I wish I've nev - er met you girl;   you'll nev-er come a-
— wo, wo.— wo,— feel - ings,   wo, wo,— wo,— feel — you   a-gain— in my

B7 *D#AD*   Em *EGB*   G

-gain.   Feel-ings,—   Feel-ings like I've nev - er lost you,—
arms.   *mp*

Am *EAC*   D7   G

and feel-ings like I'll nev - er have you—   a-gain in my heart.—

G
BCDEFGABCDEF
Em
BCDEFGABCDEF
C
BCDEFGABCDEF
Am
BCDEFGABCDEF
D7
BCDEFGABCDEF

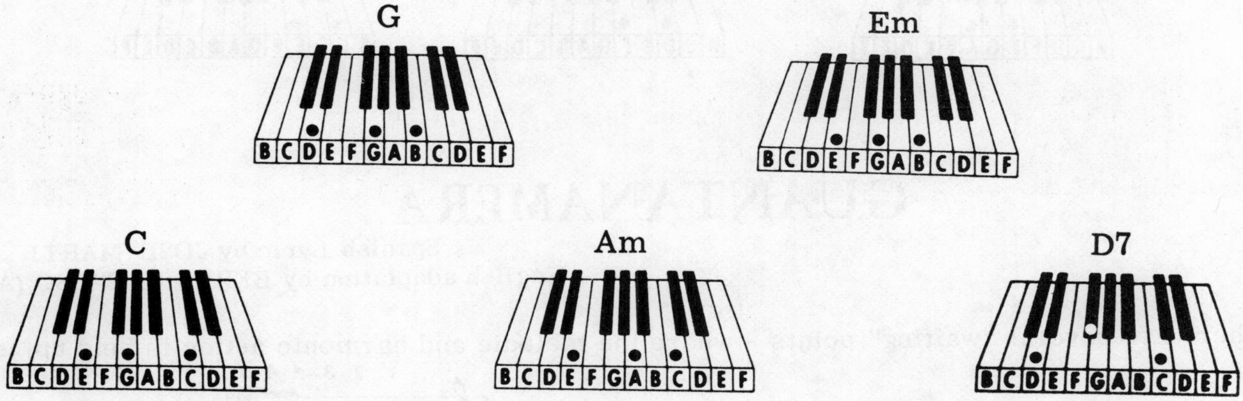

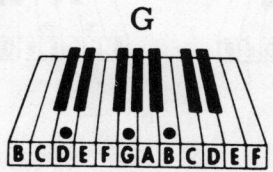

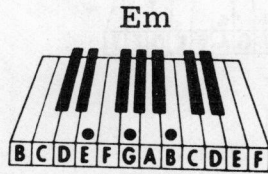

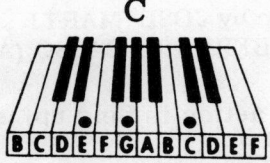

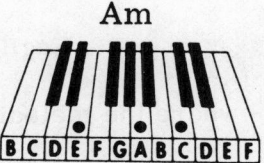

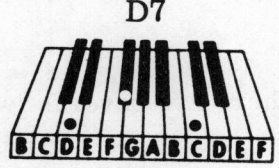

FIVE HUNDRED MILES

By
HEDY WEST

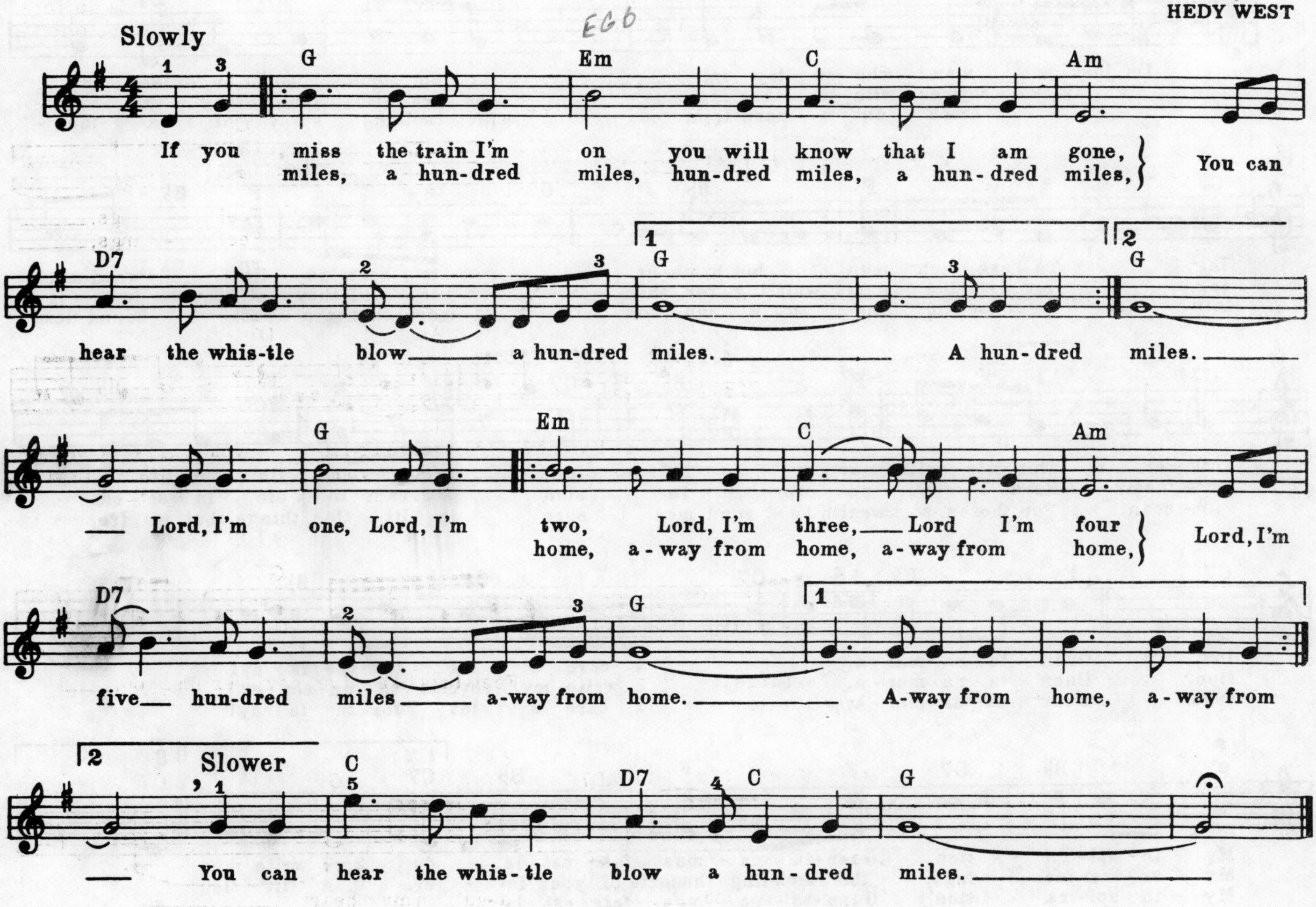

Slowly
G Em C Am
If you miss the train I'm on you will know that I am gone, You can
miles, a hun-dred miles, hun-dred miles, a hun-dred miles,
D7 G G
hear the whis-tle blow a hun-dred miles. A hun-dred miles.
G Em C Am
Lord, I'm one, Lord, I'm two, Lord, I'm three, Lord I'm four Lord, I'm
home, a-way from home, a-way from home,
D7 G
five hun-dred miles a-way from home. A-way from home, a-way from
Slower
C D7 C G
You can hear the whis-tle blow a hun-dred miles.

F
B♭
C7
BCDEFGABCDEF
BCDEFGABCDEF
BCDEFGABCDEF

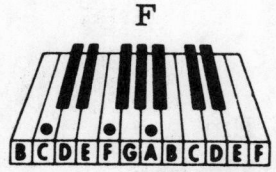

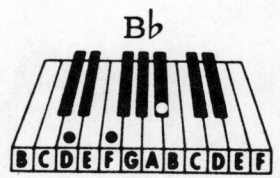

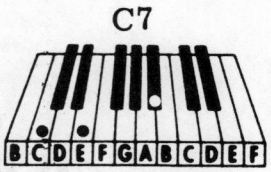

GUANTANAMERA

Spanish Lyric by JOSE MARTI
English adaptation by BERNARD GASSO (ASCAP)

There are several "waiting" points - where the melodic and harmonic action is held up, so to speak - in this song. Measure 2 is an example:-

1 2 3 & 4 &

In all cases it is essential not to hurry the time, and to count carefully.

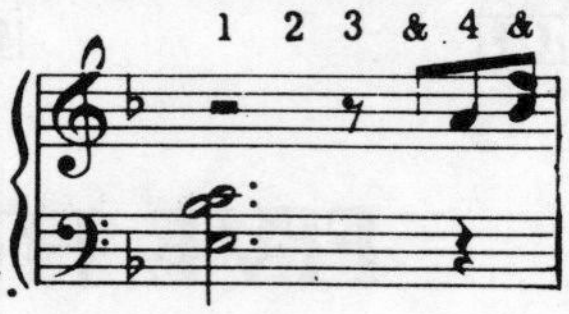

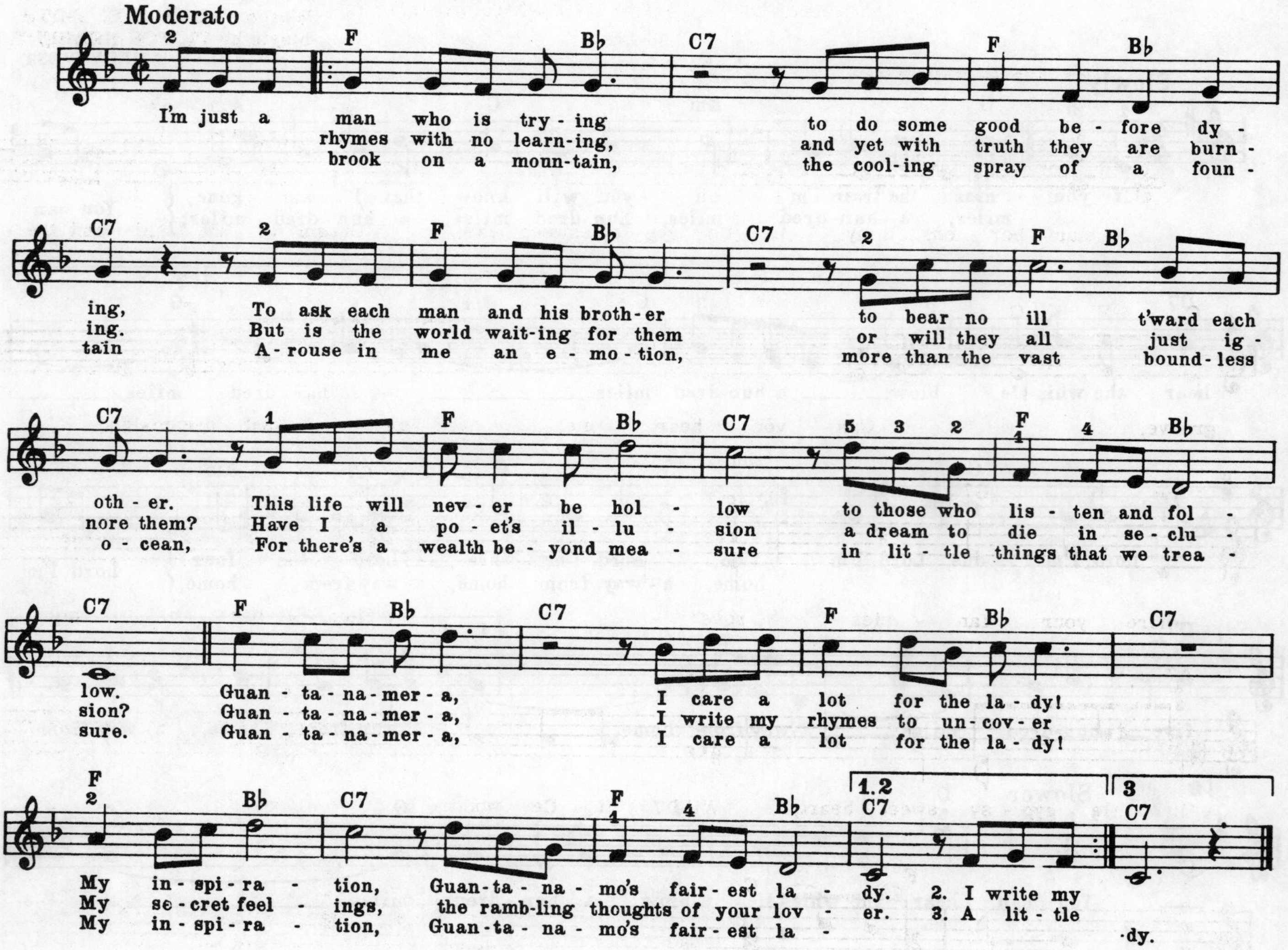

Moderato
I'm just a man who is try - ing to do some good be - fore dy - ing,
rhymes with no learn-ing, and yet with truth they are burn - ing.
brook on a moun-tain, the cool-ing spray of a foun - tain
To ask each man and his broth-er to bear no ill t'ward each oth - er.
But is the world wait-ing for them or will they all just ig - nore them?
A-rouse in me an e - mo - tion, more than the vast bound-less o - cean,
This life will nev - er be hol - low to those who lis - ten and fol - low.
Have I a po - et's il - lu - sion a dream to die in se - clu - sion?
For there's a wealth be - yond mea - sure in lit - tle things that we trea - sure.
Guan - ta - na - mer - a, I care a lot for the la - dy!
Guan - ta - na - mer - a, I write my rhymes to un - cov - er
Guan - ta - na - mer - a, I care a lot for the la - dy!
My in - spi - ra - tion, Guan - ta - na - mo's fair - est la - dy. 2. I write my
My se - cret feel - ings, the ramb - ling thoughts of your lov - er. 3. A lit - tle
My in - spi - ra - tion, Guan - ta - na - mo's fair - est la - dy.

C
F
D7
G7
A7
A♭7
BCDEFGABCDEF

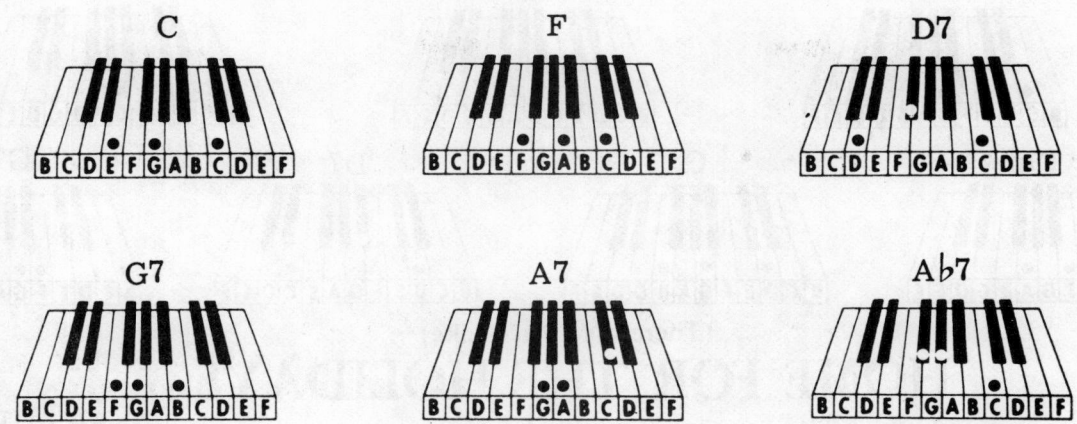

GYPSY LOVE SONG

(Slumber On, My Little Gypsy Sweetheart)

Words by HARRY B. SMITH
Music by VICTOR HERBERT
1898

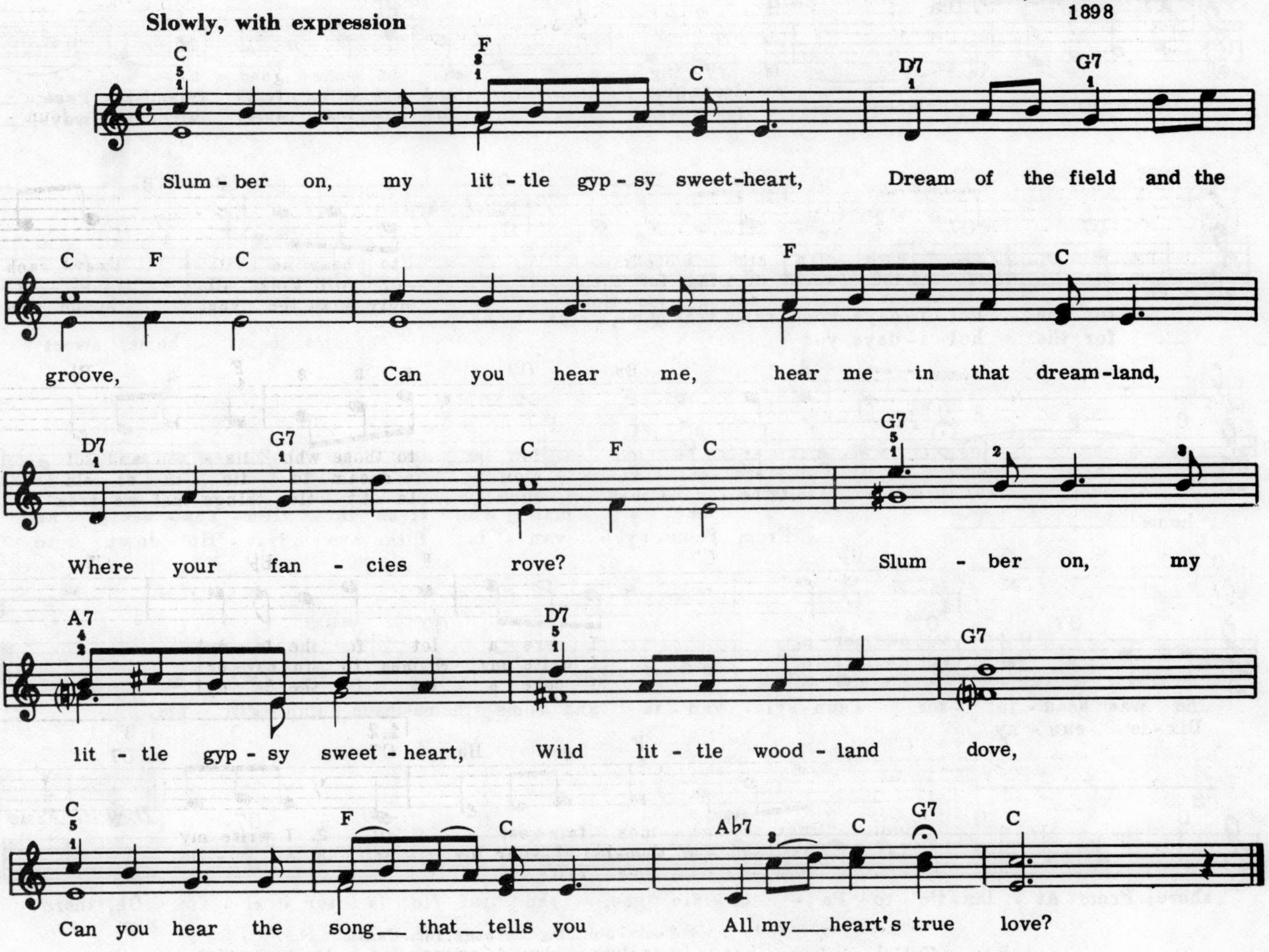

Slowly, with expression
C F C D7 G7
Slum - ber on, my lit - tle gyp - sy sweet-heart, Dream of the field and the
C F C F C
groove, Can you hear me, hear me in that dream-land,
D7 G7 C F C G7
Where your fan - cies rove? Slum - ber on, my
A7 D7 G7
lit - tle gyp - sy sweet - heart, Wild lit - tle wood - land dove,
C F C A♭7 C G7 C
Can you hear the song — that — tells you All my — heart's true love?

(There's No Place Like)

HOME FOR THE HOLIDAYS

By
AL STILLMAN and
ROBERT ALLEN

Oh, there's no place like home for the hol-i-days, __ 'cause no mat-ter how far a-way you roam, __

When you pine for the sun-shine of a friend-ly gaze, __
If you want to be hap-py in a mil-lion ways, __

1. for the hol-i-days, you can't beat home, sweet home.
2. for the hol-i-days, you can't beat home, sweet

home. __

I met a man who lives in Ten-nes-see and
From Penn-syl-van-ia folks are trav-'lin' down to

1. he was head-in' for Penn-syl-van-ia and some home-made pump-kin pie.

Dix-ie's sun-ny

2. shore; From At-lan-tic to Pa-ci-fic, gee, the traf-fic is ter-ri-fic. Oh, there's

D. S. al Fine

I DON'T CARE

Words by JEAN LENOX
Music by HARRY F. SUTTON
1905

Bright Tempo

I don't care, _____ I don't care, _____ What they may

think of me, _____ I'm hap-py go luck-y, Men say I am

pluck-y, So jol-ly and care free, I don't care _____

I don't care, _____ If I do get the mean and

sto-ny stare, If I'm nev-er suc-cess-ful, It won't be dis-

tress-ful, 'Cos I don't care. _____

B♭
B♭7
E♭
D7
Gm
C7
F7

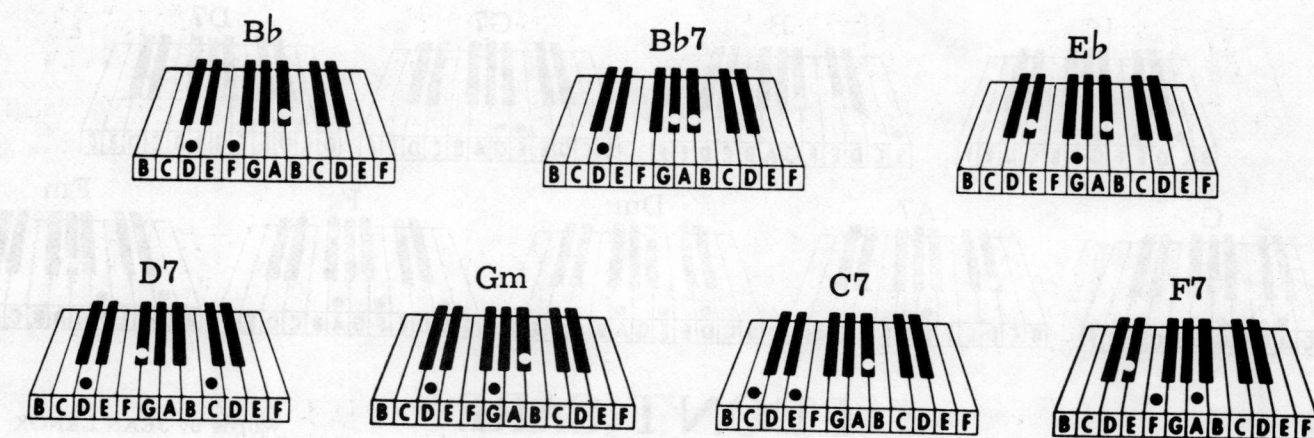

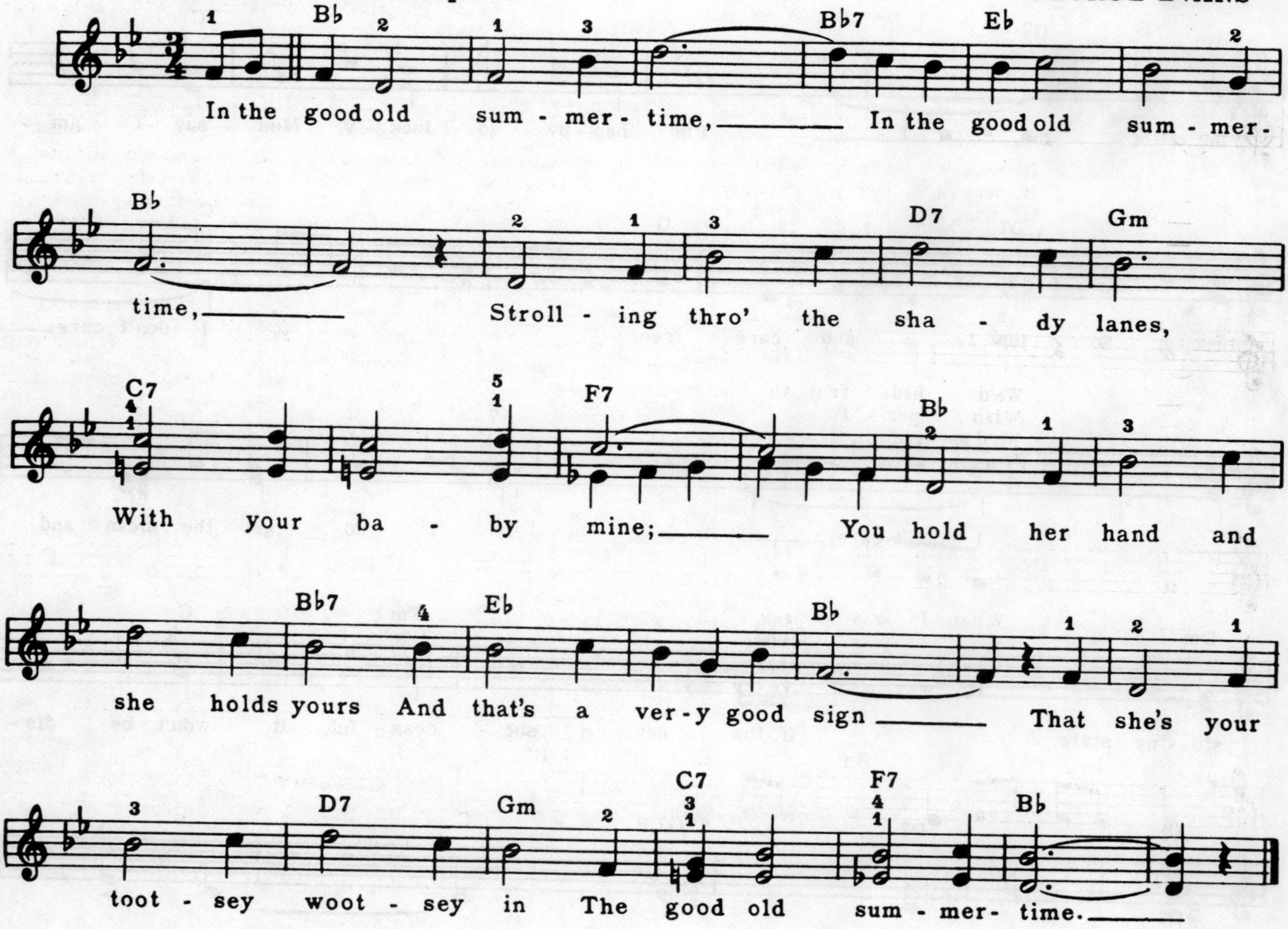

IN THE GOOD OLD SUMMERTIME

By REN SHIELDS and
GEORGE EVANS

Moderate Waltz tempo

B♭ B♭7 E♭
In the good old sum - mer - time, In the good old sum - mer -
B♭ D7 Gm
time, Stroll - ing thro' the sha - dy lanes,
C7 F7 B♭
With your ba - by mine; You hold her hand and
B♭7 E♭ B♭
she holds yours And that's a ver - y good sign That she's your
D7 Gm C7 F7 B♭
toot - sey woot - sey in The good old sum - mer - time.

Em
F
G
E
D
Bm
B7
B

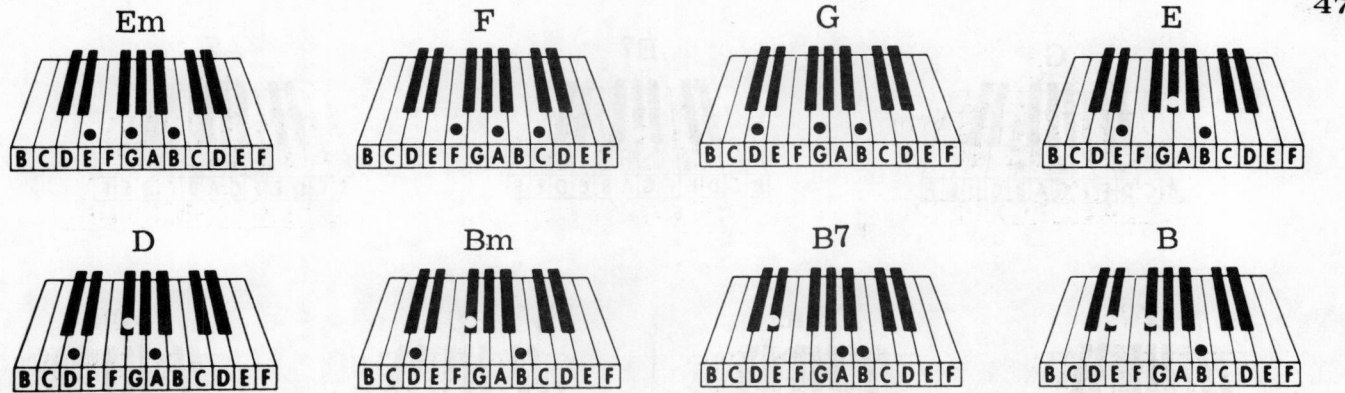

IT WAS A VERY GOOD YEAR

By
ERVIN DRAKE

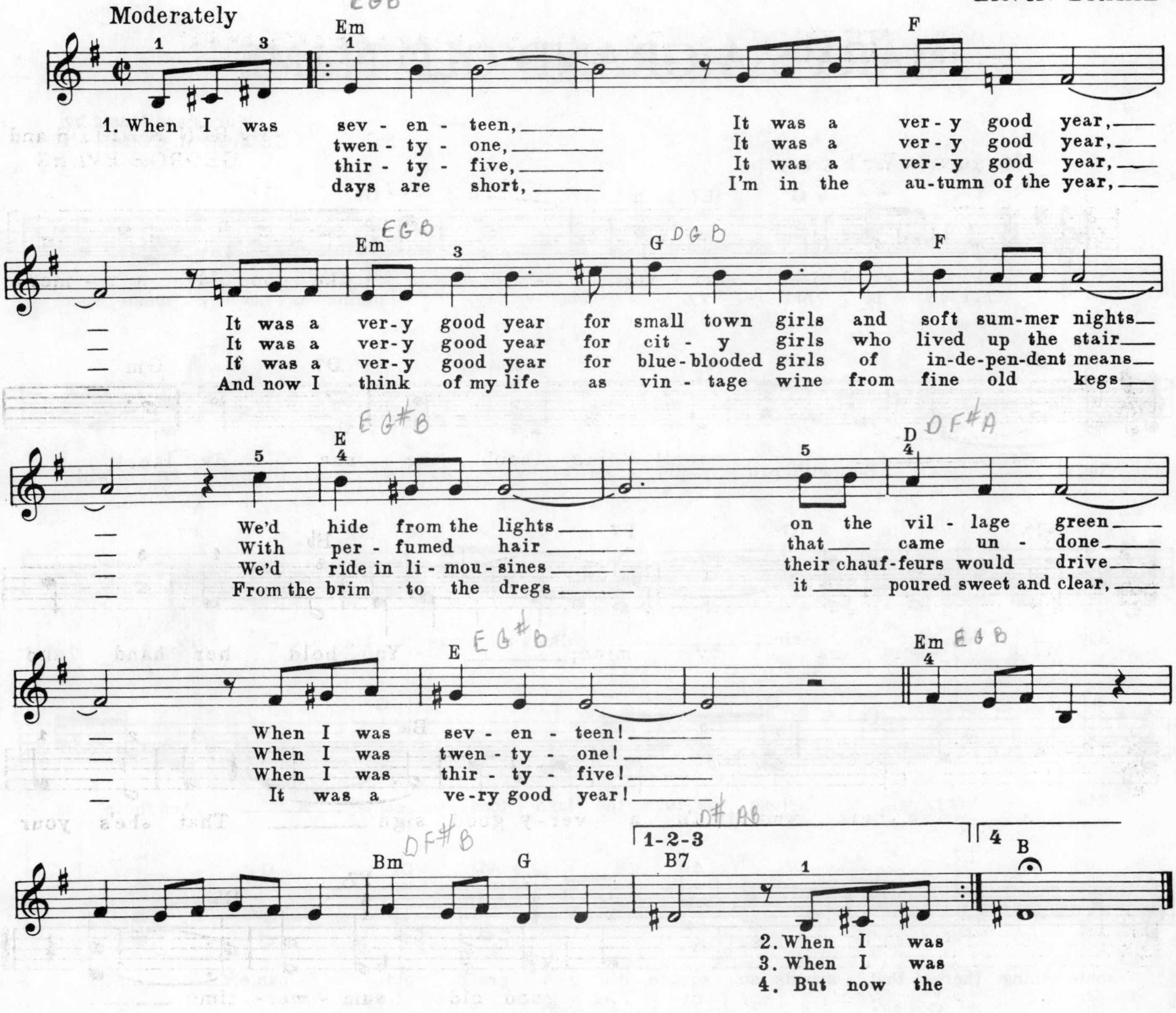

Moderately
Em
F
1. When I was sev - en - teen, It was a ver - y good year, It was a ver - y good year for small town girls and soft sum-mer nights
twen - ty - one, It was a ver - y good year, It was a ver - y good year for cit - y girls who lived up the stair
thir - ty - five, It was a ver - y good year, It was a ver - y good year for blue-blooded girls of in-de-pen-dent means
days are short, I'm in the au-tumn of the year, And now I think of my life as vin - tage wine from fine old kegs
Em
G
F
E
D
We'd hide from the lights on the vil - lage green When I was sev - en - teen!
With per - fumed hair that came un - done When I was twen - ty - one!
We'd ride in li - mou - sines their chauf-feurs would drive When I was thir - ty - five!
From the brim to the dregs it poured sweet and clear, It was a ve-ry good year!
E
Em
Bm
G
1-2-3
B7
4
B
2. When I was
3. When I was
4. But now the

G
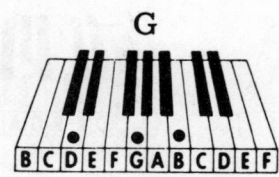

E7

A7
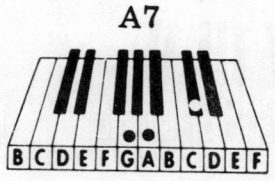

D7

Edim

F7

Am

MARY'S A GRAND OLD NAME

Words and Music by
GEORGE M. COHAN - 1905

For it is Ma - ry, Ma - ry, plain as an - y name can

be; _____ But with pro - pri - et - y, so - ci - e - ty will

say Ma - rie. _____ But it was Ma - ry,

Ma - ry, long be - fore the fash - ions came; _____ And there is

some - thing there that sounds so square, it's a grand old name. _____

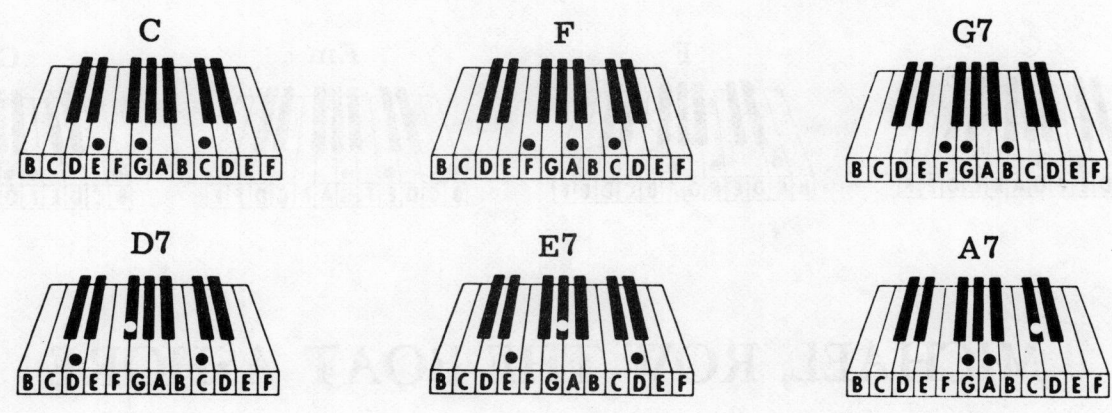

MEET ME IN ST. LOUIS

Words by ANDREW B. STERLING
Music by KERRY MILLS - 1904

Moderato

Meet me in St. Lou - is, Lou - is, Meet me at the fair. _____ Don't tell me the lights are shin - ing An - y place but there. _____ We will dance the "hooch - ee kooch-ie," _____ I will be your toot - sie woot - sie. _____ Meet me in St. Lou - is, Lou - is, Meet me at the fair. _____

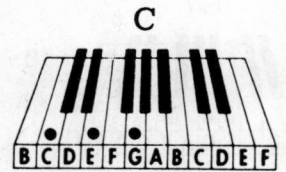 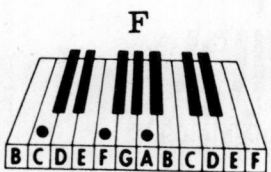 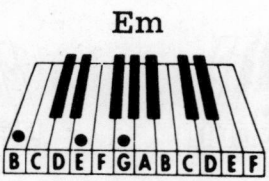 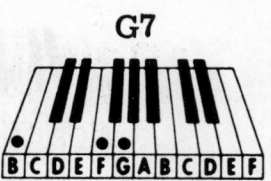

MICHAEL, ROW THE BOAT ASHORE

TRADITIONAL
Adaptation by JOHN BRIMHALL

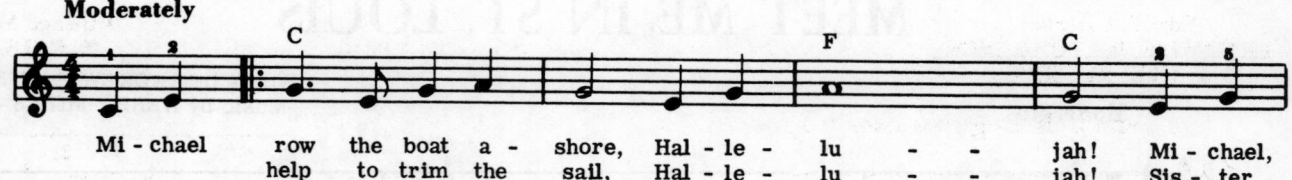

Mi - chael row the boat a - shore, Hal - le - lu - jah! Mi - chael,
help to trim the sail, Hal - le - lu - jah! Sis - ter,

row the boat a - shore Hal - le - lu - jah! Riv - er Jor - dan's wet and
help to trim the sail, Hal - le - lu - jah! Riv - er Jor - dan's deep and

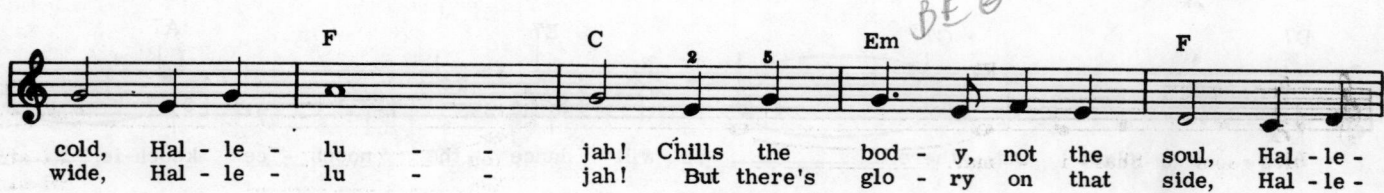

cold, Hal - le - lu - jah! Chills the bod - y, not the soul, Hal - le -
wide, Hal - le - lu - jah! But there's glo - ry on that side, Hal - le -

lu - jah! Sis - ter
jah! Trum - pet sound the ju - bi - lee, Hal - le -

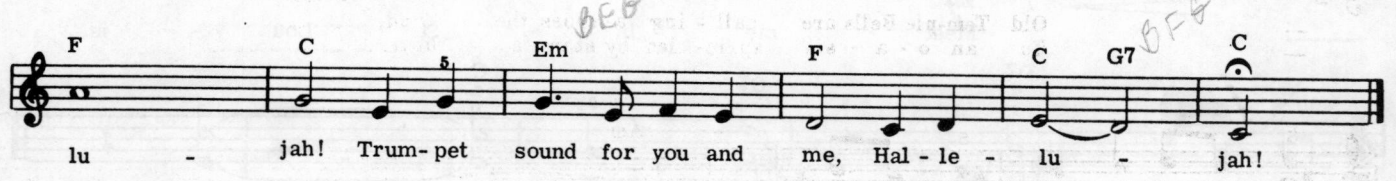

lu - jah! Trum - pet sound for you and me, Hal - le - lu - jah!

C
Dm6
E
E7
Am
G
F
F7
BCDEFGABCDEF

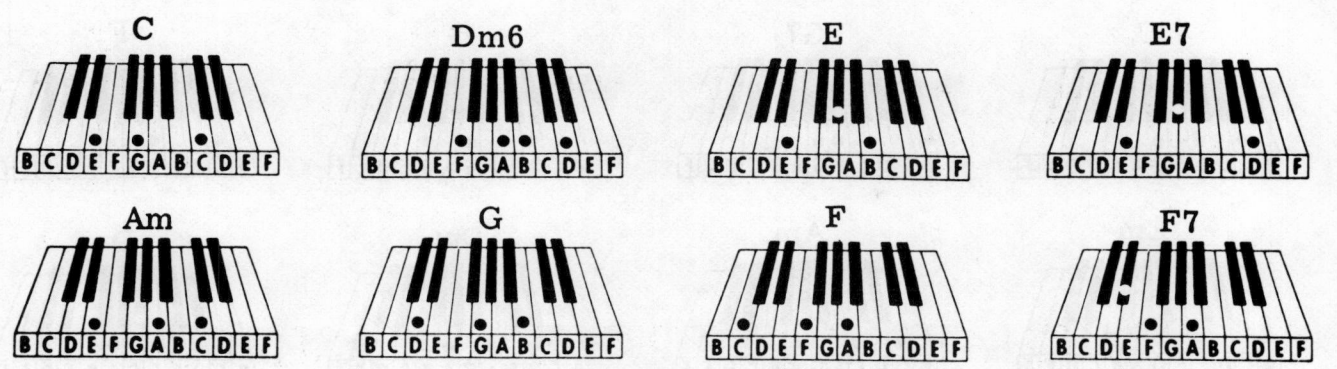

MISIRLOU

English Lyric by
FRED WISE, MILTON LEEDS
and S.K. RUSSELL

Title and Music by
N. ROUBENIS
Spanish Lyric by J. PINA

Tempo di Beguine (*not too fast*)

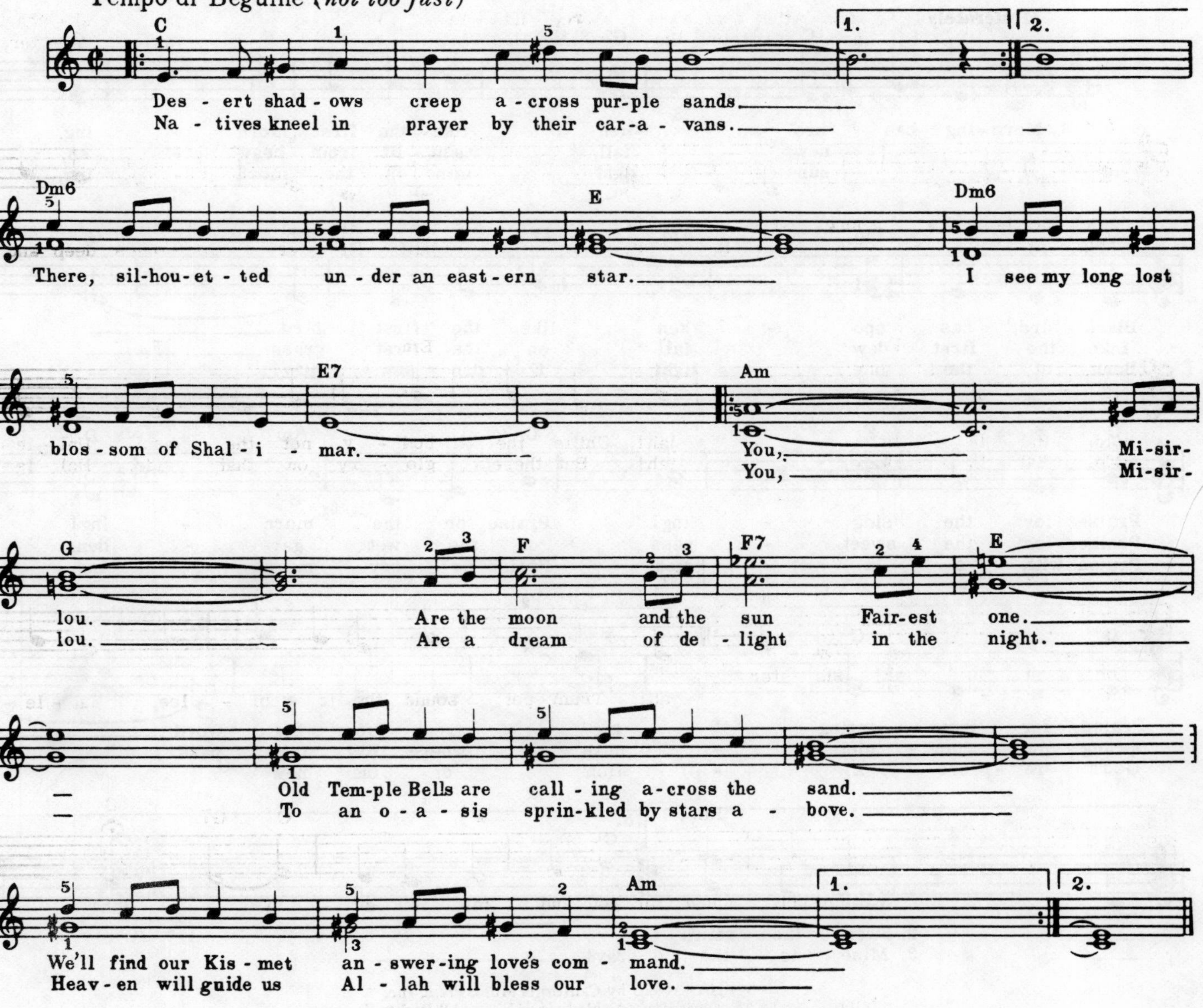

C
Des - ert shad - ows creep a - cross pur - ple sands.
Na - tives kneel in prayer by their car - a - vans.
Dm6
E
Dm6
There, sil - hou - et - ted un - der an east - ern star.
I see my long lost
E7
Am
blos - som of Shal - i - mar.
You, Mi - sir -
You, Mi - sir -
G
F
F7
E
lou. Are the moon and the sun Fair - est one.
lou. Are a dream of de - light in the night.
Old Tem - ple Bells are call - ing a - cross the sand.
To an o - a - sis sprin - kled by stars a - bove.
Am
We'll find our Kis - met an - swer - ing love's com - mand.
Heav - en will guide us Al - lah will bless our love.

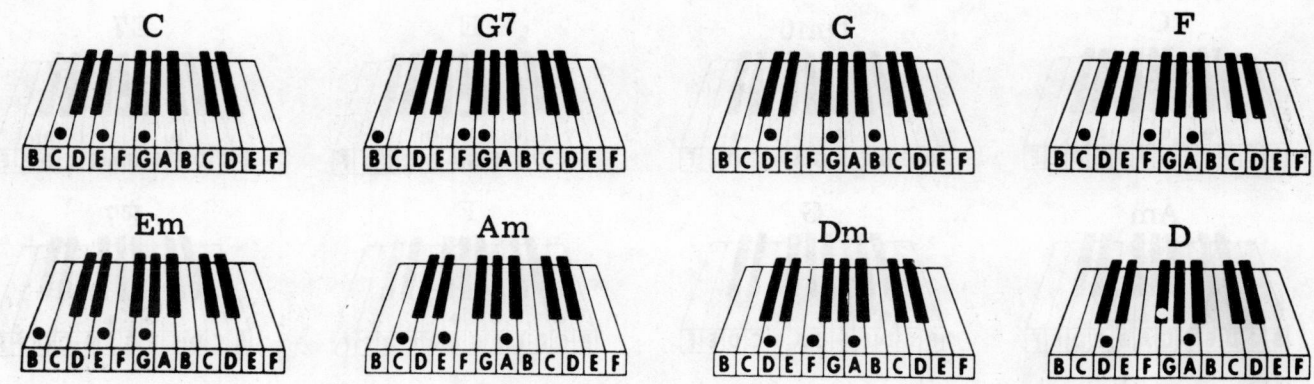

MORNING HAS BROKEN

Words by ELEANOR FARJEON
Musical Arrangement by JOHN BRIMHALL

Moderately

C　　　　G7 *BFG*　　　　　　F　　　C

1. Morn-ing has bro - ken　　like the first morn - ing.
　 new - fall,　　sun - lit from heav - en,
　 sun - light,　mine is the morn - ing,

Em *BEG*　Am *CEA*　C　　Dm *DFA*　G

Black - bird has spo - ken　like the first bird.
Like the first dew　fall　on the first grass.
Born of the one　light　E - den saw play!

C　　　F　　　　C　　Am *CEA*　D *DF#A*

Praise for the sing - ing!　Praise for the morn - ing!
Praise for the sweet - ness　of the wet gar - den,
Praise with e - la - tion,　Praise ev - ery morn - ing,

G　　　C　　　F　　G7 *BFG*　　1. 2. C

Praise for them, spring - ing　fresh from the Word.
Sprung in com - plete - ness　where His feet pass.
God's re - cre - a - tion　of the new

3. C

2. Sweet the rain's
3. Mine is the day!

NOLA

By FELIX ARNDT

O HAPPY DAY

Words by PHILIP DODDRIDGE
Music by E. F. RIMBAULT
Adapted by JOHN BRIMHALL

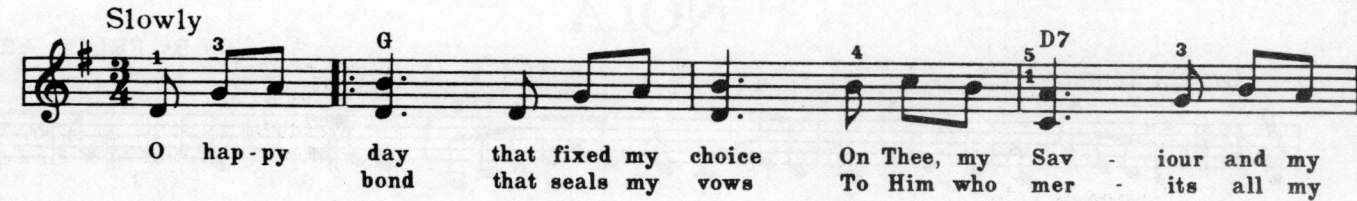

O hap-py day that fixed my choice On Thee, my Sav-iour and my
bond that seals my vows To Him who mer-its all my

God! Well may this glow-ing heart re-joice And tell its rap-tures all a-
love! Let cheer-ful an-thems fill His house, While to that sa-cred shrine I

broad. } Hap-py day, hap-py day When Je-sus washed my sins a-
move.

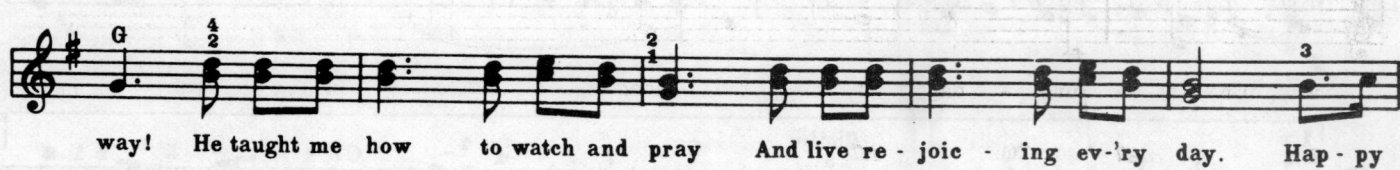

way! He taught me how to watch and pray And live re-joic-ing ev'ry day. Hap-py

day, hap-py day, When Je-sus washed my sins a-way! O hap-py way!

C
Cdim
G7
A7
Dm

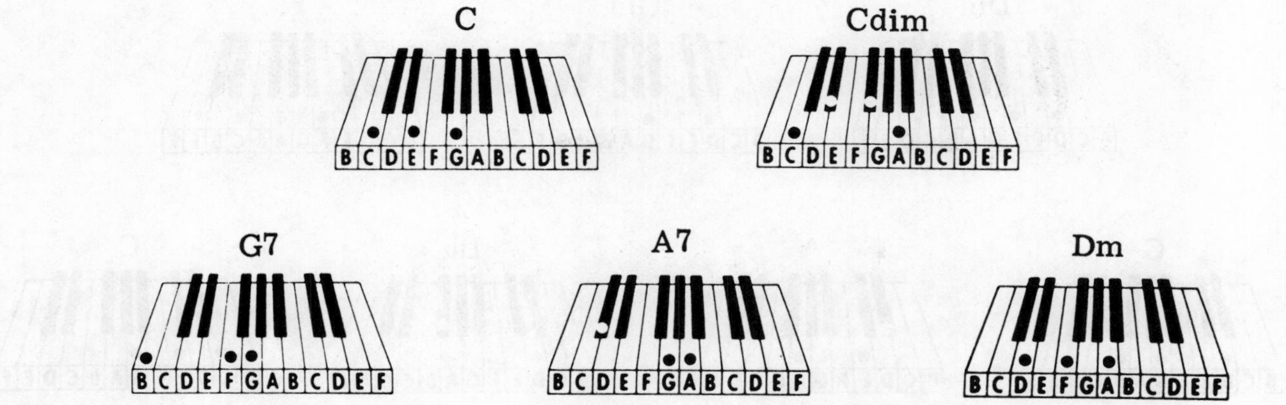

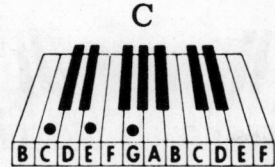

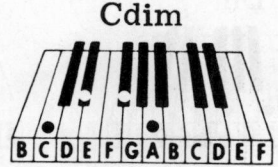

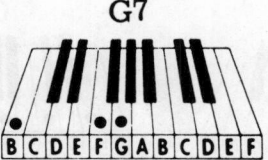

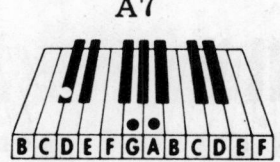

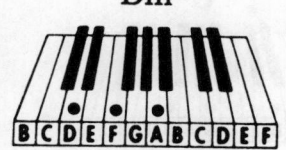

ON A SUNDAY AFTERNOON

Words by ANDREW B. STERLING
Music by HARRY VON TILZER
1902

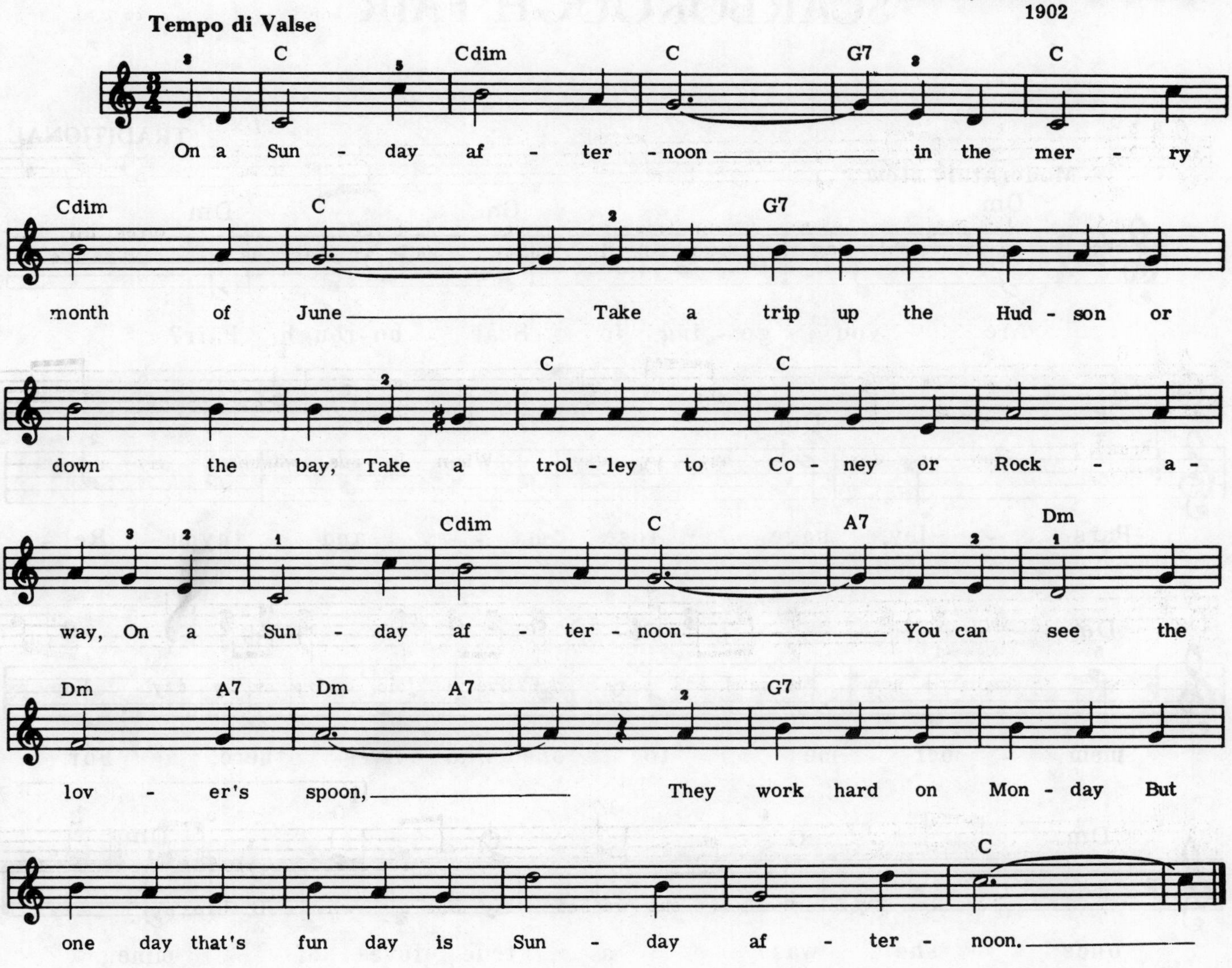

Tempo di Valse
On a Sun - day af - ter - noon in the mer - ry
month of June Take a trip up the Hud - son or
down the bay, Take a trol - ley to Co - ney or Rock - a -
way, On a Sun - day af - ter - noon You can see the
lov - er's spoon, They work hard on Mon - day But
one day that's fun day is Sun - day af - ter - noon.

Dm
Gm
F
G
A
B♭
C
BCDEFGABCDEF

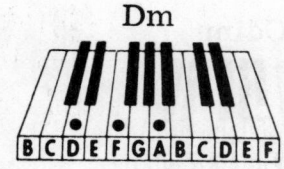

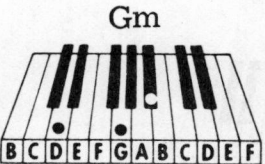

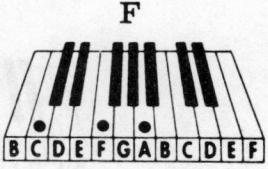

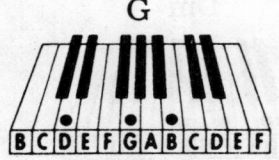

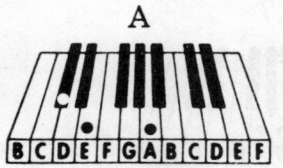

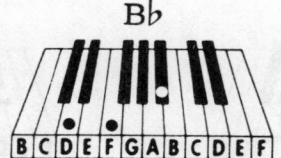

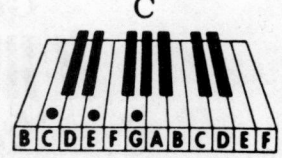

SCARBOROUGH FAIR

TRADITIONAL

Moderately slow

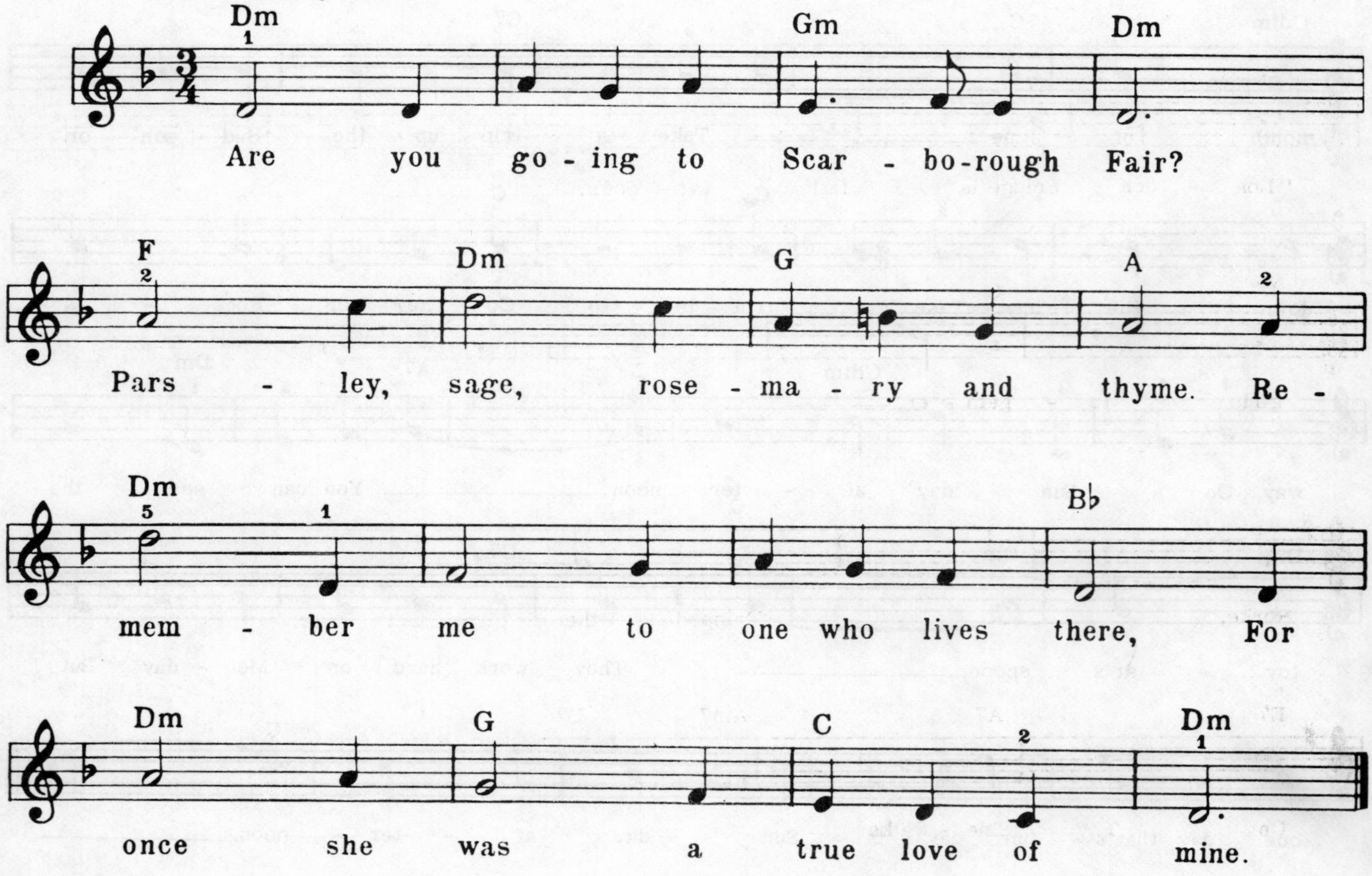

Dm Gm Dm
Are you go - ing to Scar - bo - rough Fair?
F Dm G A
Pars - ley, sage, rose - ma - ry and thyme. Re -
Dm B♭
mem - ber me to one who lives there, For
Dm G C Dm
once she was a true love of mine.

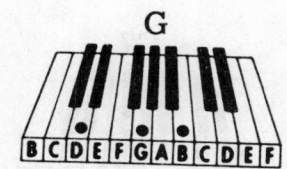

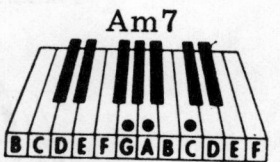

THE SIDEWALKS OF NEW YORK
(East Side, West Side, All Around The Town)

CHARLES B. LAWLOR

JAMES W. BLAKE
1894

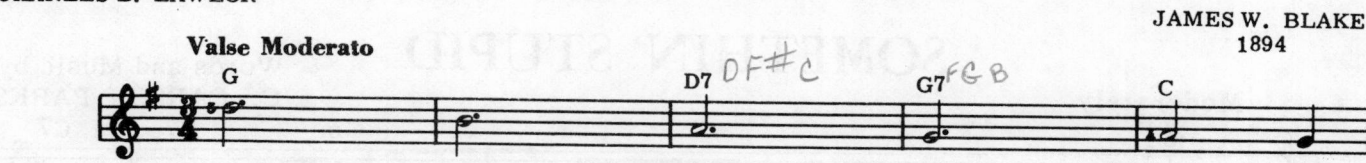

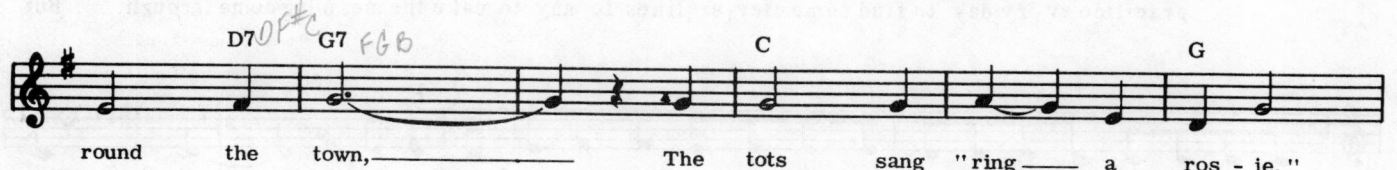

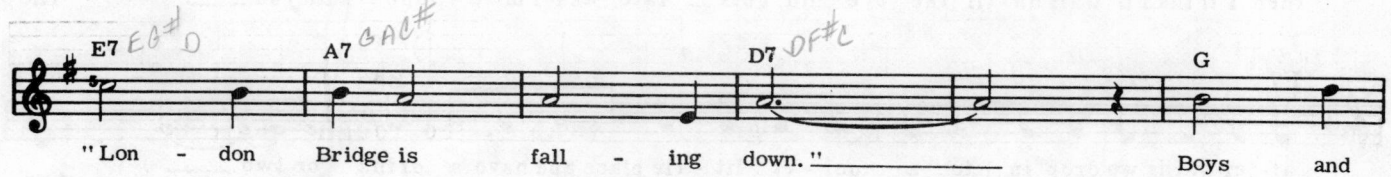

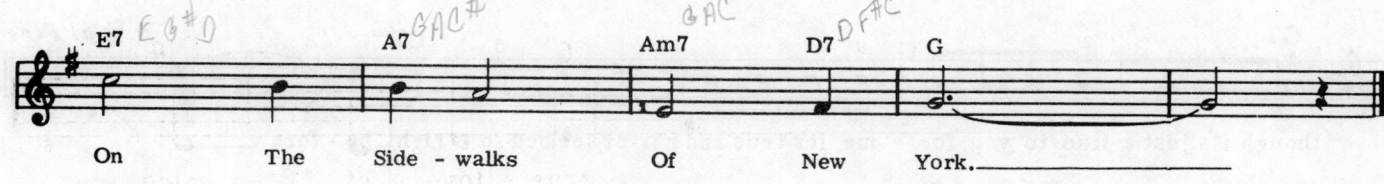

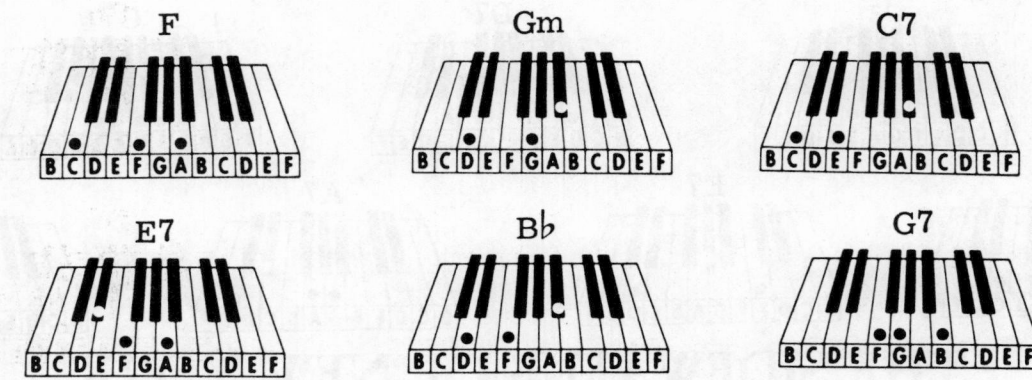

SOMETHIN' STUPID

Words and Music by
C. CARSON PARKS

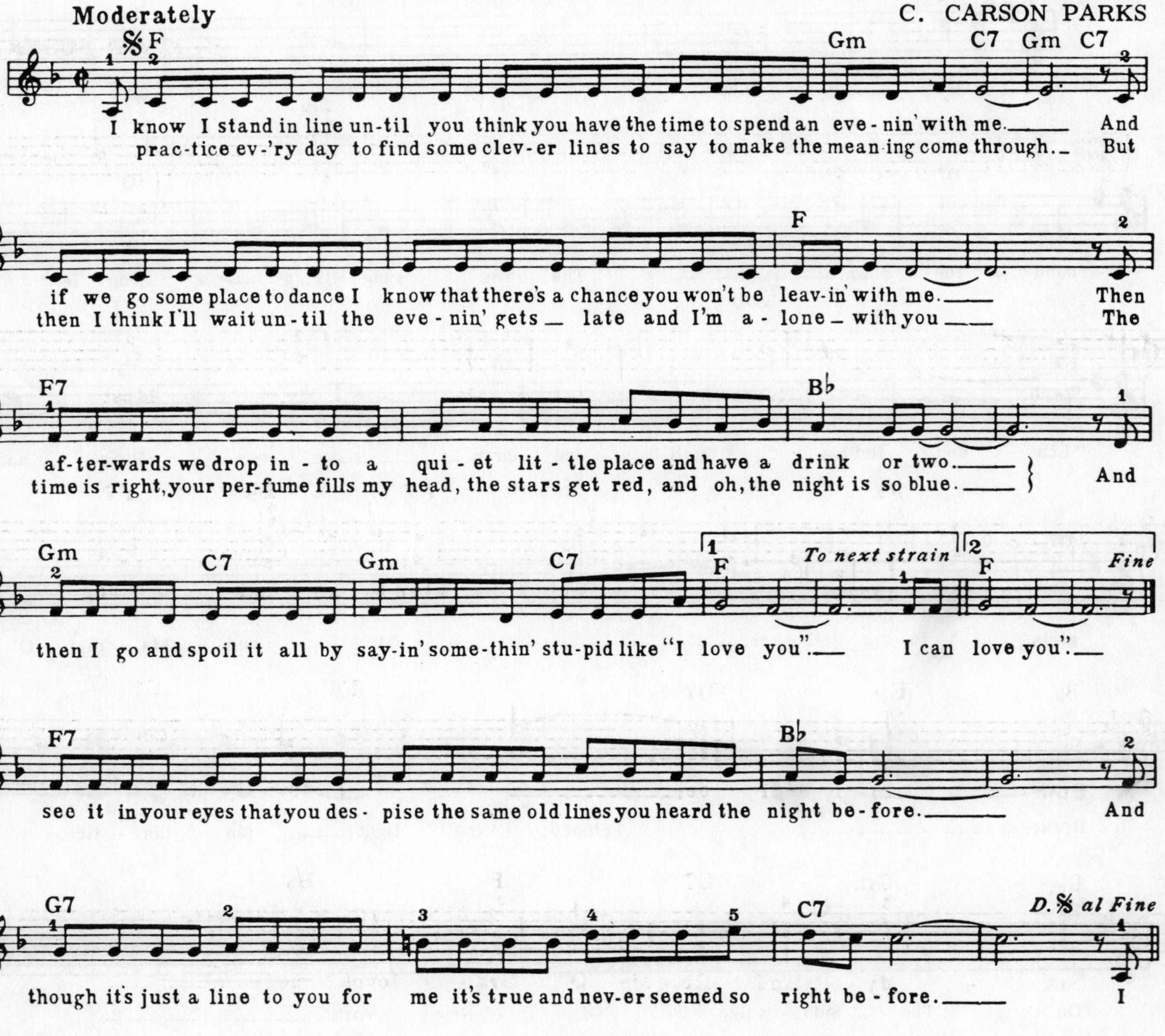

Moderately

F   Gm   C7   Gm   C7

I know I stand in line un-til you think you have the time to spend an eve-nin' with me.___ And
prac-tice ev-'ry day to find some clev-er lines to say to make the mean-ing come through.__ But

F

if we go some place to dance I know that there's a chance you won't be leav-in' with me.___ Then
then I think I'll wait un-til the eve-nin' gets __ late and I'm a-lone __ with you ___ The

F7   Bb

af-ter-wards we drop in-to a qui-et lit-tle place and have a drink or two.___ And
time is right, your per-fume fills my head, the stars get red, and oh, the night is so blue.___

Gm   C7   Gm   C7   1. F   *To next strain*   2. F   *Fine*

then I go and spoil it all by say-in' some-thin' stu-pid like "I love you".___ I can love you".___

F7   Bb

see it in your eyes that you des-pise the same old lines you heard the night be-fore.___ And

G7   C7   *D. %. al Fine*

though it's just a line to you for me it's true and nev-er seemed so right be-fore.___ I

B♭
F7
Gm
C7
E♭
D7
BCDEFGABCDEF

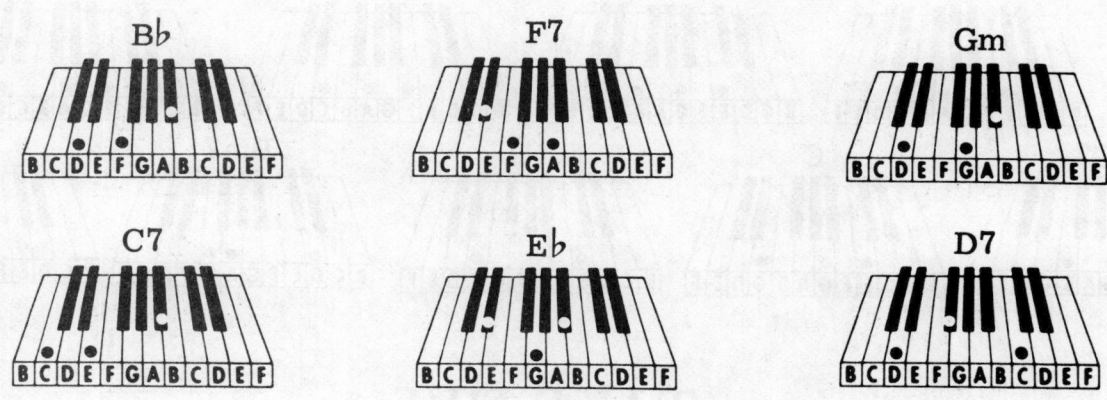

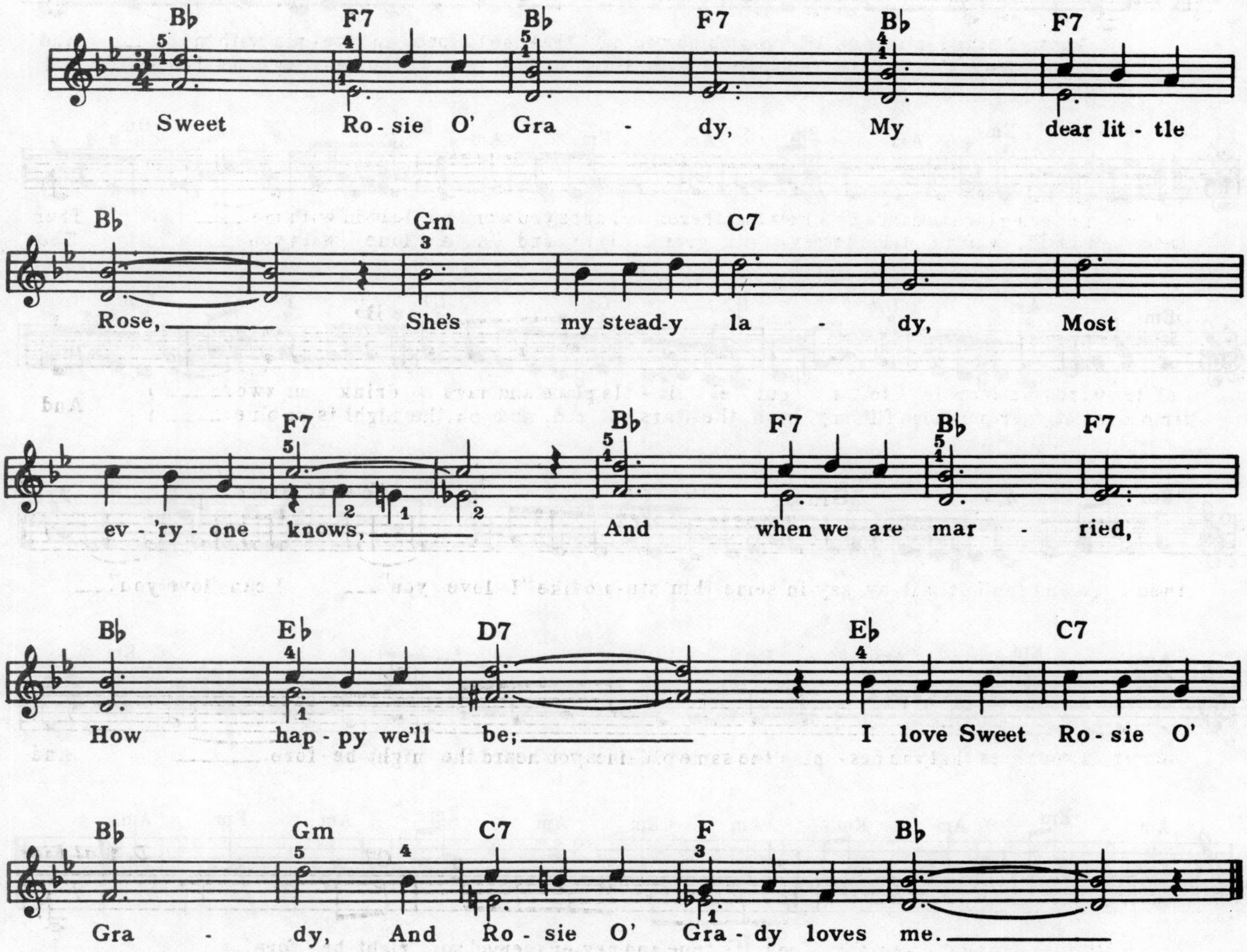

SWEET ROSIE O'GRADY

By MAUD NUGENT

Moderate waltz tempo

B♭ F7 B♭ F7 B♭ F7
Sweet Ro-sie O' Gra - dy, My dear lit-tle
B♭ Gm C7
Rose, She's my stead-y la - dy, Most
F7 B♭ F7 B♭ F7
ev-'ry-one knows, And when we are mar - ried,
B♭ E♭ D7 E♭ C7
How hap-py we'll be; I love Sweet Ro-sie O'
B♭ Gm C7 F B♭
Gra - dy, And Ro-sie O' Gra-dy loves me.

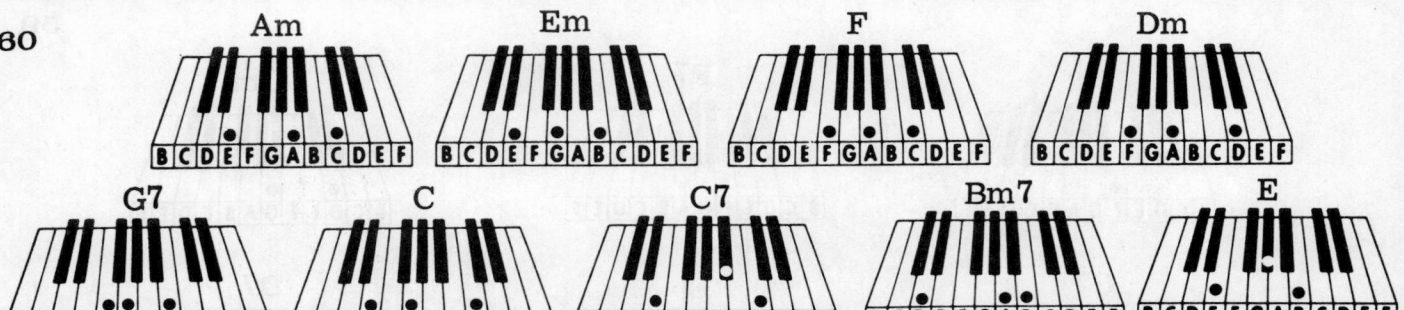

TAKE FIVE

By PAUL DESMOND

Moderately fast

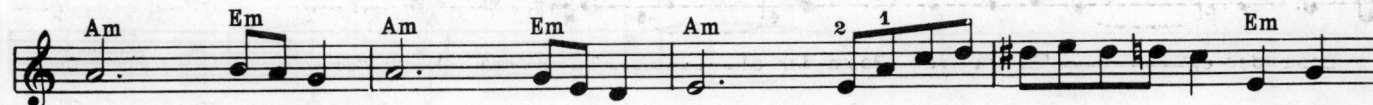

C
B C D E F G A B C D E F

G7
B C D E F G A B C D E F

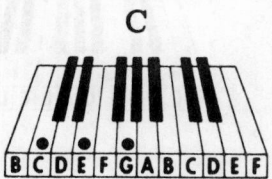

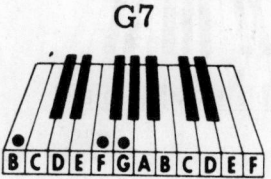

TA-RA-RA BOOM-DER-E!

HENRY SAYERS
1891

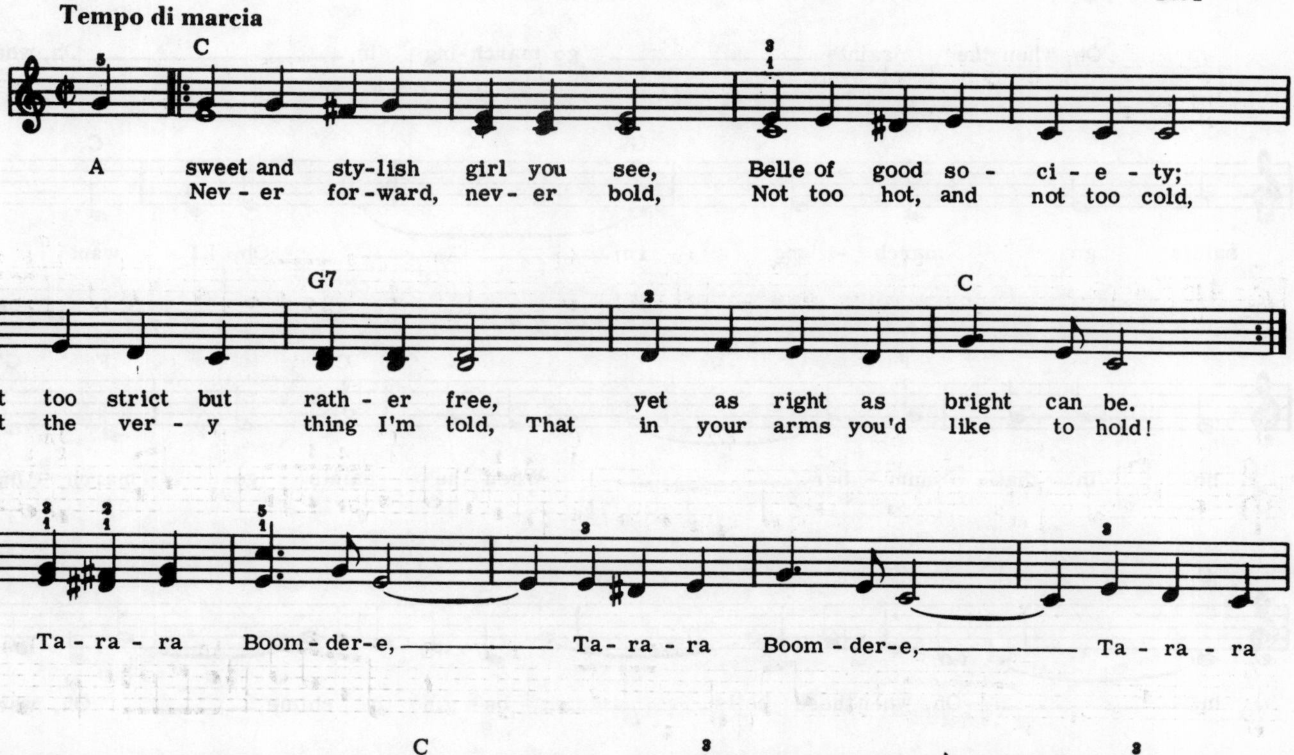

Tempo di marcia
C
A sweet and sty-lish girl you see, Belle of good so - ci - e - ty;
Nev - er for - ward, nev - er bold, Not too hot, and not too cold,
G7
C
Not too strict but rath - er free, yet as right as bright can be.
But the ver - y thing I'm told, That in your arms you'd like to hold!
C
Ta - ra - ra Boom - der - e, Ta - ra - ra Boom - der - e, Ta - ra - ra
G7
C
Boom - der - e, Ta - ra - ra Boom - der - e! Ta - ra - ra Boom - der - e, Ta - ra - ra
G7
C
Boom - der - e, Ta - ra - ra Boom - der - e, Ta - ra - ra Boom - der - e!

C
B C D E F G A B C D E F
G7
B C D E F G A B C D E F
F
B C D E F G A B C D E F

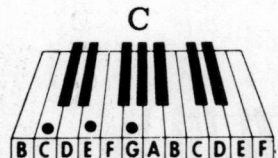

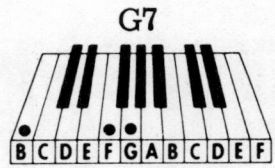

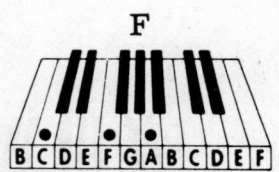

WHEN THE SAINTS GO MARCHING IN

TRADITIONAL

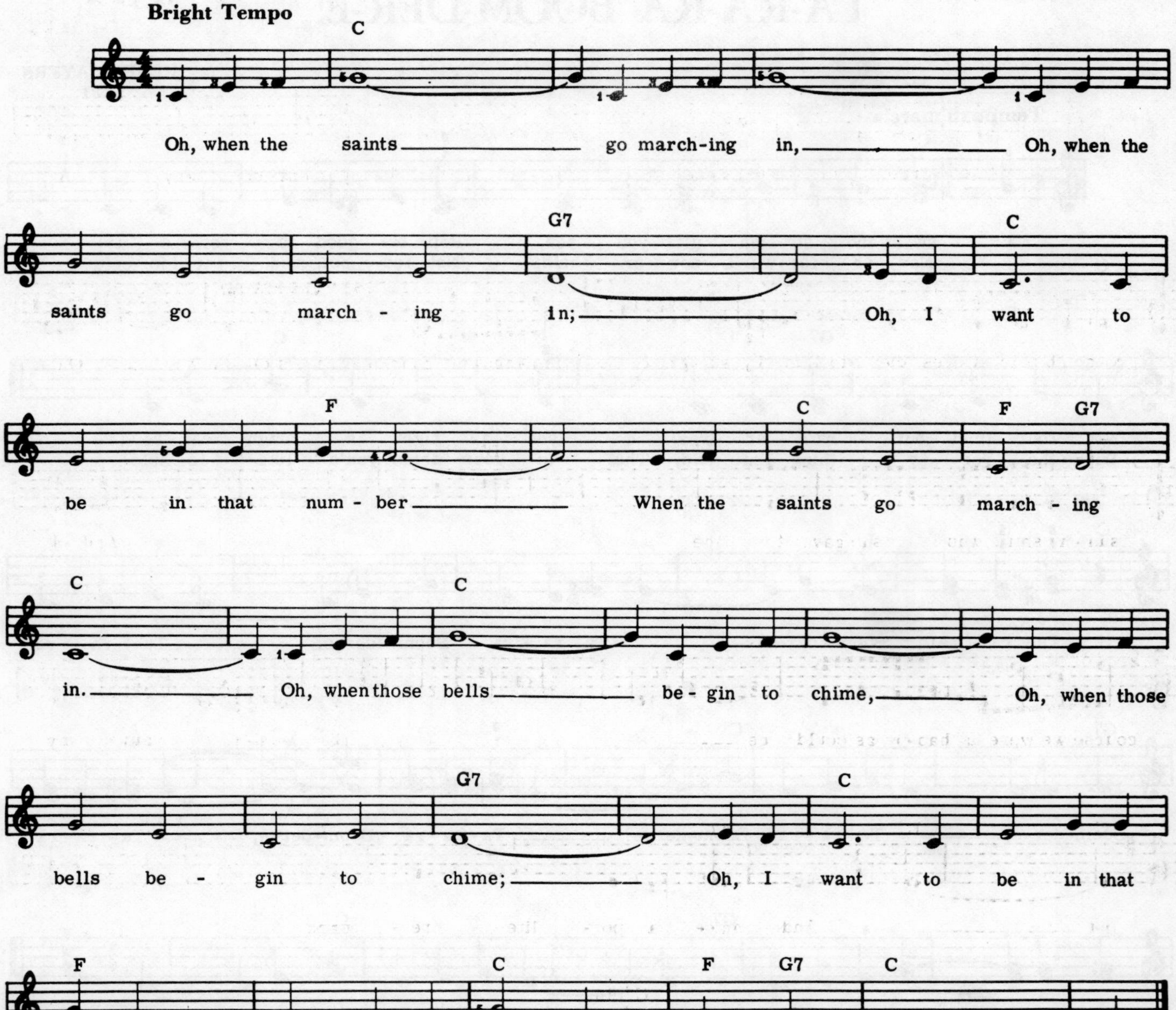

Bright Tempo
C G7 C F C F G7 C C G7 C F C F G7 C
1 3 4 5 1 3 4 5 1 5 4 1 1 5 1
Oh, when the saints go march-ing in, Oh, when the
saints go march - ing in; Oh, I want to
be in that num - ber When the saints go march - ing
in. Oh, when those bells be - gin to chime, Oh, when those
bells be - gin to chime; Oh, I want to be in that
num - ber When those bells be - gin to chime.

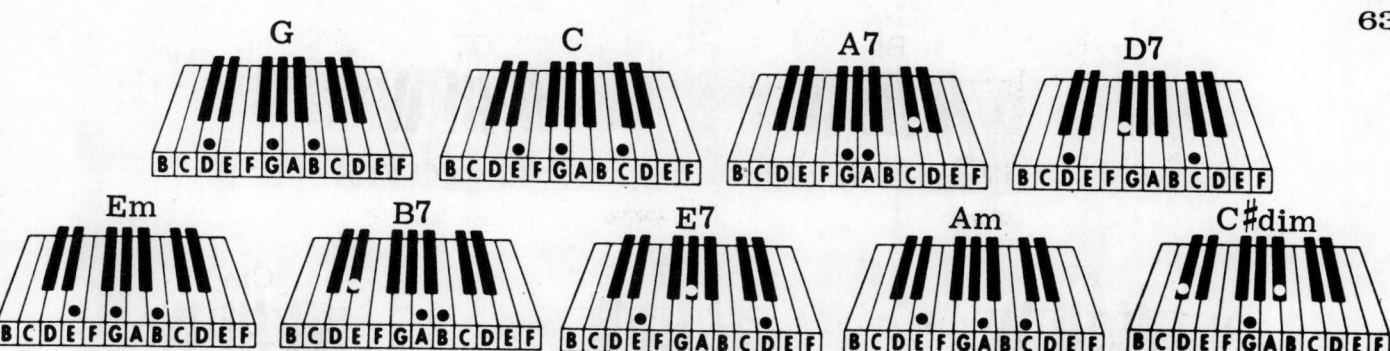

WHILE STROLLING IN THE PARK ONE DAY

ED HALEY

While stroll-ing in the park one day,_____ All in the mer-ry month of May; A

ro-quish pair of eyes, they took me by sur-prise In a mo-ment my poor heart she stole a-way. _____ Oh. a

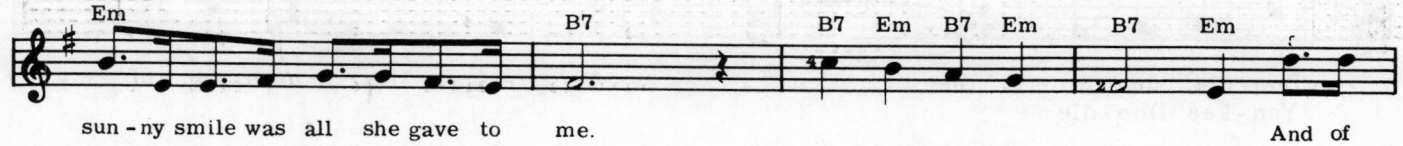

sun-ny smile was all she gave to me. And of

course we were as hap-py as could be. _____ So neat-ly I raised my

hat _____ And made a po-lite re-mark I

nev-er shall for-get that love-ly af-ter-noon, When I met her at the foun-tain in the park.

B♭

B C D E F G A B C D E F

C7

B C D E F G A B C D E F

F7

B C D E F G A B C D E F

G7

B C D E F G A B C D E F

Cm

B C D E F G A B C D E F

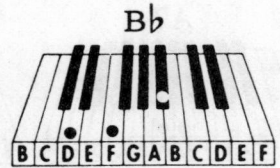

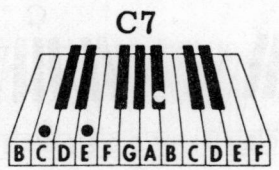

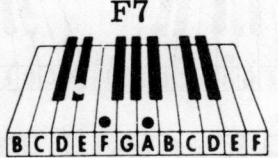

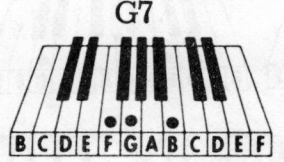

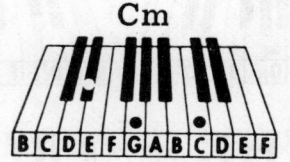

THE YANKEE DOODLE BOY

By GEORGE M. COHAN

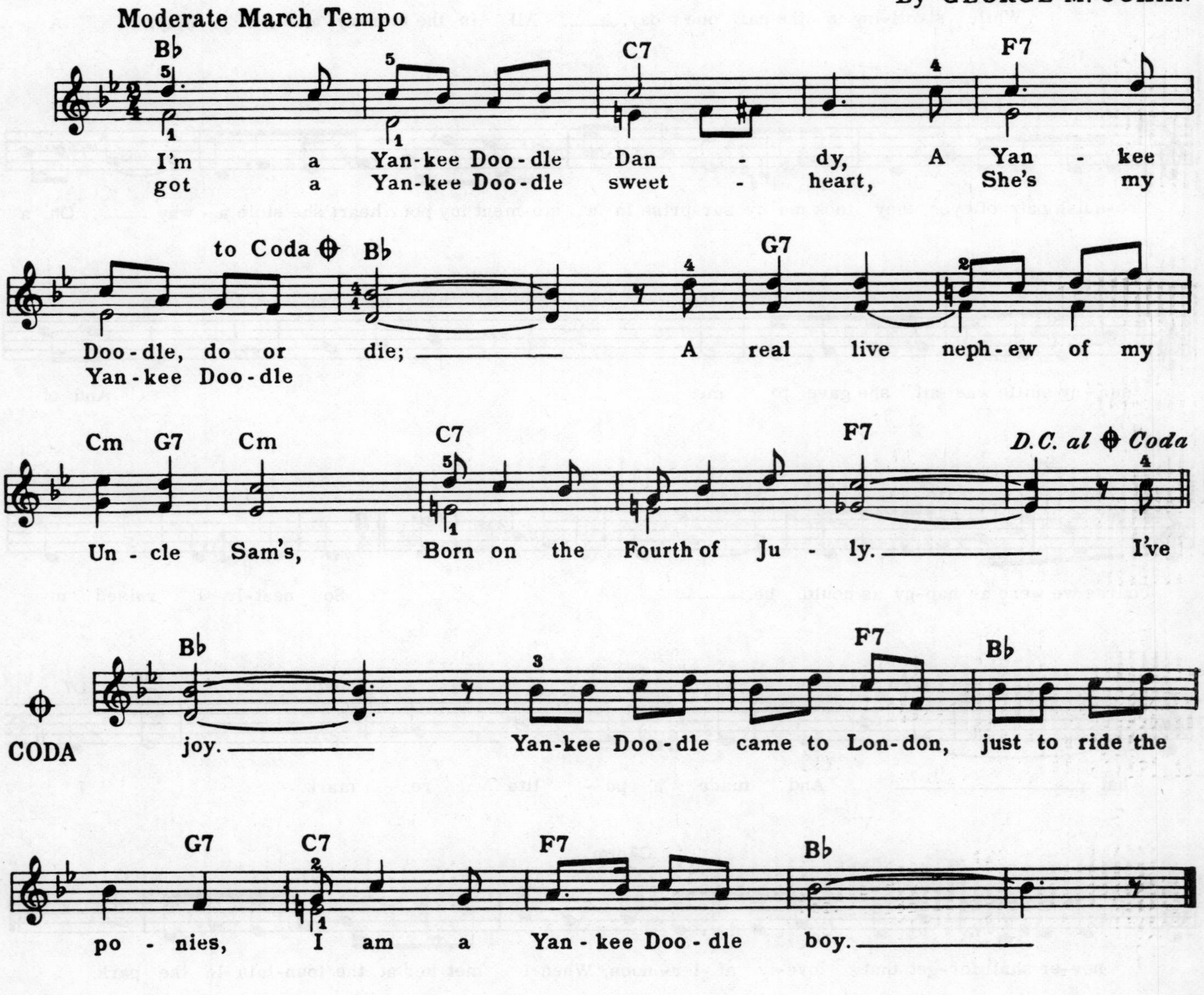

Moderate March Tempo
B♭ C7 F7
I'm a Yan-kee Doo-dle Dan - dy, A Yan - kee
got a Yan-kee Doo-dle sweet - heart, She's my
to Coda
B♭ G7
Doo-dle, do or die; A real live neph-ew of my
Yan-kee Doo-dle
Cm G7 Cm C7 F7
D.C. al Coda
Un-cle Sam's, Born on the Fourth of Ju - ly. I've
CODA
B♭ F7 B♭
joy. Yan-kee Doo-dle came to Lon-don, just to ride the
G7 C7 F7 B♭
po - nies, I am a Yan-kee Doo-dle boy.

G
Gdim
E7
Am
A7
D7
Ddim
Bm
E♭7
F♯7

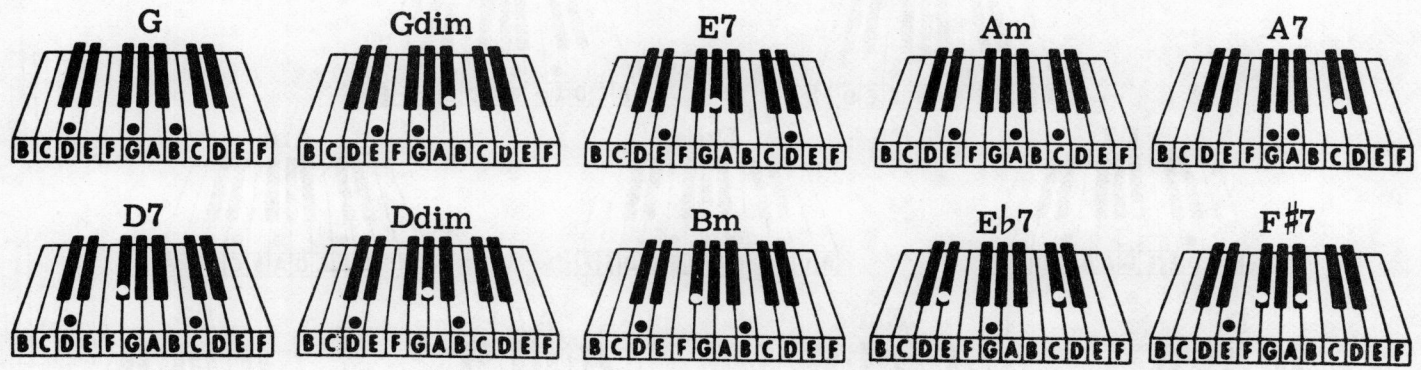

YOU TELL ME YOUR DREAM
(I'll Tell You Mine)

Words by SEYMOUR RICE and
ALBERT H. BROWN
Music by CHAS. N. DANIELS

Waltz Tempo

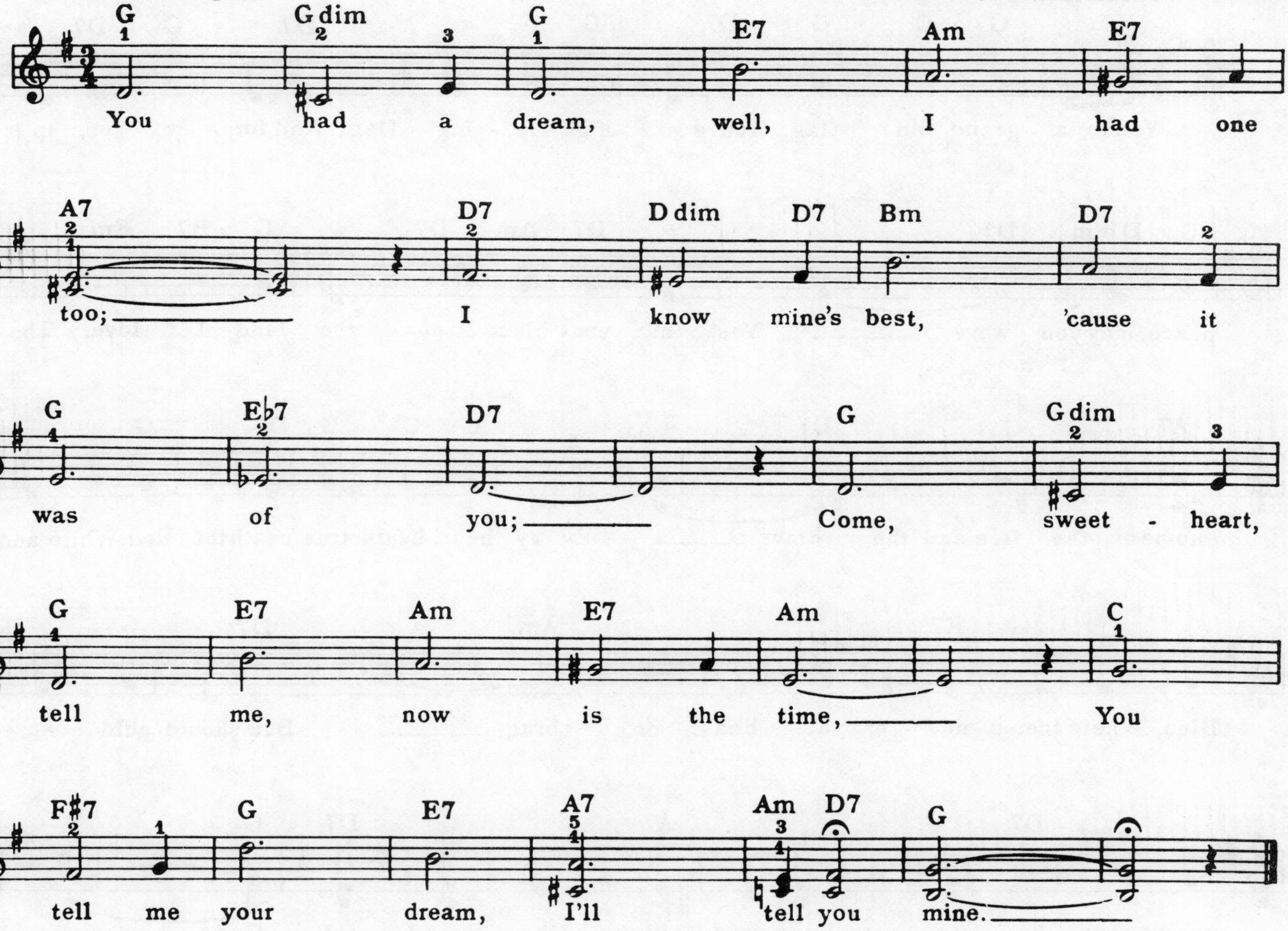

You had a dream, well, I had one too; I know mine's best, 'cause it was of you; Come, sweet - heart, tell me, now is the time, You tell me your dream, I'll tell you mine.

G
C
D7
Ddim
Am
B7
Em
A7
E7
B C D E F G A B C D E F

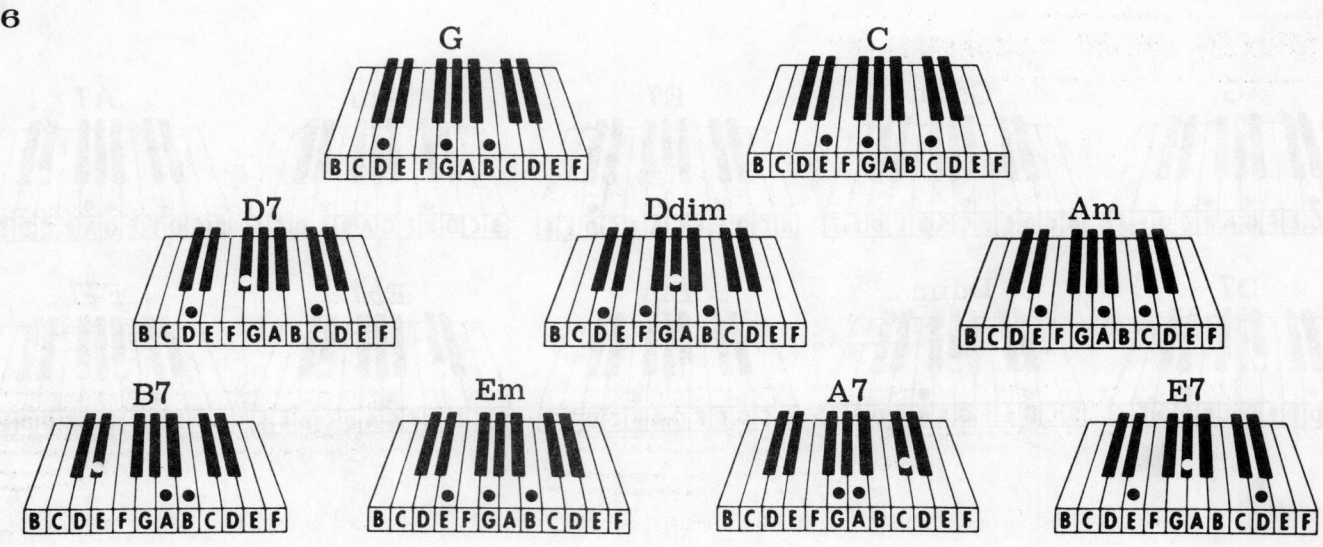

YOU'RE A GRAND OLD FLAG

By GEORGE M. COHAN

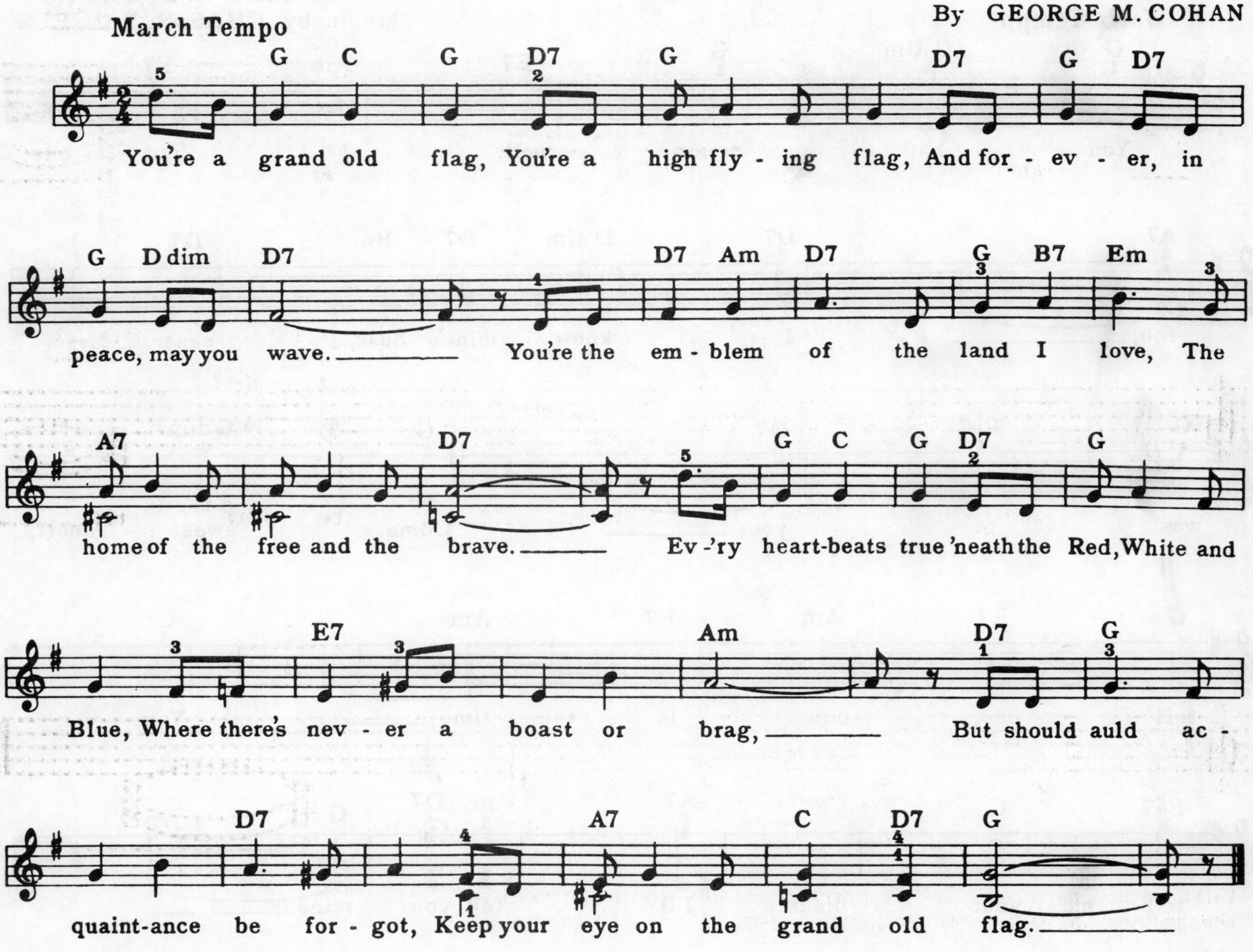

March Tempo
G C G D7 G D7 G D7
You're a grand old flag, You're a high fly - ing flag, And for - ev - er, in
G Ddim D7 D7 Am D7 G B7 Em
peace, may you wave. You're the em - blem of the land I love, The
A7 D7 G C G D7 G
home of the free and the brave. Ev - 'ry heart-beats true 'neath the Red, White and
E7 Am D7 G
Blue, Where there's nev - er a boast or brag, But should auld ac -
D7 A7 C D7 G
quaint-ance be for - got, Keep your eye on the grand old flag.

MELODY CHORD Arrangements

KUM BA YA

TRADITIONAL

Moderato

Some - one's sing - ing, Lord, _____ be with us; _____

some - one's sing - ing Lord, _____ be with us; _____

some - one's sing - ing, Lord, _____ be with us; _____

O Lord, _____ be with us.

*For all Part III songs:
Left hand plays the root of chord. Play the root each time the chord is indicated.
Use the pedal. Change pedal with each chord change.

AMAZING GRACE

TRADITIONAL

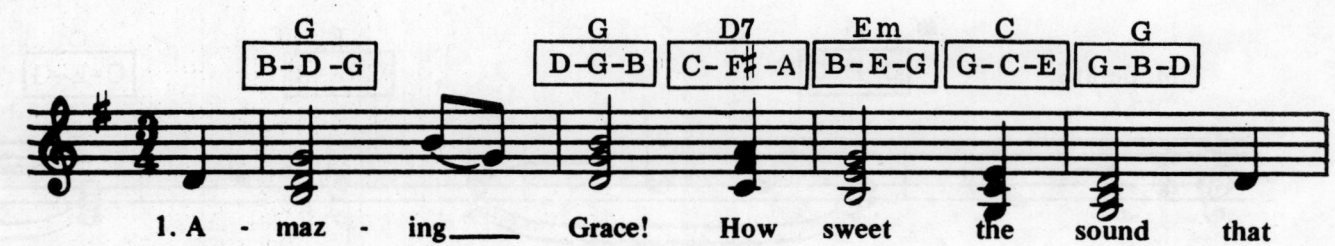

1. A - maz - ing___ Grace! How sweet the sound that

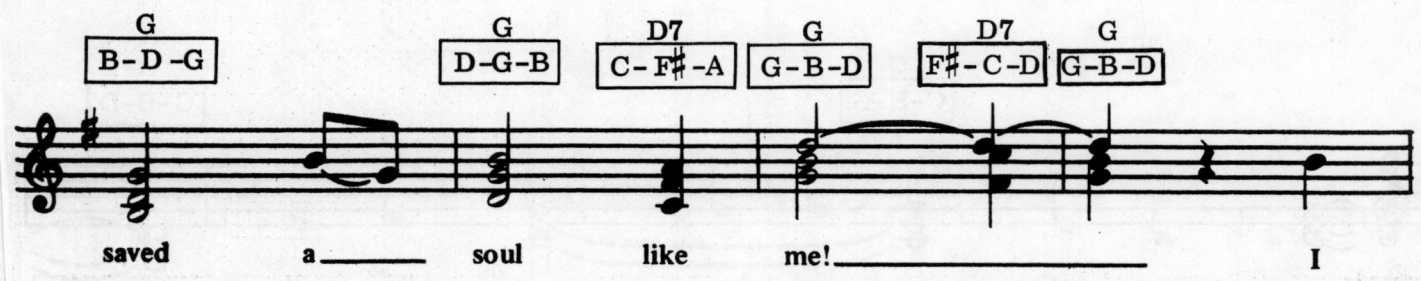

saved a ___ soul like me!_____ I

once___ was___ lost, but now___ am___ found; was

blind but___ now I see._____ 2. 'Twas

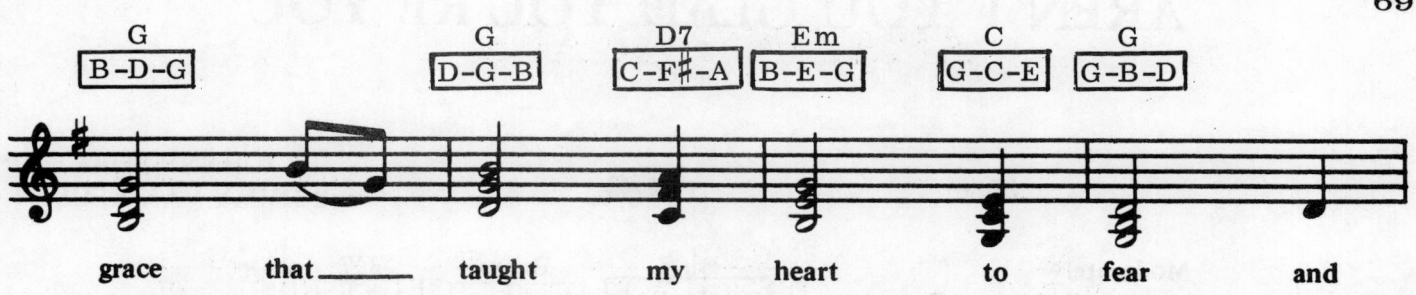

grace   that_____ taught   my   heart   to   fear   and

grace   my_____ fears   re - lieved._____ How

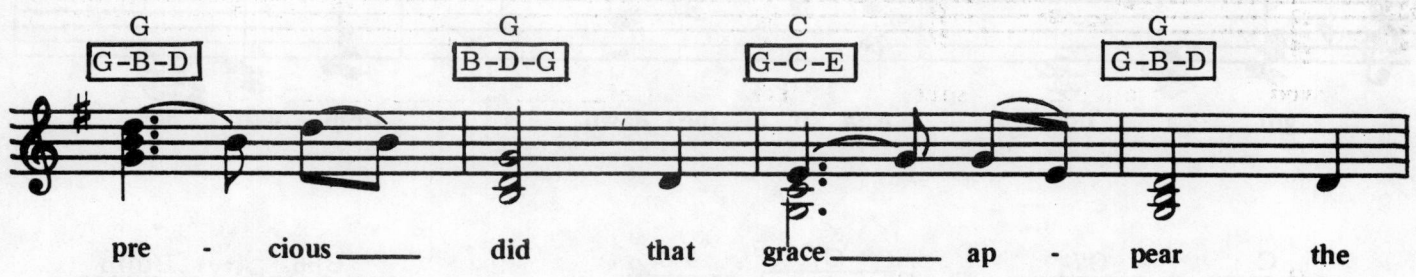

pre - cious_____ did   that   grace_____ ap - pear   the

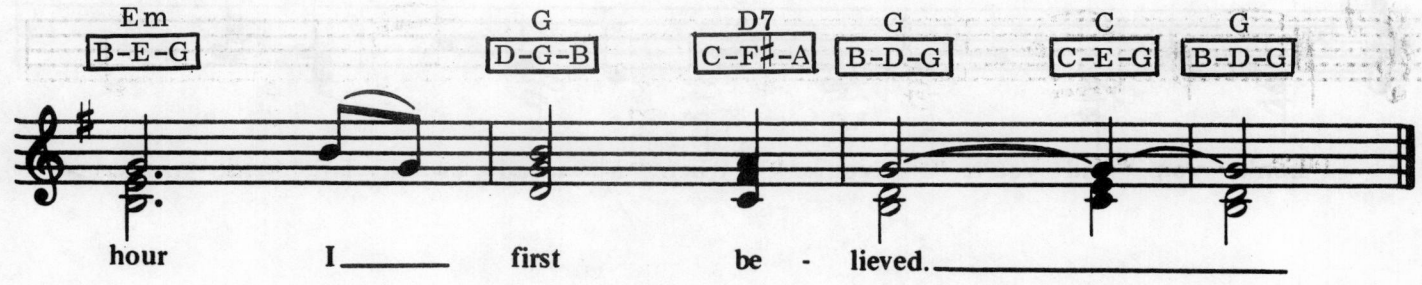

hour   I_____ first   be - lieved._____

3. Through many dangers, toils and snares
   I have already come.
   'Tis grace hath brought me safe this far
   And grace will lead me home.

4. Yes, when this heart and flesh shall fail,
   And mortal life shall cease,
   I shall possess within the veil,
   A life of joy and peace.

Amazing Grace-2-2

AREN'T YOU GLAD YOU'RE YOU

By JOHNNY BURKE
and JIMMY VAN HEUSEN

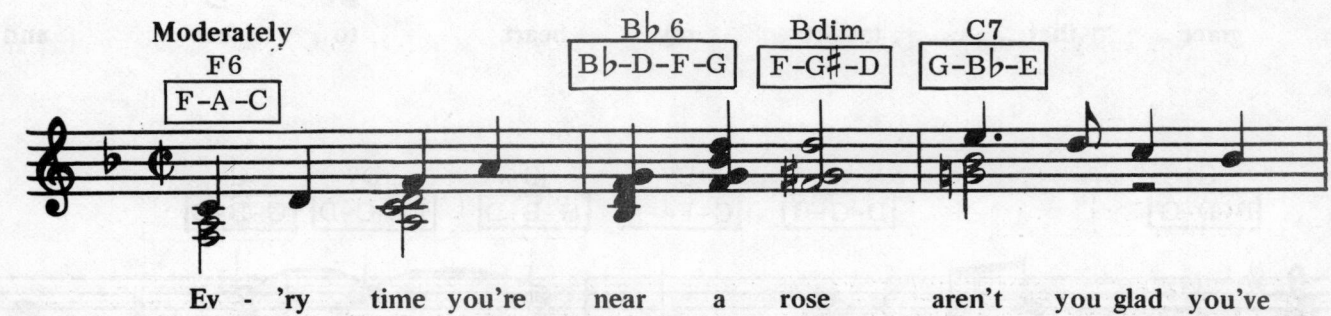

Ev - 'ry time you're near a rose aren't you glad you've

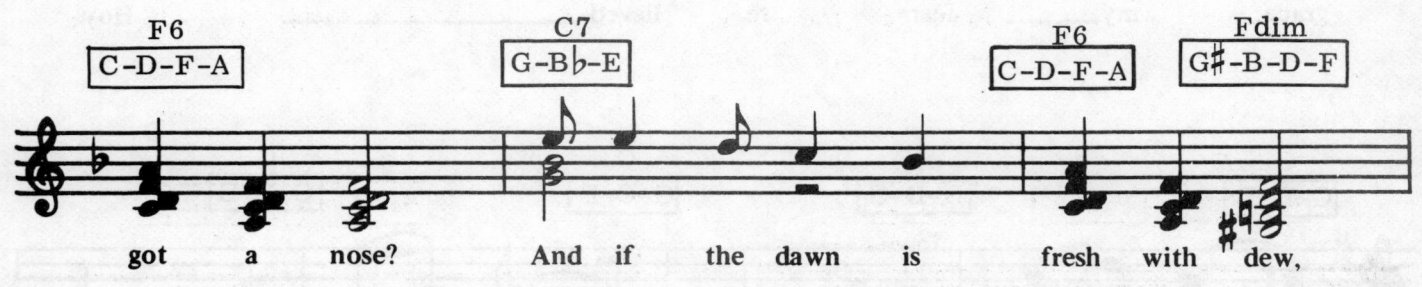

got a nose? And if the dawn is fresh with dew,

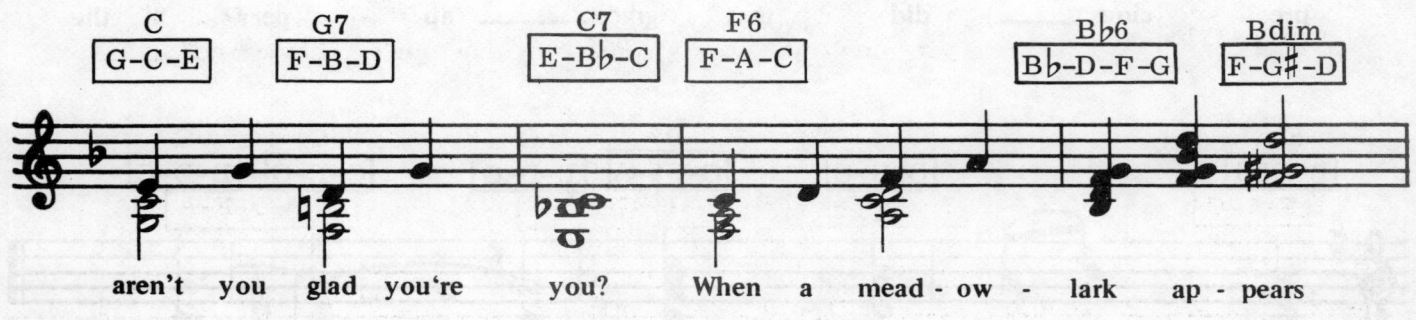

aren't you glad you're you? When a mead - ow - lark ap - pears

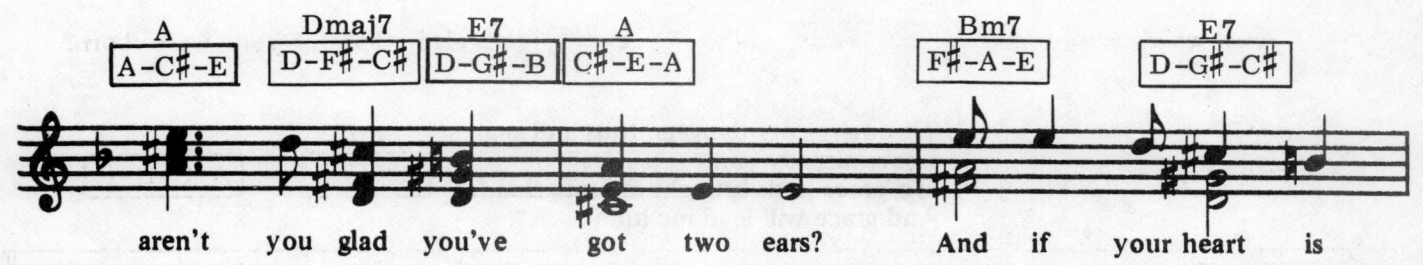

aren't you glad you've got two ears? And if your heart is

BALLADE POUR ADELINE

By PAUL de SENNEVILLE

Ballade Pour Adeline-2-2

DON'T GET AROUND MUCH ANYMORE

By BILL RUSSELL
and DUKE ELLINGTON

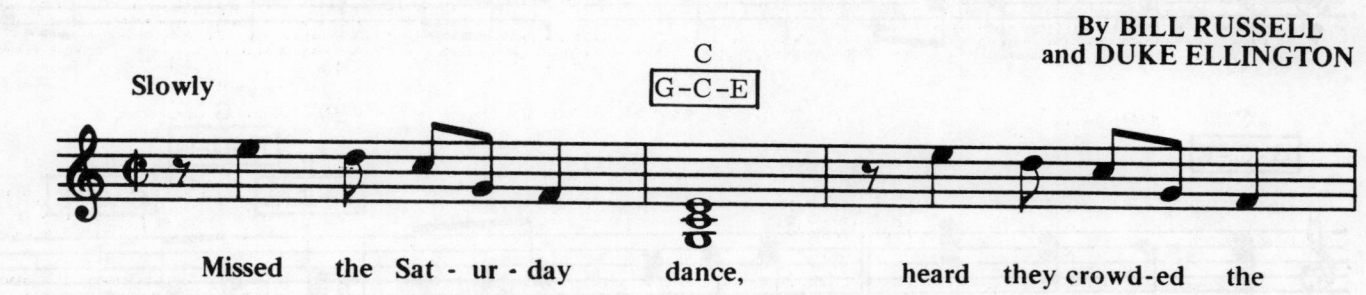

Missed the Sat - ur - day dance, heard they crowd-ed the

floor. Could - n't bear it with - out you,____

don't get a - round much an - y - more. Thought I'd vis - it the

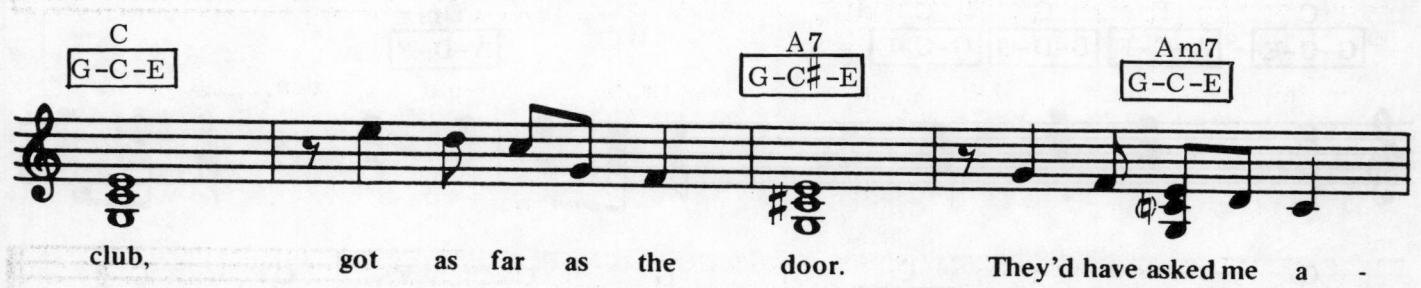

club, got as far as the door. They'd have asked me a -

Don't Get Around Much Anymore-2-2

HERE'S THAT RAINY DAY

By JOHNNY BURKE
and JAMES VAN HEUSEN

Moderately Slow

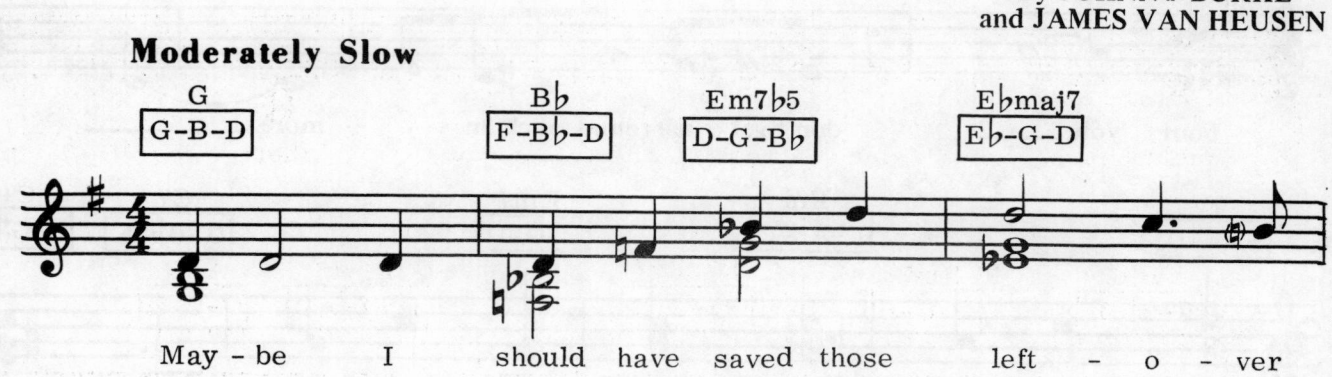

May - be I should have saved those left - o - ver

dreams; fun - ny, but here's that rain - y

day. _____ Here's that rain - y day they

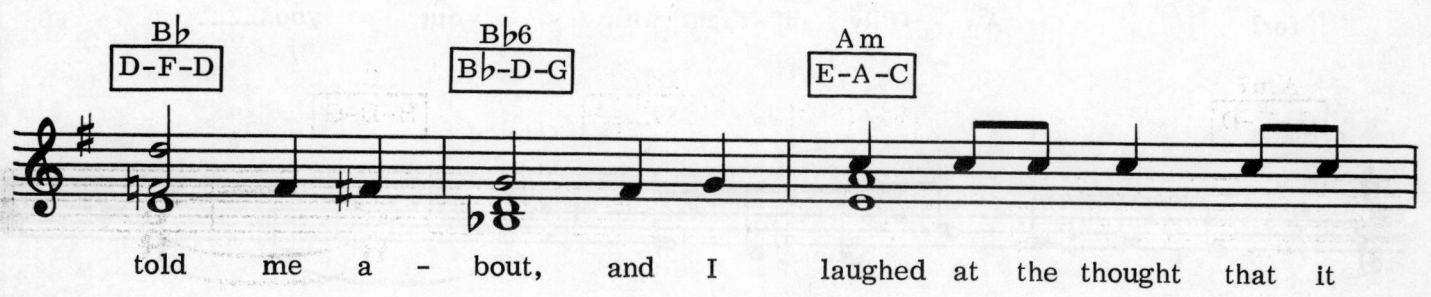

told me a - bout, and I laughed at the thought that it

Here's That Rainy Day-2-2

IMAGINATION

By JOHNNY BURKE
and JIMMY VAN HEUSEN

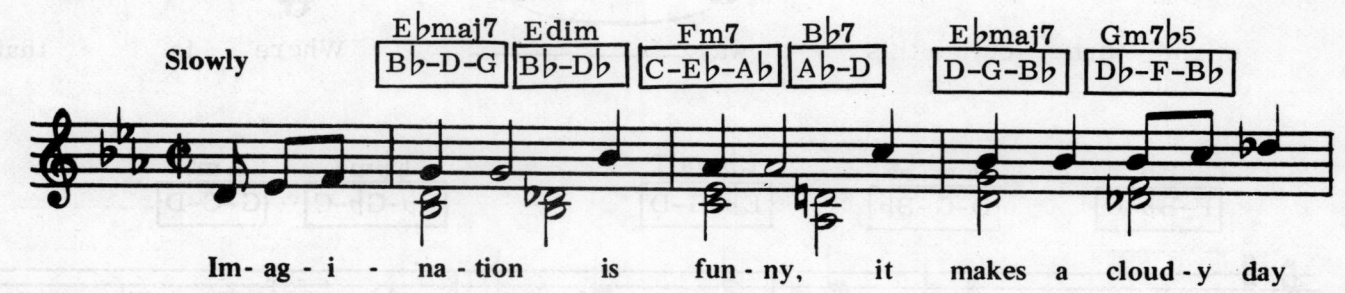

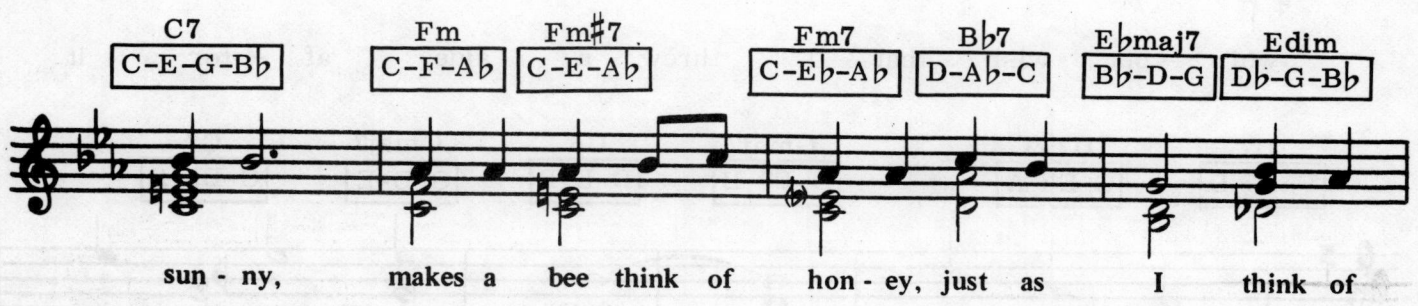

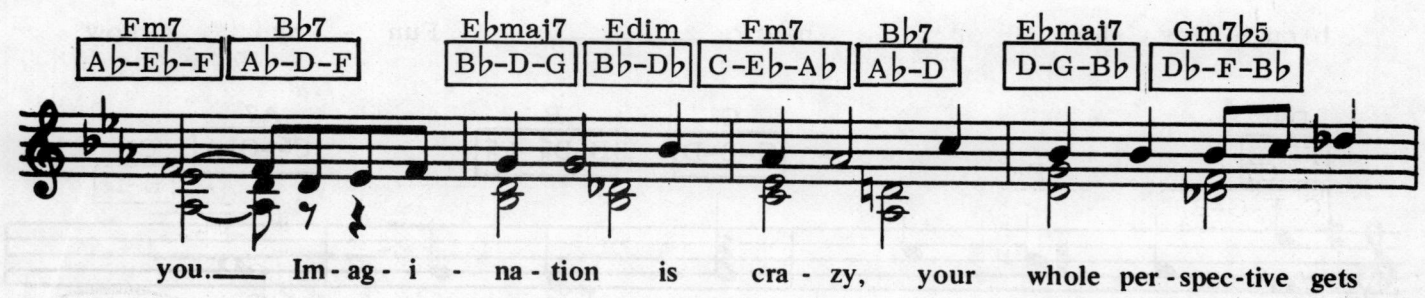

Imagination-2-2

MY WILD IRISH ROSE

By CHAUNCEY OLCOTT

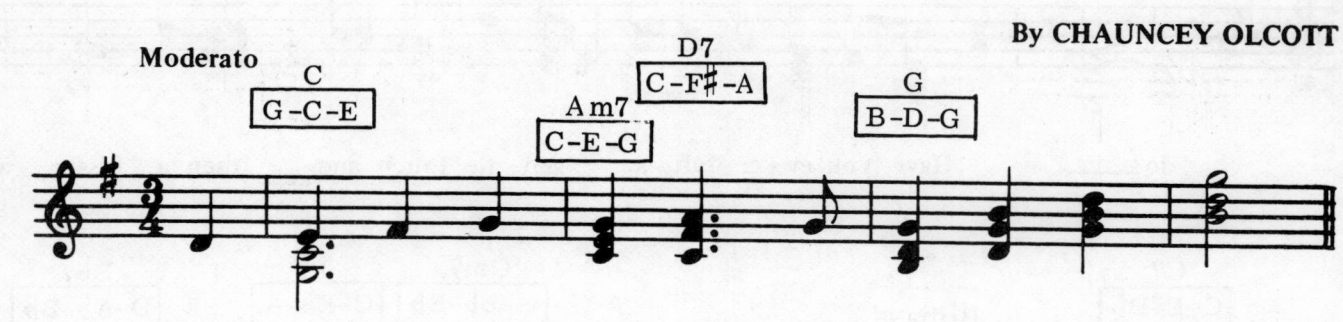

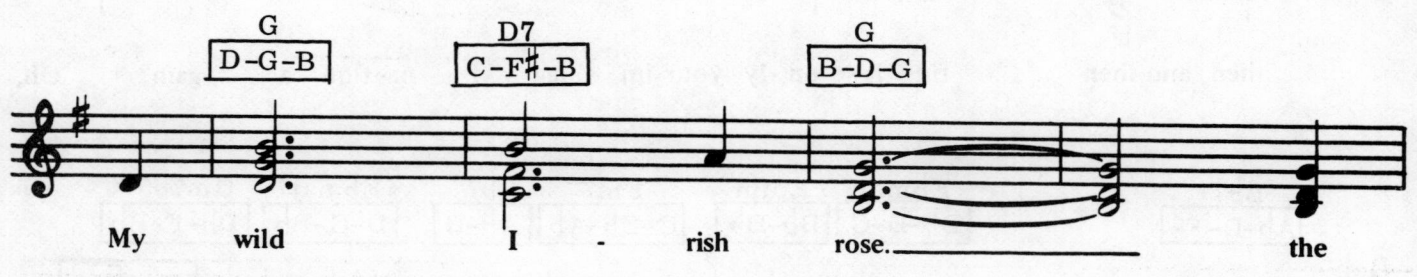

My wild I - rish rose._____ the

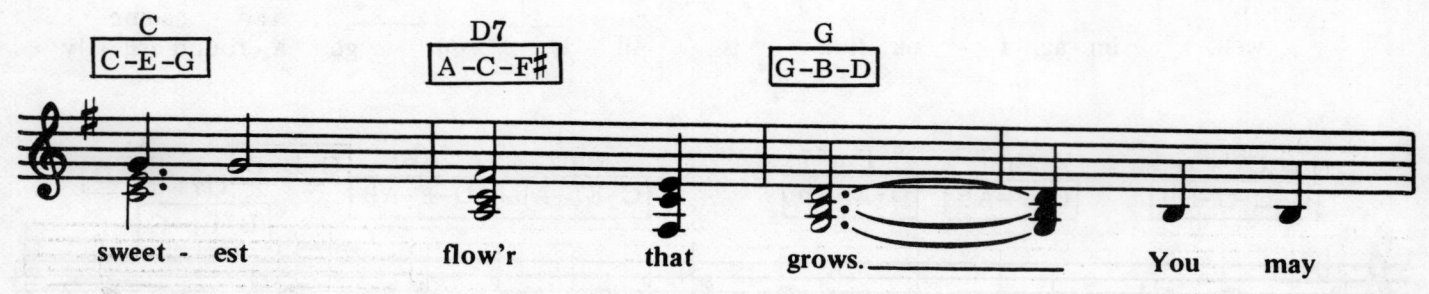

sweet - est flow'r that grows._____ You may

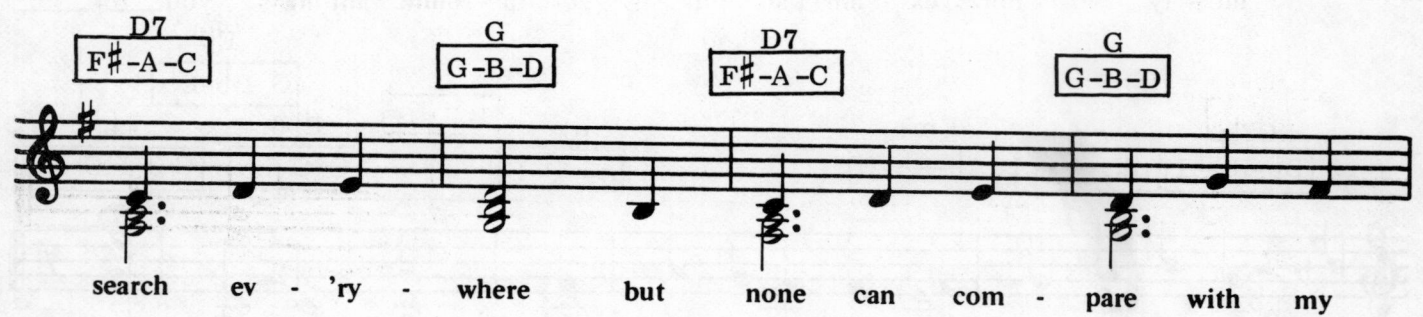

search ev - 'ry - where but none can com - pare with my

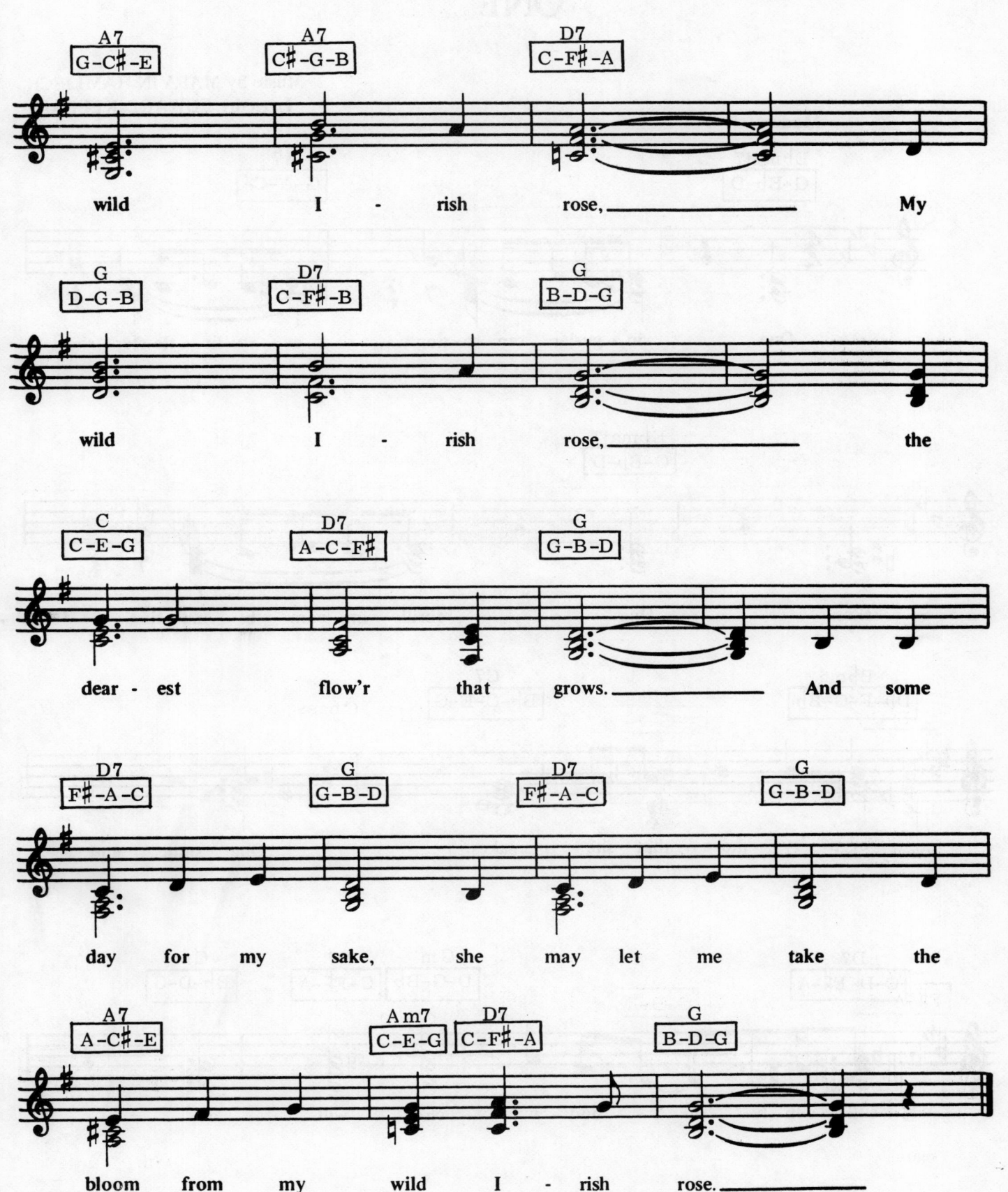

My Wild Irish Rose-2-2

From "A CHORUS LINE"

ONE

Music by MARVIN HAMLISCH
Lyric by EDWARD KLEBAN

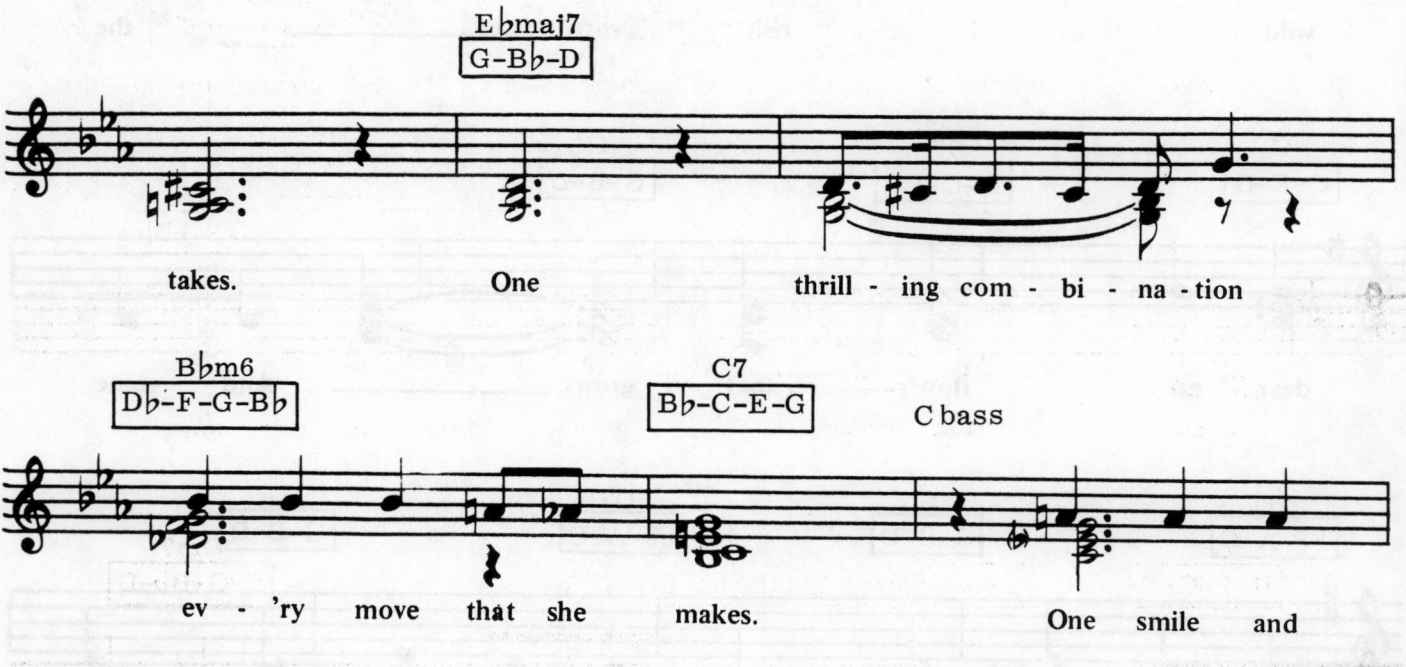

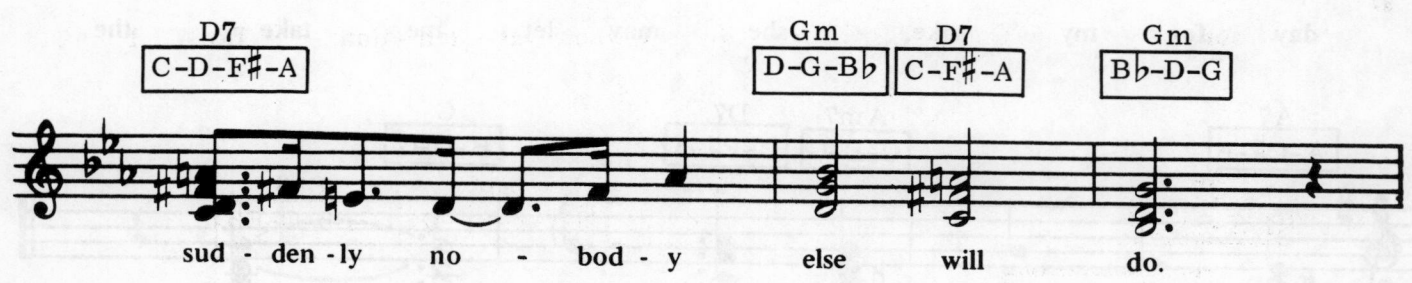

PAPER ROSES

By JANICE TORRE
and FRED SPIELMAN

I re-al-ize the way your eyes de-ceived me____

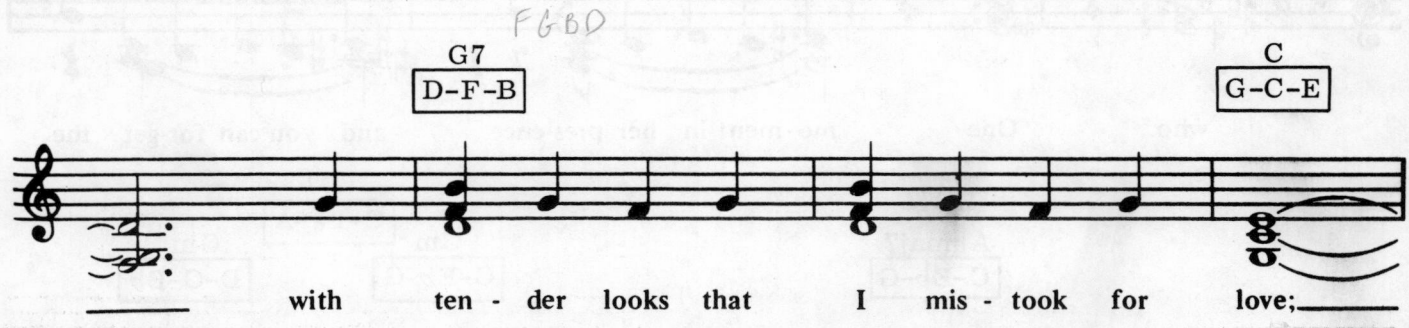

____ with ten-der looks that I mis-took for love;____

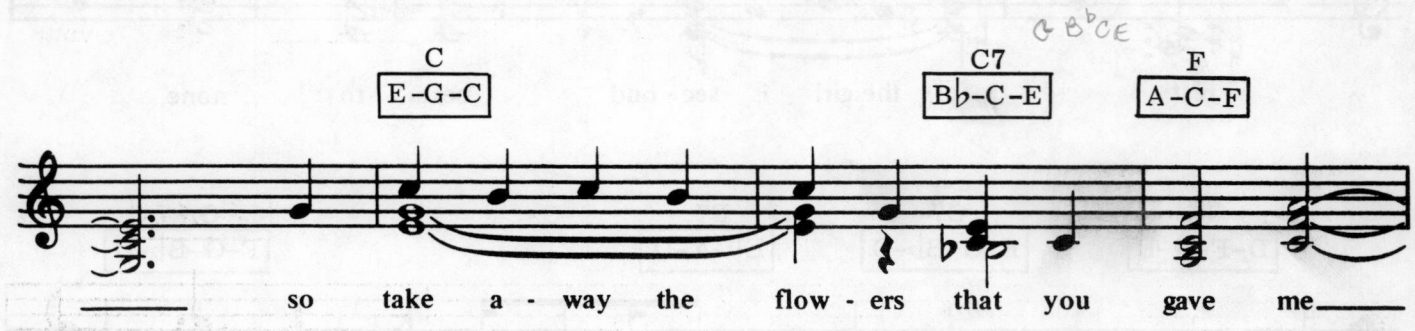

____ so take a-way the flow-ers that you gave me____

____ and send the kind that you re-mind me of.____

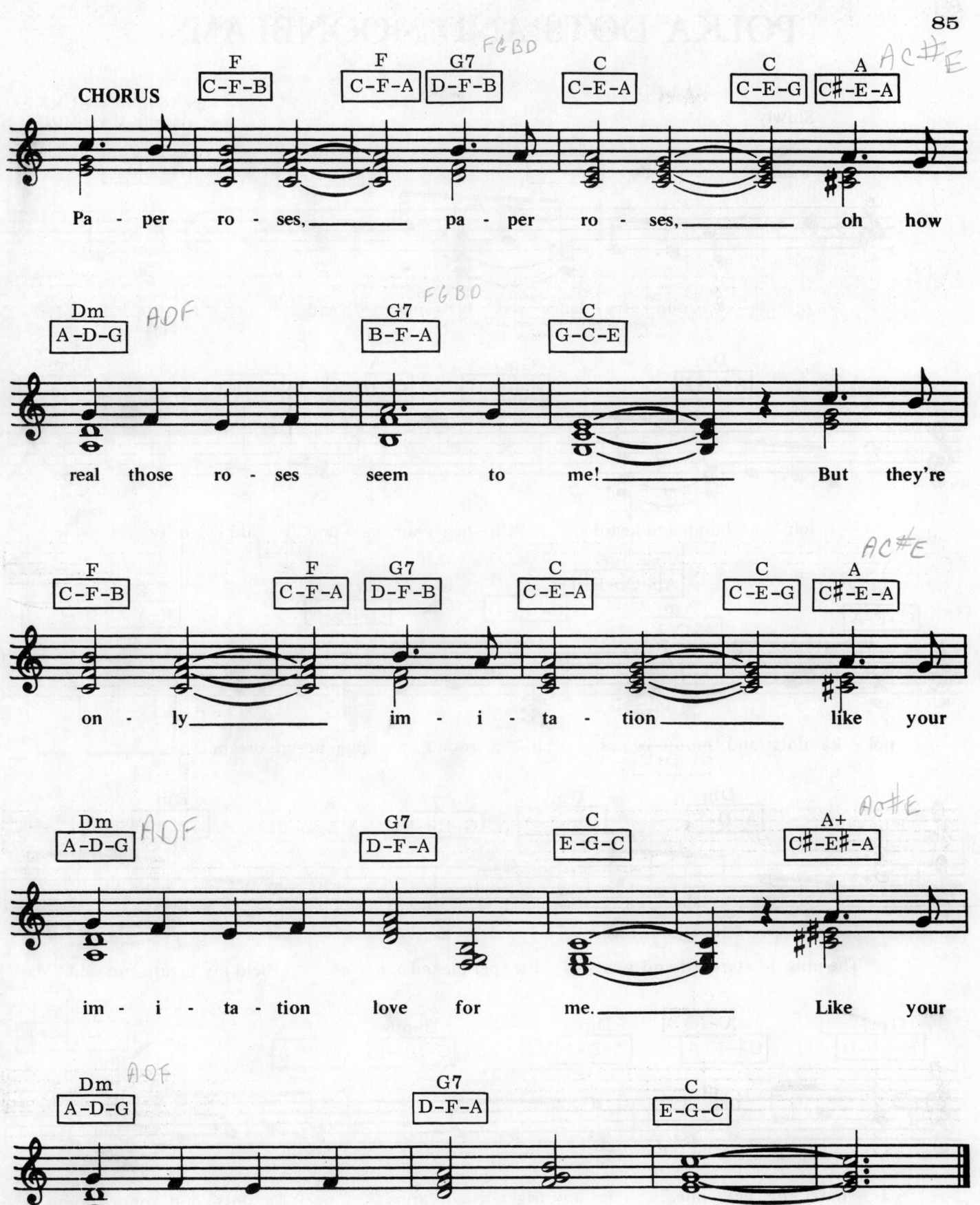

POLKA DOTS AND MOONBEAMS

By JOHNNY BURKE
and JIMMY VAN HEUSEN

Polka Dots And Moonbeams-2-2

SHOE SHINE BOY

Words by SAMMY KAHN
Music by SAUL CHAPLIN

THIS LOVE OF MINE

By FRANK SINATRA
SOL PARKER and HENRY SANICOLA

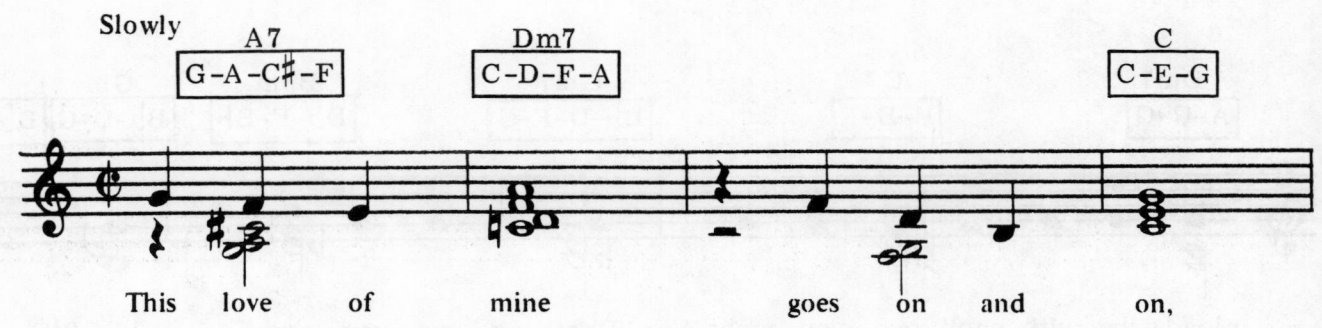

This love of mine goes on and on,

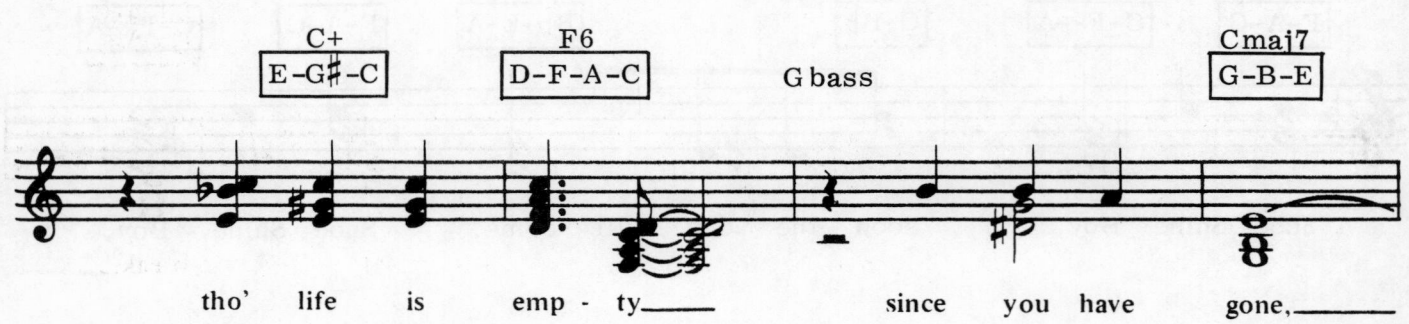

tho' life is emp-ty____ since you have gone,____

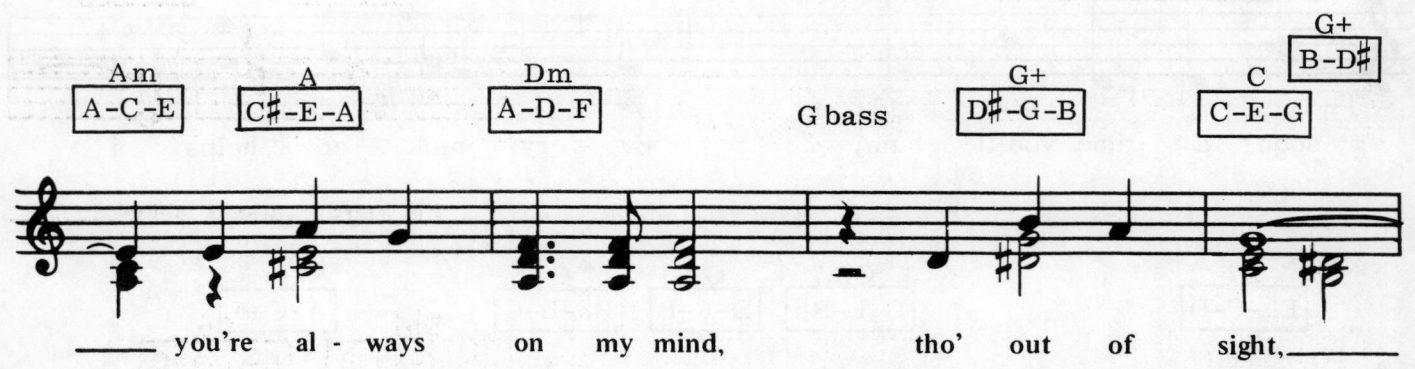

____ you're al-ways on my mind, tho' out of sight,____

From The Joseph Papp Production of Micheal Bennett's "A CHORUS LINE"

WHAT I DID FOR LOVE

Music by MARVIN HAMLISCH
Lyric by EDWARD KLEBAN

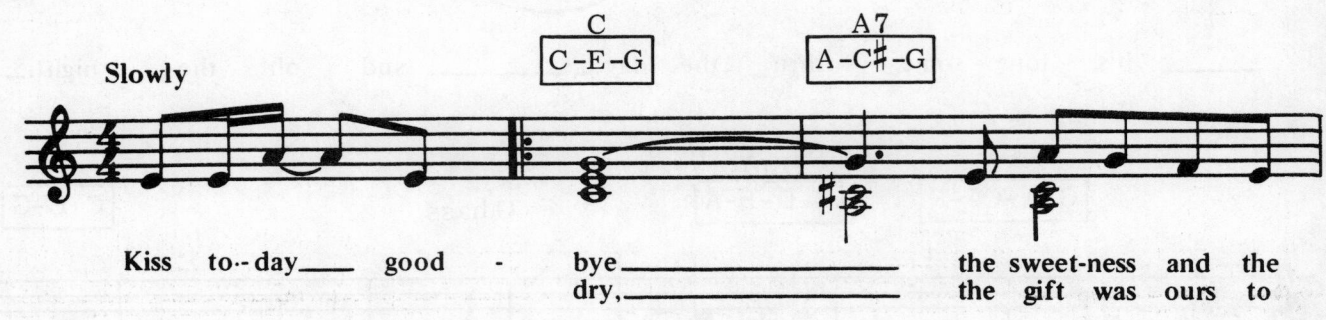

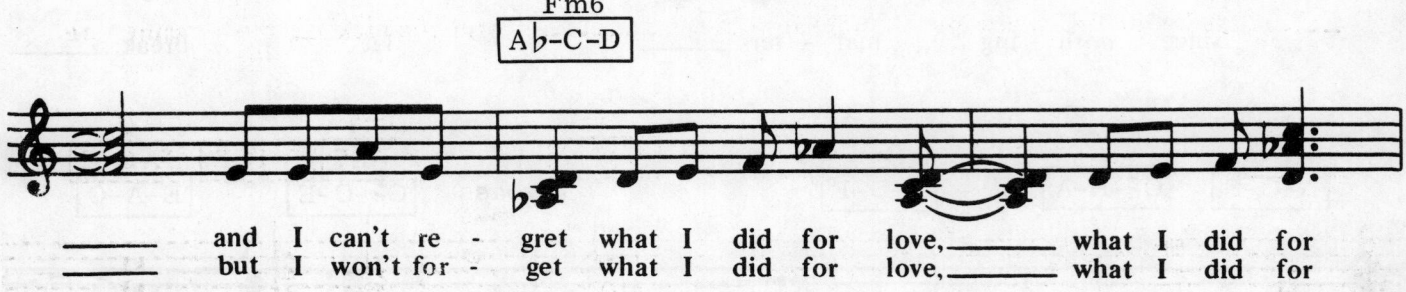

WHEN THE SAINTS GO MARCHIN' IN

TRADITIONAL

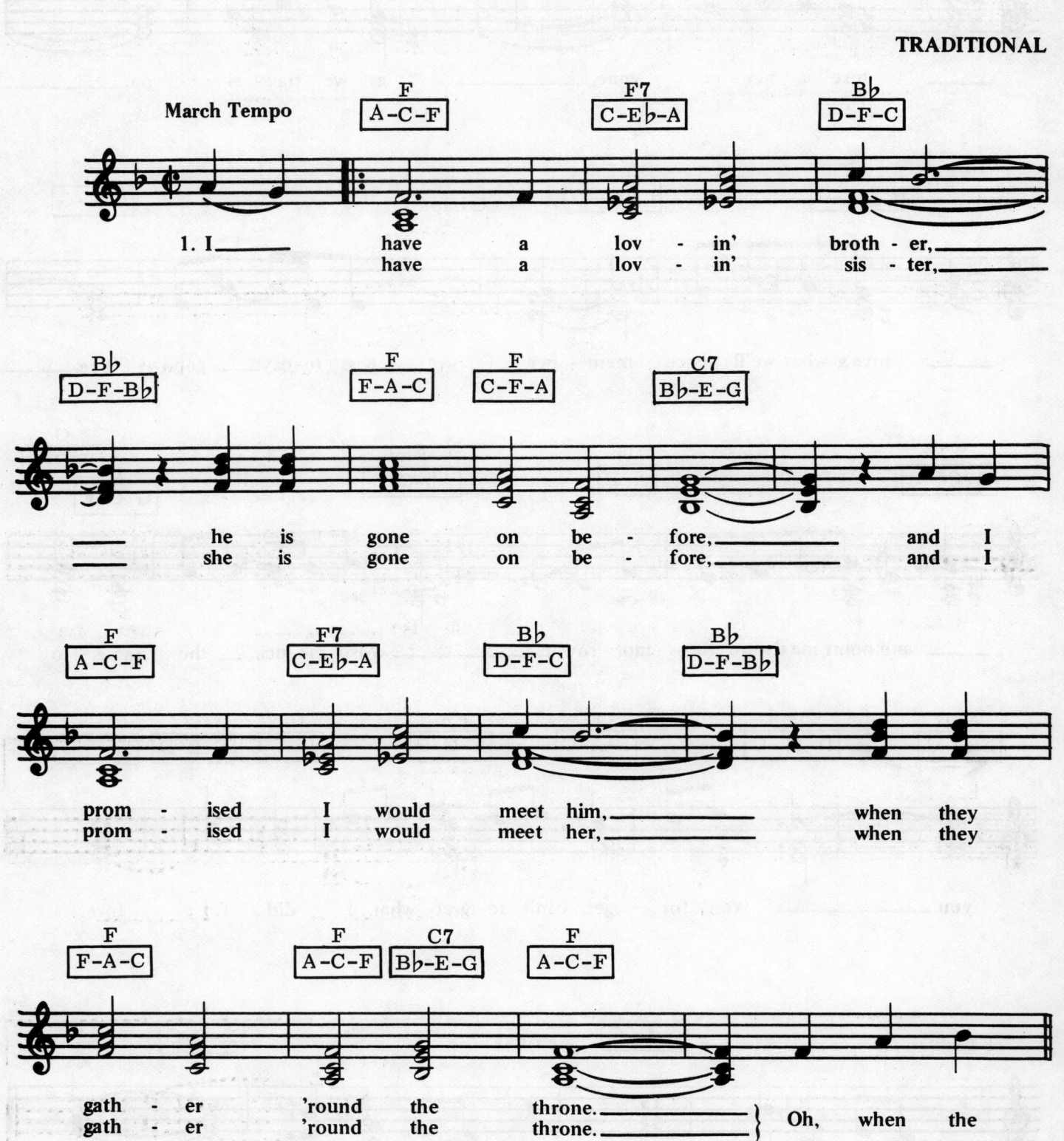

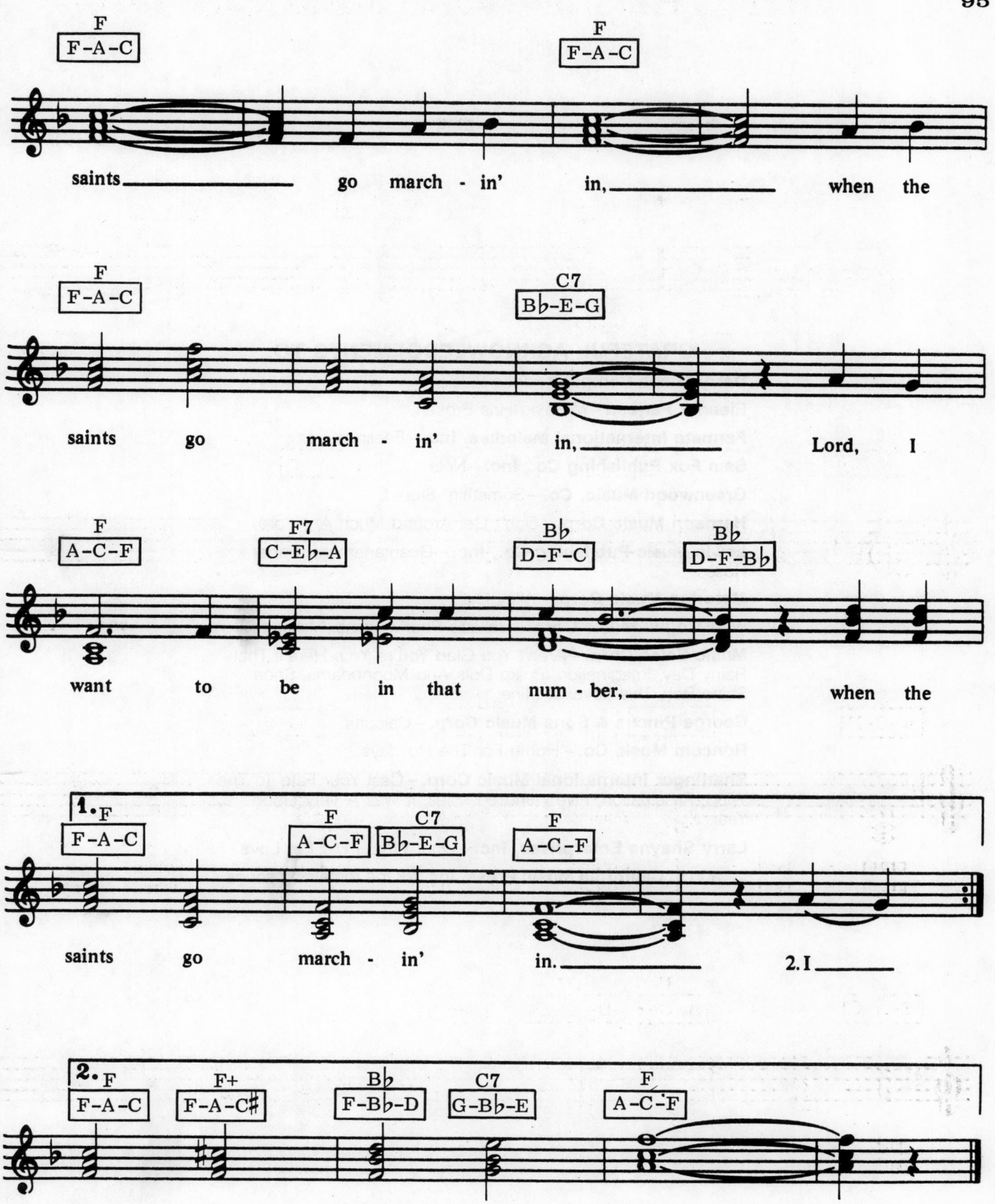

When The Saints Go Marchin' In-2-2

GRATEFUL ACKNOWLEDGEMENTS TO:

Derry Music Company – Take Five.

Eleanor Farjeon – Morning Has Broken.

Fermata International Melodies, Inc. – Feelings.

Sam Fox Publishing Co., Inc. – Nola.

Greenwood Music, Co. – Somethin' Stupid.

Harrison Music Corp. – Don't Get Around Much Anymore.

Lewis Music Publishing Co., Inc. – Guantanamera, Paper Roses.

Metorion Music Corp. – Alley Cat.

Ivan Mogull Music Corp. – Ballade Pour Adeline, Misirlou.

Music Sales Corp. – Aren't You Glad You're You, Here's That Rainy Day, Imagination, Polka Dots And Moonbeams, Shoe Shine Boy, This Love Of Mine.

George Pincus & Sons Music Corp. – Calcutta.

Roncom Music Co. – Home For The Holidays.

Shattinger International Music Corp. – Cast Your Fate To The Wind, Fascination, Five Hundred Miles, It Was A Very Good Year.

Larry Shayne Enterprises, Inc. – One, What I Did For Love

...and to **California Music Press, Inc.** for the remaining songs.

STECK-VAUGHN

ACHIEVE Indiana

English/Language Arts

5

Harcourt Achieve

Rigby · Steck-Vaughn

www.HarcourtAchieve.com
1.800.531.5015

ACKNOWLEDGMENTS

Project Authors   Carol Alexander, Judith Herbst, Estelle Kleinman, Marlene Roth, Sandra Shichtman, and Marren Simmons

Photo Credits   P. 34 ©STScI/NASA/ASU/Hester/Ressmeyer/CORBIS; p. 80 ©W. Sullivan III/Photo Researchers, Inc.

Grateful acknowledgment is made to the following authors, agents, and publishers for permission to use copyrighted materials. Every effort has been made to trace ownership of all copyrighted material and to secure the necessary permissions to reprint. We express regret in advance for any error or omission. Any oversight will be acknowledged in future printings.

"To March" by Emily Dickinson.

"The Visitor" from *The Queen of Eene,* by Jack Prelutsky. Text copyright © 1978 by Jack Prelutsky. Used by permission of HarperCollins Publishers.

From *Earthquakes* by Seymour Simon. Copyright © 1991 by Seymour Simon. Used by permission of HarperCollins Publishers.

From *Soaring with the Wind: The Bald Eagle* by Gail Gibbons. Copyright © 1998 by Gail Gibbons. William Morrow, 1998.

"The Bugs That Aren't" by Gary Raham. Copyright © 1998 by Highlights for Children, Inc., Columbus, Ohio. Reprinted with permission.

"Happily Ever After" by Beth Thompson. Copyright © 1997 by Highlights for Children, Inc., Columbus, Ohio. Reprinted with permission.

"Think like a Horse" by Tamara Duncan. Copyright © 1997 by Highlights for Children, Inc., Columbus, Ohio. Reprinted with permission.

"Zoo in the Sky" by Edmund A. Fortier. Copyright © 1999 by Highlights for Children, Inc., Columbus, Ohio. Reprinted with permission.

From *The Secret Garden* by Frances Hodgson Burnett. New York: Frederick A. Stokes Company, 1911.

"My Early Home" from *Black Beauty* by Anna Sewell (1877).

ISBN 0-7398-9914-7

© 2005 Harcourt Achieve Inc.

1 2 3 4 5 6 7 8 9 10 073 11 10 09 08 07 06 05 04

Achieve Indiana
Contents

Indiana English/Language Arts Standards

Achieve Indiana will help you get ready for a test that has been organized according to standards set up by the state of Indiana. Standards are the goals that have been developed to make sure that you have all the skills necessary to be successful in school.

Standard 1: You will understand the characteristics of words. You will see letter patterns and know how to turn them into spoken language.

Standard 2: You will read and understand a written work. You will ask and answer important questions, make predictions, and compare information to understand what is read.

Standard 3: You will read and respond to many different written works. You will name and discuss the characters, theme (the main idea of a story), plot (what happens in a story), and the setting (where a story takes place) of stories that you have read.

Standard 4: You will write clear sentences and paragraphs that form a main idea. You will use the stages of the writing process, including prewriting, drafting, revising, and editing drafts.

Standard 5: You will write compositions that describe and explain familiar objects, events, and experiences. Your writing will show a knowledge of Standard English and the stages of the writing process.

Standard 6: You will write using Standard English language rules.

To the Student

This book will help you prepare for the Indiana Statewide Testing for Educational Progress-Plus *(ISTEP+)* English/Language Arts test. The first part of the book gives you practice on different kinds of items you will see on the real test. It also gives you a tip for answering each item.

The second part of the book is a practice test that is similar to the *ISTEP+* English/Language Arts test. Taking this test will help you know what the actual test is like.

Kinds of Items

The *ISTEP+* English/Language Arts test includes items about reading and writing. It will ask you to write about what you have read.

Multiple-Choice Items

After each multiple-choice item are four answer choices. For both the Modeled Instruction part of this book and the Practice Test, fill in the circle next to your answer. Remember to pick the choice that you think is the best answer. Mark your answers in the book.

Open-Ended Items

These items will not give you answer choices. You will need to write out your answers. There are three kinds of open-ended items:

- **Short-Response Items**

  These items will be scored on reading comprehension. They will not be scored on writing.

- **Extended-Response Items**

   When you see this symbol next to an extended-response item, you know this item will be scored on reading comprehension and on writing. Be sure to plan before you write and check your writing for correct grammar, punctuation, capitalization, spelling, and paragraph organization.

- **Writing Activities**

   You will also see this symbol on the first page of Test 3. Test 3 is one writing activity. For this test, you will be scored only on writing. Be sure to plan before you write and check your writing for correct grammar, punctuation, capitalization, spelling, and paragraph organization.

DIRECTIONS: In Test 1, you will read a story and an article. You will answer questions based on each passage. Now read the story "Think like a Horse" and do Numbers 1 through 6.

Think like a Horse

by Tamara Duncan

So here they were, exploring the well-marked bridle paths of the county park, and Kristi was riding her very own pony, not a pony that her father was training for someone else or a pony that would be sold at the next auction. Kristi was so happy that she could have laughed out loud, but she just turned in the saddle and smiled at her father, who was following on his big palomino. When the path widened, they trotted and cantered together, with little Babe doing her best to keep up with the palomino's long strides.

After a few minutes, Kristi gradually slowed Babe to a walk. A little muddy stream, about three feet wide but quite shallow, was just ahead. Some of Kristi's friends tried to jump their ponies across, but Kristi's father had been very firm about teaching his horses to walk calmly through streams. Kristi thought her father was the very best horse trainer in the world, so she followed his rules. She wanted Babe to walk calmly through the water, too.

Go On ➡

Babe had other ideas. A few feet from the bank, she arched her neck, snorted, and planted her feet. Kristi squeezed with her legs and clucked to urge Babe forward, but the pony refused to move. Kristi tried again, using her heels a little more sharply. Babe moved sideways a few steps, but she would not cross the stream.

Kristi knew that some riders carried whips or wore spurs to help their horses know what to do, but her father didn't like to use those things. Kristi turned to her father, who had been watching quietly. "Could you give us a lead across?" she asked him.

"I could," her father said, "and Babe would probably follow, but would that really solve the problem? Someday you may be out riding by yourself. What would you do then? Keep trying. I want to see if you can think like a horse."

Think like a horse, Kristi thought. If I were Babe, why wouldn't I want to walk through the stream? Did I fall in a stream once and hurt myself? Kristi began to worry. She had seen her father work with horses that had become terribly frightened or that had been abused. It took many long, patient hours to retrain them.

Kristi dismounted and decided to try leading Babe through the stream instead of riding her. Still, Babe planted her feet and refused to take one step nearer the water. Kristi was beginning to feel angry, so she took a deep breath and let it out. Then she stood on the bank of the stream to think, still holding Babe's reins. Idly she threw a pebble into the dark water. It made a little splash.

At the sound, Babe snorted and stared at the stream. Cautiously the pony took a step forward. Kristi held her breath. She picked up another pebble and threw it into the water. Ears pricked forward, Babe lowered her head and snorted again. Then she took another step.

"Oh, Babe," said Kristi, "didn't you know it was water? What did you think it was?" Suddenly she remembered a time when her father's horse had shied at a place in the road where a hole had been filled.

"Horses don't understand the different color of the road," her father had explained. "They think a dark place is a hole, and they don't know how deep it is. When this horse is older and more experienced, he'll learn not to be afraid."

Kristi walked to Babe's head and looked at the stream. The dark sluggish water did look like a hole or a ditch. "I'm sorry, Babe. You didn't know that it was water and not some bottomless pit that I was asking you to step into."

Kristi was wearing her rubber riding boots, so she splashed into the stream. Babe extended one foreleg and pawed at the water before setting her hoof down firmly. Kristi let her take her time, and they soon crossed the stream and climbed up the opposite bank. Kristi's father followed.

Kristi patted her pony, checked the saddle girth to make sure it was still snug, and swung onto Babe's back. As she adjusted her stirrups, Kristi smiled. "Now I know the secret of thinking like a horse," she said. "You have to see things like a horse!"

Her father nodded, then teased, "Just so you don't start smelling like one!" Their laughter mixed with the sound of hoofbeats as they continued down the trail.

Go On

1 Which of the following BEST states the major theme of the story?

○ Try to see things from a different point of view.

○ You'll become more relaxed if you learn to think like an animal.

○ Your parents will understand you better if your family has animals.

○ Become close friends with an animal.

Tip: The theme is a truth about life that is found in a story. You should always be able to relate the events in a story to a theme. Review the story and think about the general truth that Kristi learns.

2 Why does Kristi not use spurs or a whip on Babe to make the horse cross the stream?

○ She does not want to do the same things her friends do.

○ She is afraid it will make Baby angry and harder to handle.

○ She knows that Babe is smart enough to figure out a solution.

○ She trusts her father's rules about how to best train a horse.

Tip: You can tell a lot about characters by their actions. You can also try to figure out why characters behave they way they do. Review the story to learn more about Kristi's thoughts and feelings and her reasons for acting the way she does.

Go On

Indiana English/Language Arts Standards
1. **4.3.2:** Identify the main events of the plot, including their causes and the effects of each event on future actions, and the major theme from the story action.
2. **4.3.3:** Use knowledge of the situation, setting, and a character's traits, motivations, and feelings to determine the causes for that character's actions.

3 Read these sentences from the story.

> **Babe had other ideas. A few feet from the bank, she arched her neck, snorted, and planted her feet.**

Which word means the SAME as *snorted*?

○ sniffed

○ sneezed

○ bucked

○ trotted

☺ Tip: The words *big* and *large* are examples of words that have the same basic meaning. Try each choice in the sentence. Then choose the answer that has the same meaning as the word *snorted*.

4 Based on what you know about Kristi, what do you think she will do the next time she has trouble with her horse?

○ Kristi will walk her horse through the stream.

○ Kristi will try to think like a horse.

○ Kristi will call for her father's help.

○ Kristi will use a whip or spurs to get her horse moving.

☺ Tip: Sometimes you must make a prediction about what might happen next. To make a good prediction, you must use your own knowledge and the ideas presented in the text. Think about what Kristi is like and decide which answer choice can be supported based on clues from the article. Then choose the answer that is most likely to be true.

Go On

Indiana English/Language Arts Standards

3. 4.1.2: Apply knowledge of synonyms (words with the same meaning), antonyms (words with opposite meanings), homographs (words that are spelled the same but have different meanings), and idioms (expressions that cannot be understood just by knowing the meanings of the words in the expression, such as *couch potato*) to determine the meaning of words and phrases.

4. 4.2.3: Make and confirm predictions about text by using prior knowledge and ideas presented in the text itself, including illustrations, titles, topic sentences, important words, foreshadowing clues (clues that indicate what might happen next), and direct quotations.

5 Read this sentence from the story.

> Some of Kristi's friends tried to jump their ponies across, but Kristi's father had been very firm about teaching his horses to walk calmly through streams.

Which of these words means about the SAME as the word *firm*?

- ○ determined
- ○ different
- ○ open
- ○ weak

🌀 **Tip:** *Happy* and *glad* are examples of words that mean about the same thing. Try each answer choice in the sentence. See which word will have about the same meaning as the word *firm* in the sentence.

6 Based on the actions of Kristi's father, which of the following BEST describes his character?

- ○ Kristi's father is hard to talk to.
- ○ Kristi's father is smart and kind.
- ○ Kristi's father doesn't understand Kristi's problem.
- ○ Kristi's father likes to have fun and laugh a lot.

🌀 **Tip:** An author tells what a character is like by how he or she chooses to have the character talk and act. Always look for evidence in the passage before you come to a conclusion about what a character is like. Based on what the author has told you about Kristi's father, choose the answer that can be supported by evidence in the passage.

Go On

Indiana English/Language Arts Standards

5. 4.1.2: Apply knowledge of synonyms (words with the same meaning), antonyms (words with opposite meanings), homographs (words that are spelled the same but have different meanings), and idioms (expressions that cannot be understood just by knowing the meanings of the words in the expression, such as *couch potato*) to determine the meaning of words and phrases.

6. 4.3.3: Use knowledge of the situation, setting, and a character's traits, motivations, and feelings to determine the causes for that character's actions.

DIRECTIONS: In Test 1, you will read an article. You will answer questions based on the passage, as well as some others. Now read "Desert Wildlife." Then do Numbers 7 through 10. Then you will answer more questions about writing, research, spelling, and grammar.

Desert Wildlife

North America is home to four major deserts. They are all in the western half of the United States. Their names are Great Basin, Mojave, Sonoran, and Chihuahuan Deserts. All of them are quite beautiful.

A desert is a dry region that gets about ten inches of rain or less per year. Deserts can be very hot during the day and very cold at night. It is not easy to live in a desert. However, many kind of animals do live in this harsh land. They have a number of different ways to survive.

Water

Desert animals have adapted to the dry conditions of their homes. Very little water is available. Many desert animals don't need as much water as other animals. They get most of the moisture they need from eating certain plants or other creatures. Other desert animals have ways to store water in their bodies. The desert tortoise can store about a quart of water in its bladder, so it has a supply whenever it needs to drink. The kangaroo rat never has to drink at all because its body makes its own water.

Staying Cool

Desert animals use different methods to stay cool during the day. Some, such as the coyote, stay in shady dens during the hottest part of the day. Vultures and some other birds fly high in the air because the temperature is cooler there. Other animals, such as the kangaroo rat, dig burrows and stay underground when the sun is out. The kangaroo rat fills the opening of its burrow from the inside to keep the burrow cooler. A lizard's scales keep it from drying out in the sun. Many desert animals are most active during the coolest parts of the day, early in the morning and again at dusk. They go to their homes or find a shady spot to rest in when the sun is high. Other animals only come out at night to hunt and to drink.

Building Homes

Do all desert animals live in burrows or dens? Believe it or not, some birds build their homes in cactus! The sharp spines of the cactus keep other animals away. This helps protect the birds and their babies. Other animals, such as the mule deer, tend to rest in open areas.

All of the creatures that make their homes in the desert are special. They have developed many ways to change, or adapt, according to their harsh surroundings. Various small animals and birds will just go to sleep for several months if they are not able to find enough food. The animals are able to change their behavior to fit a new situation. That's called adaptation! It's what helps animals in the desert survive.

Go On

7 Which of the following from the article would help you find facts about how animals deal with the desert heat?

○ the introduction

○ the title

○ the headings

○ the drawing

Tip: People read for different reasons. Sometimes they read to be entertained. Other times they read to find information. Sometimes a passage is organized in ways that help the reader find detailed information. Read the question and ask yourself which answer choice will give you the exact information you need.

8 Using information from the article, which of the following can you predict is true?

○ American deserts grow larger each year.

○ All desert birds build their nests in cactus.

○ Desert animals have developed ways to stay warm at night.

○ Most of the animals that live in the desert are small animals.

Tip: When you make a prediction, you use both your own knowledge and the ideas presented in the text. Read all of the choices carefully. Decide which answer choice can be supported based on facts in the article. Then choose the answer that is most likely to be true.

Go On

Indiana English/Language Arts Standards
7. 4.2.1: Use the organization of informational text to strengthen comprehension.
8. 4.2.3: Make and confirm predictions about text by using prior knowledge and ideas presented in the text itself, including illustrations, titles, topic sentences, important words, foreshadowing clues (clues that indicate what might happen next), and direct quotations.

9 Read the following sentence from the article.

> **Desert animals have *adapted* to the dry conditions of their homes.**

Which of the following means about the SAME as *adapted*?

- ○ run
- ○ seen
- ○ adjusted
- ○ surrendered

Ⓢ Tip: Many words are the same or opposite in meaning. Words with the same meaning can be used in place of each other. Words with opposite meanings cannot. Try replacing the word *adapted* with each answer choice. Choose the answer that makes the most sense.

10 According to the article, what kind of animal can store a quart of water in its bladder?

- ○ coyote
- ○ kangaroo rat
- ○ mule deer
- ○ desert tortoise

Ⓢ Tip: One good way to find the facts you need is to skim the article. Reread the question first, so you will know exactly what you're looking for. Skim the article and look for facts about desert animals and water.

Go On

Indiana English/Language Arts Standards

9. 4.1.2: Apply knowledge of synonyms (words with the same meaning), antonyms (words with opposite meanings), homographs (words that are spelled the same but have different meanings), and idioms (expressions that cannot be understood just by knowing the meanings of the words in the expression, such as *couch potato*) to determine the meaning of words and phrases.

10. 4.2.2: Use appropriate strategies when reading for different purposes.

For Number 11, choose the sentence that shows the correct punctuation.

11 ○ Every day, my teacher reads a chapter from <u>Pippi Longstocking</u>.

○ Every day, my teacher reads a chapter from *Pippi Longstocking*.

○ Every day, my teacher reads a chapter from "Pippi Longstocking."

○ Every day, my teacher reads a chapter from *"Pippi Longstocking."*

> **Tip:** Mark titles using quotation marks, italics, or underlining. Quotation marks are used to mark the title of a chapter in a book. Titles of books are italicized if they are typed. If they are handwritten, titles of books are underlined.

For Number 12, choose the sentence that shows the correct capitalization.

12 ○ Jim said, "members of the group wildlife rescue are coming to speak to our class."

○ Jim said, "Members of the group wildlife rescue are coming to speak to our class."

○ Jim said, "members of the group Wildlife Rescue are coming to speak to our class."

○ Jim said, "Members of the group Wildlife Rescue are coming to speak to our class."

> **Tip:** Learn the rules that tell you which words must begin with a capital letter. Magazines, newspapers, works of art, and the names of special groups are capitalized. The first word in a quotation is usually capitalized, too. Read the sentences above, keeping the rules of capitalization in mind.

Go On

Indiana English/Language Arts Standards
11. 4.6.6: Use underlining, quotation marks, or italics to identify titles of documents.
12. 4.6.7: Capitalize names of magazines, newspapers, works of art, musical compositions, organizations, and the first word in quotations, when appropriate.

13 Read this sentence.

> **My grandmother will be 80 years old next week, and we are throwing her a surprise birthday party.**

How should *grandmother* be divided into syllables?

- ○ grand•mot•her
- ○ grand•mother
- ○ grand•moth•er
- ○ grandmoth•er

⊚ Tip: A syllable is a part of a word that can be pronounced by itself. Read the choices carefully to decide which one is divided correctly into syllables.

For Number 14, choose the sentence that shows the correct punctuation.

14
- ○ Trent's mother asked him to prepare the dog's food.
- ○ Trents mother asked him to prepare the dogs food.
- ○ Trent's mother asked him to prepare the dogs food.
- ○ Trents' mother asked him to prepare the dog's food.

⊚ Tip: Apostrophes are used to show possession. For example, to say that a bicycle belongs to Cara, you could write *Cara's bicycle.* Read the sentences above and remember the ways apostrophes are used to show possession in writing.

Indiana English/Language Arts Standards

13. 4.6.8: Spell correctly roots (bases of words, such as *un*necessary, *coward*ly), inflections (words like *care/careful/caring*), words with more than one acceptable spelling (like *advisor/adviser*), suffixes and prefixes (*-ly, -ness, mis-, un-*), and syllables (word parts each containing a vowel sound, such as *sur•prise* or *e•col•o•gy*).

14. 4.6.5: Use parentheses to explain something that is not considered of primary importance to the sentence, commas in direct quotations *(He said, "I'd be happy to go.")*, apostrophes to show possession *(Jim's shoes, the dog's food)*, and apostrophes in contractions *(can't, didn't, won't)*.

DIRECTIONS: In Test 2, you will read a poem and an article. You will also answer questions based on each passage. Now read the poem "To March." And do Numbers 1 through 5. You may look back at the poem as often as you like.

To March

by Emily Dickinson

DEAR March, come in!
How glad I am!
I looked for you before.
Put down your hat—
You must have walked—
How out of breath you are!
Dear March, how are you?
And the rest?
Did you leave Nature well?
Oh, March, come right upstairs with me,
I have so much to tell!

I got your letter, and the birds';
The maples never knew
That you were coming,—I declare,
How red their faces grew!
But, March, forgive me—
And all those hills

You left for me to hue;
There was no purple suitable,
You took it all with you.

Who knocks? That April!
Lock the door!
I will not be pursued!
He stayed away a year, to call
When I am occupied.
But trifles look so trivial
As soon as you have come,
That blame is just as dear as praise
And praise as mere as blame.

Go On

1 What are the speaker's feelings about March?

○ The speaker treats March in an unfriendly manner.

○ The speaker wants March to leave.

○ The speaker welcomes March as an old friend.

○ The speaker has not met March before.

Tip: A speaker's feelings are shown by the way he or she acts or speaks. Look at the speaker's choice of words and the effects those words may have on the reader. Also look at the actions that go with those words to help you decide the speaker's feelings.

2 Which of the following BEST expresses the theme of the poem?

○ The author likes spring better than summer.

○ The author likes March better than April.

○ The author likes to welcome each month.

○ The author likes to open her house to each season.

Tip: The theme of a poem is the author's message. You can find the theme by asking yourself what the author is trying to say, or what idea the author is sharing. Sometimes the theme can be stated in several different ways.

3 Which of the following lines from the poem is an example of personification?

○ How glad I am!

○ The maples never knew that you were coming . . .

○ There was no purple suitable . . .

○ I will not be pursued!

Tip: Personification is a way of showing how a thing is like a person. Read the lines from the poem. Try to figure out which one takes a thing and makes it like a person, with qualities that only a person has.

Go On

Indiana English/Language Arts Standards

1. 4.3.3: Use knowledge of the situation, setting, and a character's traits, motivations, and feelings to determine the causes for that character's actions.

2. 4.3.2: Identify the main events of the plot, including their causes and the effects of each event on future actions, and the major theme from the story action.

3. 4.3.5: Define figurative language, such as similes, metaphors, hyperbole, or personification, and identify its use in literary works.

4 Read the following lines from the poem.

> That you were coming,—I declare,
> How red their faces grew!

Which of the following words means about the SAME as *declare*?

○ forget

○ demand

○ state

○ admire

> ⊚ **Tip:** The way that a word is used in a sentence can help you understand its meaning. Read each of the answer choices. Try to substitute each of the choices in place of the word in the sentence. Choose the word that fits the meaning of the word the best.

5 Read these lines from the poem.

> Who knocks? That April!
> Lock the door!

Based on these lines, what would the speaker MOST LIKELY do next?

○ The speaker will send March away.

○ The speaker will welcome April.

○ The speaker will expect March to go with April.

○ The speaker will keep April out.

> ⊚ **Tip:** To predict what will happen in a passage, think what might happen next. To do this, use your own experiences, such as how you've felt or known other people to feel. Also, look for important clues in the text that can support your answer.

Go On

Indiana English/Language Arts Standards

4. 4.1.2: Apply knowledge of synonyms (words with the same meaning), antonyms (words with opposite meanings), homographs (words that are spelled the same but have different meanings), and idioms (expressions that cannot be understood just by knowing the meanings of the words in the expression, such as *couch potato*) to determine the meaning of words and phrases.

5. 4.2.3: Make and confirm predictions about text by using prior knowledge and ideas presented in the text itself, including illustrations, titles, topic sentences, important words, foreshadowing clues (clues that indicate what might happen next), and direct quotations.

DIRECTIONS: Now you will read the article "The Bugs That Aren't" and do Numbers 6 through 10. Then you will answer more questions about writing, research, spelling, and grammar.

The Bugs That Aren't

by Gary Raham

You have probably seen pill bugs. These animals are bean-sized and gray or brownish in color. They are shaped like a jelly bean cut in half lengthwise.

Pill bugs are divided into many segments, which make them look like tiny armadillos. When you touch one of these bugs, it rolls up into a ball that looks like a pill. That's why it's often called a pill bug, even though it isn't really a "bug" at all.

All true bugs are very different animals. They belong to a special group of insects. The pill bug is more closely related to animals like crayfish and brine shrimp. If you have pet fish you may have given them brine shrimp to eat.

The pill bug is also related to some of the tiny, darting animals you can just barely see when you look at a jar of pond water. All of these animals are crustaceans.

Go On ➡

The Wet Life

Most crustaceans live in water. Unlike insects, they do not need waterproof coatings to keep their bodies moist.

But pill bugs do not live in water. To survive, they behave in ways that save water. For example, pill bugs spend most of their time in moist places under rocks and leaf litter.

They tend to stay under cover during the day. They go out at night to eat spider's eggs, dead plants, ripe fruit, and ant droppings.

If you lift up a rock and find pill bugs there, they are likely to be all bunched together. They prefer one another's odor, and they like to be touching something on all sides. Bunching up also helps keep moisture from evaporating. The smell of other pill bugs is probably how they find their way home at night, too.

Little Sips

You can also watch pill bugs drink water. Place a pill bug or two in a shallow pan or dish. Put a small drop of water near the edge.

When they begin to dry out, they will lower their rear ends into the water and move them up and down. They are drawing water up between their tail "fins," much like our way of sucking water through a straw. The water follows grooves along their legs, helped along by the movements of tiny hairs. The water ends up near their mouths, where they can drink it.

When you pick up a pill bug in the spring and summer months, you may find one whose underside looks milky. If you look closely, you may also see shadowy oval shapes.

The oval shapes are young pill bugs. They are in a brood pouch formed by flat plates that grow from the female's legs. When the young are ready to leave, the mother pill bug will release them. They will look like tiny white copies of the adults.

Young pill bugs live in a dangerous world. If conditions are too dry, the young will die. If the ground is too wet, they will be attacked by molds. The survivors will become more darkly colored each time they shed their skins and grow. After a year, they can produce their own young.

Old Beliefs

People used to believe many myths about pill bugs. Some thought that a pill bug in the house would bring bad luck. Others thought that feeding pill bugs to cows or people could cure stomachaches.

But pill bugs are just unusual crustaceans that have found a way to live on land. In fact, except when pill bugs munch on ripe tomatoes, these crustaceans and people get along pretty well.

The next time you see one, take a closer look at this tiny neighbor. Then let it wander off to take care of pill-bug business.

Go On

6 What happens when pill bugs use their tail "fins"?

○ They shed their skins.

○ They are able to drink.

○ They are able to swim.

○ They can keep molds away.

☺ Tip: A *cause* is something that brings about a result, and an *effect* is that result. Ask yourself why pill bugs put their rear ends in water. The answer to that question will give you the effect.

7 Which would be the MOST helpful if you wanted to find out what people used to think about pill bugs?

○ the title "The Bugs That Aren't"

○ the section "The Wet Life"

○ the section "Little Sips"

○ the section "Old Beliefs"

☺ Tip: A passage may be constructed in a way that helps you find information. Some of the ways a passage can be organized include the title, section headings, lists, outlines, and pictures. Look back at the passage and think about each answer before you choose.

8 After reading the title of this article, you can predict that

○ pill bugs live in water

○ pill bugs are not really bugs

○ all bugs are actually crustaceans

○ pill bugs are not real

☺ Tip: The title is the name of the article. Read it carefully. Determine what it tells you about the subject of the article.

Go On

Indiana English/Language Arts Standards
6. 4.2.6: Distinguish between cause and effect and between fact and opinion in informational text.
7. 4.2.1: Use the organization of informational text to strengthen comprehension.
8. 4.2.3: Make and confirm predictions about text by using prior knowledge and ideas presented in the text itself, including illustrations, titles, topic sentences, important words, foreshadowing clues (clues that indicate what might happen next), and direct quotations.

9 Which of the following helps a pill bug to save water?

○ bunching up together

○ following one another's scent

○ living in water

○ rolling into a ball

☉ Tip: To find the cause for something, you can start by looking at the effect, or result. In this question, the effect is that the pill bugs save water. Examine each answer choice to find which is a cause, or a way, that the pill bugs save water.

10 Read the following sentence from the article.

Pill bugs are divided into many segments, which make them look like tiny armadillos.

Which of the following words means about the SAME as *segments*?

○ parts

○ bodies

○ insects

○ arms

☉ Tip: Many words have similar meanings. Read the sentence. Then read the answer choices. Determine which word is most like the word *segments*.

Go On

Indiana English/Language Arts Standards
9. 4.2.6: Distinguish between cause and effect and between fact and opinion in informational text.
10. 4.1.2: Apply knowledge of synonyms (words with the same meaning), antonyms (words with opposite meanings), homographs (words that are spelled the same but have different meanings), and idioms (expressions that cannot be understood just by knowing the meanings of the words in the expression, such as *couch potato*) to determine the meaning of words and phrases.

For Number 11, choose the correct definition of the word.

11 Read this sentence.

> **Madison enjoyed the book he read so much that he looked at its** *bibliography* **to get ideas for other books to read.**

The word *bibliography* comes from the Greek root word *biblion*, meaning "small book" and the Greek root word *graphein*, meaning "to write." What does *bibliography* mean in this sentence?

○ a place where books are kept

○ a hobby of collecting rare books

○ a book written about a person's life

○ a list of books related to a single subject

⑤ Tip: Common root words can help you understand the meaning of words. The root of the word *bibliography* means book. That means that the answer must somehow be related to books. Read the example sentence, and then read each answer choice. Put each answer choice in the example sentence, in place of the word *bibliography*. This will help you make the best choice.

12 Choose the BEST way to combine the following sentences.

> **Sally has a large dog.**
> **She walks the dog every day.**
> **She walks it in the park.**

○ Sally walks every day, and so does her dog.

○ Sally's large dog walks every day in the park.

○ Sally walks her dog in the park every week.

○ Sally walks her large dog in the park every day.

⑤ Tip: When you revise writing, you make changes that make it better or clearer. One way to do this is to combine simple sentences. Read the answer choices and determine which one keeps the information contained in the three original sentences.

Go On

Indiana English/Language Arts Standards
11. 4.1.4: Use common roots (*meter = measure*) and word parts (*therm = heat*) derived from Greek and Latin to analyze the meaning of complex words (*thermometer*).
12. 4.4.12: Revise writing by combining and moving sentences and paragraphs to improve the focus and progression of ideas.

For Number 13, choose the sentence that is written MOST clearly and correctly.

13 ○   The tired hikers were climbing up the hill happy to see their cars.

   ○   Climbing up the hill, the tired hikers were happy to see their cars.

   ○   Climbing up the hill happy to see their cars were the tired hikers.

   ○   The tired hikers were happy to see their cars climbing up the hill.

> ⟳ **Tip:** When you revise writing, you make changes that make it clearer and easier to read. Read each answer choice and determine exactly what the writer is trying to say. Then pick the choice that is most clearly written.

For Number 14, choose the phrase that is correct and BEST completes the sentence.

14 The sunburned sailor slipped on the deck while running ＿＿＿＿＿＿＿.

   ○   before the boat

   ○   across the boat

   ○   through the boat

   ○   under the boat

> ⟳ **Tip:** Interesting sentences often have good detail in them. One way to add detail is to use descriptive phrases. The writer tries to paint a picture using words. Ask yourself which phrase gives the most accurate description.

For Number 15, choose the sentence that is written MOST clearly and correctly.

15 ○   The clown ran noisy through the crowd.

   ○   Pink and orange clouds total filled the sky.

   ○   The tired dog curled up in the corner and quiet took a nap.

   ○   The girl carefully placed the baby bird back in its nest.

> ⟳ **Tip:** Adverbs can be used to modify verbs, adjectives, or other adverbs. Adverbs usually describe *how* or *when.* Often an adverb will end in *-ly.* Read each sentence to yourself. Choose the sentence that uses adverbs correctly.

Indiana English/Language Arts Standards

13. **4.4.10:** Review, evaluate, and revise writing for meaning and clarity.

14. **4.6.3:** Create interesting sentences by using words that describe, explain, or provide additional details and connections, such as adjectives, adverbs, appositives, participial phrases, prepositional phrases, and conjunctions.

15. **4.6.4:** Identify and use in writing regular *(live/lived, shout/shouted)* and irregular verbs *(swim/swam, ride/rode, hit/hit),* adverbs *(constantly, quickly),* and prepositions *(through, beyond, between).*

Test 3

Celebrating a Birthday

Read the writing prompt below and complete the writing activity.

 Write a story about your favorite birthday celebration. Tell how you celebrated your birthday and why it was your favorite celebration. You may write about an imaginary celebration if you like.

Describe your favorite celebration. Describe how you felt that day. Be sure to include details in your story. Tell about who was there at the celebration and what everyone did. What made this celebration better than all the others?

Be sure to include

- a description of your favorite birthday celebration

- how you felt during your celebration

- what made your celebration so special

- a beginning, middle, and an end to your story

- details to make your story interesting

Tip: When you write a story, make sure that you include colorful details to make the writing interesting. Think about stories you like to read and what makes them interesting to you. It might be action verbs, good descriptions, or snappy dialogue. When you write your story, think about your audience and what will make the story interesting for them to read.

 **Go On**

Indiana English/Language Arts Standards
WRITING: Writing Process [4.4.2, 4.4.4, 4.4.10, 4.4.11, 4.4.12]
WRITING: Writing Applications [4.5.1, 4.5.5, 4.5.6]
WRITING: Written English [4.6.1, 4.6.2, 4.6.3]

The Pre-Writing/Planning space on the next two pages, or a separate sheet of paper, can be used for notes, outlines, lists, or any other tools to help plan your writing. When you have finished planning, write your essay neatly on pages 26–29 in this book. Your final essay on the lined pages will be the only writing scored. Be sure to create a title for your essay. Proofread your essay using the Editing Checklist on page 29. The Editing Checklist will help you check your writing for correct paragraphing, spelling, grammar, and punctuation, and for the use of Standard English.

Pre-Writing/Planning

Pre-Writing/Planning

Go On

Story

Title: _____

_____

_____

_____

_____

_____

_____

_____

_____

_____

_____

_____

_____

_____

_____

_____

_____

_____

_____

_____

Go On

Go On

Go On

_____

_____

_____

_____

_____

_____

_____

_____

_____

_____

_____

_____

_____

Check your writing with the Editing Checklist.

Editing Checklist

1 Have you checked capitalization and punctuation?

2 Are all the words spelled correctly?

3 Are there any run-on sentences or fragments?

4 Have you kept verb tense consistent?

5 Do the subject and verb agree?

6 Is your essay written according to the rules of Standard English?

7 Do you use paragraphs correctly?

STOP

DIRECTIONS: In Test 4, you will read a story and an article. You will answer questions based on each passage. Then you will do some writing on a related topic.

The first story is about a girl who works at a bakery and who does things differently from most people. Read the story. Then do Numbers 1 through 5. You may look back at the story as often as you like.

Happily Ever After

by Beth Thompson

"It's an extraordinary day for a wedding," Mrs. Bidgely chirped as she spread thick vanilla icing on the third layer of an enormous cake. "And if I do say so myself, this is an extraordinary cake! Don't you agree, Rowena?"

When there was no answer, Mrs. Bidgely glanced over her shoulder . . . and almost dropped her frosting knife. "Rowena!" she cried. "What *are* you cooking?"

Rowena Skittles, assistant baker at Bidgely's Bakery, was stirring a huge, steaming pot. "It's rice, Mrs. B.!" Rowena explained. Her orange corkscrew curls bounced up and down. "All weddings need rice. Should I add the butter now?"

"Oh, Rowena!" Mrs. Bidgely sputtered. "The rice is to throw, not to eat! We need *uncooked* rice! Now let me handle things. It's not every day that Bidgely's Bakery is selected to make a wedding cake for the mayor's only daughter."

"Bert said they picked us because of his birthday cake," said Rowena. "He said that the mayor still talks about that cake!"

"Yes, I'm sure he does!" Mrs. Bidgely said. She shuddered, remembering the chocolate-mint-rainbow-iced cake that Rowena had made, topped with purple pandas and sparklers. It was nothing like the vanilla cake with blue roses that Mrs. Bidgely would have made. After all, Bidgely's motto was printed right on the front window: Always in Good Taste. But Inglebert Fenton Killebrew III (also known as Bert) had said it was the best cake he'd ever tasted. And his father, the mayor, had agreed.

Mrs. Bidgely decided that *this* cake would be in very good taste. It was decorated with creamy white icing, sugar roses, and doves, with a tiny china bride and groom on top. And Mrs. Bidgely would deliver *this* cake personally.

"It's your day off, Rowena, so go and enjoy yourself," Mrs. Bidgely said. She was afraid to let Rowena get too close to the cake.

"Well, Mrs. B., if you're sure, then I will. I'm going to try out my new in-line skates in the park."

The park was crowded with skaters zipping and zooming along the paths. Rowena laced up her skates and tried to stand, but . . . SPLAT! Every time she stood up, down she sat!

"Need some help, Rowena?" A pair of bright green in-line skates skidded expertly to a stop. It was Bert Killebrew!

Go On ➡

"I could use a hand," said Rowena, "or even two." Holding on to Bert, she wobbled over to a bench. "But why aren't you at your sister Millicent's wedding?"

"Millicent said I was in the way," explained Bert. "I'm just supposed to show up on time to carry the ring down the aisle—and no skates!" Bert looked disgusted. "Weddings are boring!"

"Then you can help me with these wheely-wobblers!" said Rowena happily. "The last time I skated, skates had two rows of wheels. It was easier to stay up!"

After an hour of practice, Rowena was able to roll slowly and unsteadily along the path. She bought Bert a raspberry snow cone to thank him, and she got one, too.

"You're doing great, Rowena," said Bert, "but I've got to roll! It's time for Millicent's boring old wedding. Bye!" And he skated away.

Rowena started thinking about the wedding and stopped looking where she was going. Suddenly she was rolling down a hill . . . and picking up speed! Rowena almost hit old Mr. Timmons, who was feeding the pigeons. He dived for cover, scattering birdseed all over Rowena. On she rolled, followed by a flock of flapping birds.

Then she just missed June the Balloon Lady . . . but Rowena's waving arms got tangled in the strings. Purple and green balloons bobbed around her like giant grapes.

"Look out!" cried Rowena. "Skater out of control!" People jumped out of her way as she rolled toward the park gate.

When Rowena rocketed past the rose garden, she grabbed at a bush to stop herself, but all she got were rose petals in her hair and a thorn in her thumb.

Still clutching her raspberry snow cone, Rowena roared on, heading straight for the center of town!

Meanwhile, as Mrs. Bidgely carried the cake on a silver tray out to her delivery van, she discovered two flat tires. How could she get to the wedding on time? Then she heard a rumble approaching.

"Help!" cried Mrs. Bidgely as a colorful streak with bobbing balloons and orange curls raced toward her, but it was too late. Unstoppable Rowena raced by, grabbing the cake, tray and all! Horrified, Mrs. Bidgely ran after her, crying, "Stop! Stop!"

The wedding lay right in the path of runaway Rowena!

On rolled Rowena, trailing balloons and pigeons and petals. The tall cake swayed on its tray, but Mrs. Bidgely's icing held like cement, and not a layer was lost. As Rowena bounced up the church steps, the china bride and groom flew off. Rowena tried to grab them, but her hands were full of cake and snow cone.

"Rowena, use your brakes!" yelled Bert. Brakes! Why hadn't she thought of that? Rowena screeched to a stop and plopped down the tray in a shower of pink rose petals. Safe!

Go On

"It's beautiful!" cried Millicent. "But where are the little bride and groom?"

Triumphantly, Rowena fished them out of her raspberry snow cone. "Here they are!" she cried, plopping them pinkly on top of the cake. Poor Mrs. Bidgely fainted at the sight, but Millicent and her parents were delighted.

"Boy, Rowena," said Bert, "if Millicent's marriage is half as exciting as her wedding, she's sure to live happily ever after!"

1 Read the following sentence from the story.

> **After an hour of practice, Rowena was able to roll slowly and unsteadily along the path.**

What does the word *unsteadily* mean?

- ○ shakily
- ○ angrily
- ○ carefully
- ○ gracefully

ⓢ Tip: Root words can help you figure out the meaning of words you don't know. Start by deciding what the root of *unsteadily* is. Ask yourself what the root word means. Remember to add the prefix *un-* and suffix *-ly* before deciding what the whole word means.

2 Which of the following BEST expresses the story's theme?

- ○ There is only one right way to do things.
- ○ Learning new things helps people to grow.
- ○ Maintaining order and control is very important.
- ○ Unplanned events can be exciting and enjoyable.

ⓢ Tip: The theme is a truth about life that is found in a story. You can find more than one example of the theme in the story. Read each answer choice and decide which one best represents a truth about life in the story.

Indiana English/Language Arts Standards
1. **4.1.3:** Use knowledge of root words *(nation, national, nationality)* to determine the meaning of unknown words within a passage.
2. **4.3.2:** Identify the main events of the plot, including their causes and the effects of each event on future actions, and the major theme from the story action.

Go On

3 Which of the following sentences from the story contains a simile?

○ Her orange corkscrew curls bounced up and down.

○ Mrs. Bidgely decided that this cake would be in very good taste.

○ The wedding lay right in the path of runaway Rowena.

○ Purple and green balloons bobbed around her like giant grapes.

🌀 **Tip:** A simile is a comparison of two different things, usually using the words *like* or *as.* For example, the sentence *"He is as tall as an oak tree"* contains a simile. The man is compared to an oak tree because he is tall. Read each sentence and look for two things being compared to one another.

4 In the story, Rowena and Mrs. Bidgely are very different. On the lines below, write TWO things that Rowena does that are unusual.

_____

_____

_____

🌀 **Tip:** Sometimes making a list can help you better understand a character in a story. Look back at the story for some of the examples the author gives about how Rowena is a bit different. The author gives you lots of clues about Rowena and what she is like.

5 Write a brief description of Rowena, telling what kind of person she is. Look beyond the things that Rowena does to find out why she does them. Give at least TWO examples from the story.

_____

_____

_____

_____

🌀 **Tip:** After reading a story, you can tell what a character is like. Look at the story to find examples of what kind of person Rowena is.

Indiana English/Language Arts Standards
3. **4.3.5:** Define figurative language, such as similes, metaphors, hyperbole, or personification, and identify its use in literary works.
4. **4.3.3:** Use knowledge of the situation, setting, and a character's traits, motivations, and feelings to determine the causes for that character's actions.
5. **4.3.3:** Use knowledge of the situation, setting, and a character's traits, motivations, and feelings to determine the causes for that character's actions.

Go On

DIRECTIONS: This passage is about stars. Read the article. Then do Numbers 6 through 11. You may look back at the article as often as you like.

Zoo in the Sky

by Edmund A. Fortier

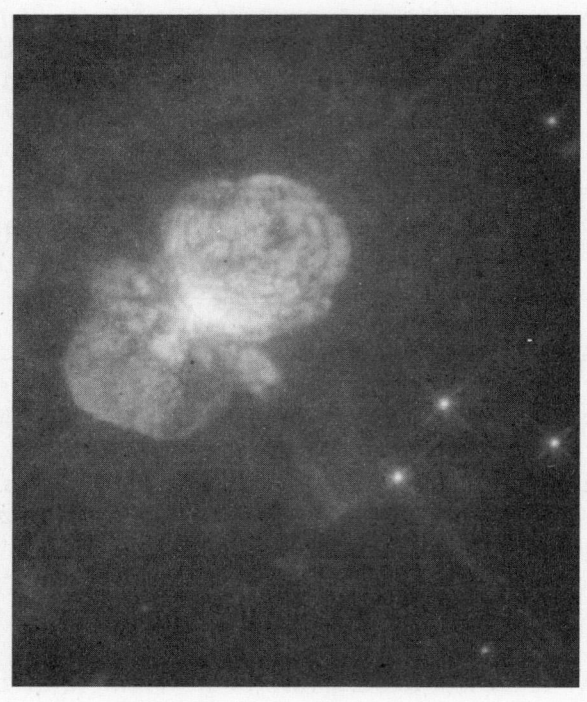

If you wanted to see a pelican, a crab, or a swan, where would you look? The answer is simple—a zoo!

But if you were an astronomer, you wouldn't have to go to a zoo at all. With a powerful telescope and a little imagination, you could spot each of these creatures in the night sky.

This isn't as strange as it sounds. The night sky has always excited people's imaginations. When people of long ago looked up at the stars, they thought they could see the shapes of beasts, birds, and mythical heroes. Some of their fanciful sky pictures became our present-day constellations.

Much later, when astronomers began exploring the sky with telescopes, they saw—well, mostly they saw more stars. But they also saw strange, hazy patches of light.

Huge Clouds

Astronomers called each of these patches a "nebula" (NEB-you-lah), from the Latin word for cloud. A nebula really is a cloud. But it's a cloud of gas and dust.

The more astronomers studied nebulae (NEB-you-lee), which means more than one nebula, the more familiar some of them looked. Just as you might see the figure of a clown or a cow in a cloud, astronomers saw ghostly shapes floating in space. For example, they called one nebula "the Swan" and another "the Crab." They even named one of them "the Horsehead."

Nebulae, like clouds, are in constant motion. But you would have to watch a nebula for years to notice a change. Nebulae are so huge and so far away that, to us, they seem frozen in space.

Star Birth

Some nebulae are the birth-places of new stars, and others are the debris from dead or dying stars. But all nebulae have one thing in common. They are made of the same materials as stars.

The nebulae where stars are born are made of hydrogen gas, helium gas, and dust. Some of them are dark. We know dark nebulae exist because some of them block out the light of stars behind them. The most famous of all dark nebulae, the Horsehead, lies in front of a bright nebula.

Over many millions of years, stars can form inside a dark nebula. If one of these stars is very hot—much hotter than the Sun—that star could transform the dark cloud into a bright nebula. These nebulae appear red in photographs because of the energy they receive from the hot stars within them. Astronomers think that every star—including our Sun—was born in a nebula like the Swan, the Horsehead, or the Pelican.

When Stars Die

Stars die, too. Most die quietly, creating another kind of nebula. The outer layers of these stars expand into thin gaseous shells called planetary nebulae, such as "the Cat's Eye."

At the center of these nebulae are the stars' super-hot, shrunken cores, which are called white dwarfs. The white dwarfs cause the nebulous shells to glow with a pale light.

These nebulae are smaller than other nebulae. In fact, when they were discovered, astronomers thought the nebulae looked like planets. That's why scientists called them planetary nebulae.

But not all dying stars are so well-behaved. Very massive stars end their lives in tremendous explosions called supernovae. No event in our galaxy is more violent. For a few brilliant moments, a supernova can out-shine a billion suns. About nine hundred years ago, one blazed so brightly it could be seen in the daytime. The nebula it left behind is named "the Crab."

Go On

6 Information in the article is presented as a

    ○ summary of opinions

    ○ list of causes and effects

    ○ scientific description

    ○ comparison of facts

🌀 **Tip:** An article can be organized in ways that make it easier to understand. Authors have many different ways of presenting information. Look at each answer choice. Then look back at the article to see how the author organized the article.

7 Which of the following sentences from the story contains an example of personification?

    ○ But it's a cloud of gas and dust.

    ○ But they also saw strange, hazy patches of light.

    ○ This isn't as strange as it sounds.

    ○ But not all dying stars are so well-behaved.

🌀 **Tip:** Personification gives human qualities to something that is not human. Read each sentence and look for the "thing" that is being given human qualities.

8 If you wanted to read about how stars are formed, which of the following would you do?

    ○ Study the title *Zoo in the Sky.*

    ○ Read the section called "Star Birth."

    ○ Look for the first place the word *star* is used.

    ○ Read the section called "Huge Clouds."

🌀 **Tip:** There are many ways to find what you need in a passage. One method is reading, or rereading, the passage more slowly to help you understand its meaning. Another way is to look at how the article is labeled. Labels often help you know what is coming next.

Indiana English/Language Arts Standards
6. **4.2.1:** Use the organization of informational text to strengthen comprehension.
7. **4.3.5:** Define figurative language, such as similes, metaphors, hyperbole, or personification, and identify its use in literary works.
8. **4.2.2:** Use appropriate strategies when reading for different purposes.

Go On

9 Which of the following sentences is an OPINION from the article?

    ○ This isn't as strange as it sounds.

    ○ A nebula really is a cloud.

    ○ Nebulae, like clouds, are in constant motion.

    ○ Stars die, too.

⑤ Tip: To fully understand a passage, you must be able to tell the difference between fact and opinion. A fact is true and can be proved to be true. An opinion is what someone thinks about something. An opinion cannot be proved to be true. It is just one point of view. Read each answer choice. Decide which sentence is the author's opinion.

10 Why is this article titled *Zoo in the Sky?* Write a short paragraph that explains why you think the author chose that title. Be sure to include an example from the article to support your answer.

_____

_____

_____

_____

_____

_____

_____

_____

⑤ Tip: Sometimes a passage gives you enough information so that you can draw conclusions about something. In this passage, you are asked to tell why the author chose the title that he did. This passage is full of clues to give you the answer.

Go On

Indiana English/Language Arts Standards
9. 4.2.6: Distinguish between cause and effect and between fact and opinion in informational text.
10. 4.2.3: Make and confirm predictions about text by using prior knowledge and ideas presented in the text itself, including illustrations, titles, topic sentences, important words, foreshadowing clues (clues that indicate what might happen next), and direct quotations.

11 Write a summary of the article *Zoo in the Sky*. In your summary, be sure to include the main ideas of the article and the most important details. Remember to put the information in your own words.

Use the Pre-Writing/Planning space below to plan your writing. Only the essay on pages 39–40 will be scored. The Editing Checklist on page 40 will help you proofread your writing for correct paragraphing, spelling, grammar, and punctuation, and the use of Standard English. **Your essay should have an introduction, a body, and a conclusion and should be well organized.**

> ☺ **Tip:** Remember that a summary only tells the most important things that happened. In a summary, you use your own words to describe main events and key details. Look back at the story to decide which events you will include in your summary.

Pre-Writing/Planning

Go On

Indiana English/Language Arts Standards
11. **4.4.10** Review, evaluate, and revise writing for meaning and clarity.
   4.4.11 Proofread one's own writing, as well as that of others, using an editing checklist or set of rules, with specific examples of corrections of frequent errors.
   4.5.4 Write summaries that contain the main ideas of the reading selection and the most significant details.
   4.6.4 Identify and use in writing regular *(live/lived, shout/shouted)* and irregular verbs *(swim/swam, ride/rode, hit/hit)*, adverbs *(constantly, quickly)*, and prepositions *(through, beyond, between)*.

Summary

Go On

_____

_____

_____

_____

_____

_____

_____

_____

_____

_____

_____

_____

Check your writing with the Editing Checklist.

Editing Checklist

1 Have you checked capitalization and punctuation?

2 Are all the words spelled correctly?

3 Are there any run-on sentences or fragments?

4 Have you kept verb tense consistent?

5 Do the subject and verb agree?

6 Is your essay written according to the rules of Standard English?

7 Do you use paragraphs consistently?

Test-Taking Tips

Now you are ready to take a practice test to help you prepare for the *ISTEP+* English/Language Arts test. The first two parts of the practice test are the Basic Skills Assessment. The third and fourth parts of the practice test are the Applied Skills Assessment.

Remember these hints when you are taking the practice tests:

- Pay careful attention to the directions.
- Read the entire item and all of the answer choices.
- Be sure you clearly understand the item.
- Narrow down possible answers by eliminating incorrect answer choices.
- Sometimes more than one answer may seem correct—choose the best answer.
- Be sure to mark answers clearly in the correct empty circle.
- Do not spend too much time on any one item.
- Mark items to return to if time permits.
- Use any time remaining to review your answers.

Also try using the following strategies as you write your writing activity and extended response:

- Plan what you want to say before you begin writing.
- Write neatly on the lines within the box.
- Be sure to answer all parts of the question.
- Revise and edit your work.
- Use any time remaining to review your writing.

Sometimes people get nervous when they take a test. Try to remember what you have learned about taking tests. Knowing what to expect should help you feel more confident and improve your score.

ISTEP+

Indiana Statewide Testing for Educational Progress

Practice Test

Basic Skills Assessment
English/Language Arts
Grade 5

For Test 1, you will read a story and an article. You will answer questions based on each passage. After responding to these questions, you will answer more questions about writing, research, spelling, and grammar.

The first passage is a story about a secret garden. In the story, Mary finds an old key and wonders what secrets it might unlock. Read the story. Then do Numbers 1 through 5. Refer back to the story as often as you like.

Go On

from
The Secret Garden

by Frances Hodgson Burnett

Mary looked at it, not really knowing why the hole was there, and as she looked she saw something almost buried in the newly-turned soil. It was something like a ring of rusty iron or brass and when the robin flew up into a tree nearby she put out her hand and picked the ring up. It was more than a ring, however; it was an old key which looked as if it had been buried a long time.

Mistress Mary stood up and looked at it with an almost frightened face as it hung from her finger.

"Perhaps it has been buried for ten years," she said in a whisper. "Perhaps it is the key to the garden!"

She looked at the key quite a long time. She turned it over and over, and thought about it. As I have said before, she was not a child who had been trained to ask permission or consult her elders about things. All she thought about the key was that if it was the key to the closed garden, and she could find out where the door was, she could perhaps open it and see what was inside the walls, and what had happened to the old rose-trees. It was because it had been shut up so long that she wanted to see it. It seemed as if it must be different from other places and that something strange must have happened to it during ten years. Besides that, if she liked it she

Go On

could go into it every day and shut the door behind her, and she could make up some play of her own and play it quite alone, because nobody would ever know where she was, but would think the door was still locked and the key buried in the earth. The thought of that pleased her very much.

Living as it were, all by herself in a house with a hundred mysteriously closed rooms and having nothing whatever to do to amuse herself, had set her inactive brain to working and was actually awakening her imagination. There is no doubt that the fresh, strong, pure air from the moor had a great deal to do with it. Just as it had given her an appetite, and fighting with the wind had stirred her blood, so the same things had stirred her mind. In India she had always been too hot and languid and weak to care much about anything, but in this place she was beginning to care and to want to do new things. Already she felt less "contrary," though she did not know why.

She put the key in her pocket and walked up and down her walk. No one but herself ever seemed to come there, so she could walk slowly and look at the wall, or, rather, at the ivy growing on it. The ivy was the baffling thing. Howsoever carefully she looked she could see nothing but thickly growing, glossy, dark green leaves. She was very much disappointed. Something of her contrariness came back to her as she paced the walk and looked over it at the tree-tops inside. It seemed so silly, she said to herself, to be near it and not be able to get in. She took the key in her pocket when she went back to the house, and she made up her mind that she would always carry it with her when she went out, so that if she ever should find the hidden door she would be ready.

Go On

1 Based on the story, which of the following can you predict will happen?

○ Mary will find the hidden door.

○ Mary will move back to India.

○ Mary will become a gardener.

○ Mary will capture the robin.

2 Which of the following events is the MOST important part of the story?

○ Mary sees a robin.

○ Mary finds a key.

○ Mary makes a new friend.

○ Mary plays in the garden.

3 What will Mary do if she finds the gate to the garden?

○ She will go in by herself.

○ She will give the key to a friend.

○ She will bury the key where she found it.

○ She will ask an adult for permission to enter.

Go On

4 Read the following sentence from the story.

She put the key in her pocket and walked up and down her walk.

What is the meaning of the word *walk* as it is used in this sentence?

○ a paved pathway

○ a trip outside for a dog on a leash

○ movement on foot

○ behaving in a certain way

5 Read the following sentences from the story.

There is no doubt that the fresh, strong, pure air from the moor had a great deal to do with it. Just as it had given her an appetite, and fighting with the wind had stirred her blood, so the same things had stirred her mind.

What do the words "fighting with the wind had stirred her blood" mean in this sentence?

○ Taking long hikes kept her warm.

○ Exercising had helped to calm her down.

○ Feeling angry had caused her to misbehave.

○ Being in new surroundings had made her feel more active.

Go On

English/Language Arts

This passage is from a book called *Earthquakes*. Do you know much about earthquakes? Have you ever been in an earthquake?

For some interesting facts about earthquakes, read the passage. Then do Numbers 6 through 10. You may look back at the passage as often as you like. After you respond to questions based on the passage, you will answer more questions about writing, research, spelling, and grammar.

Go On

Earthquakes

by Seymour Simon

Most earthquakes take place in the earth's crust, a five- to thirty-mile deep layer of rocks that covers the earth. Cracks in the rocks, called faults, run through the crust. The rocks on one side of a fault push against the rocks on the other side, causing energy to build up. For years, friction will hold the rocks in place. But finally, like a stretched rubber band, the rocks suddenly snap past each other. The place where this happens is called the focus of an earthquake.

From the focus, the energy of the quake speeds outward through the surrounding rocks in all directions. The shocks may last for less than a second for a small quake to several minutes for a major one. Weaker shocks, called aftershocks, can follow a quake on and off for days or weeks.

Sometimes one side of a fault will slip higher than the other. This kind of up-and-down movement is called a dip-slip fault.

Why do most earthquakes in the United States occur in California? The answer lies deep within the earth. The earth's solid rocky crust floats on the mantle, an 1,800-mile-thick layer of very heavy, melted rock that moves up and down and around. Over the years, these movements have cracked the crust like an eggshell into a number of huge pieces called plates.

The plates float slowly about on the mantle up to four inches a year. As the plates move, they run into or pull away from each other, producing enormous strains in the rocks along their edges. The United States and Canada are riding on the North American plate, which is slowly moving into the Pacific plate. The colliding plates are what causes most of the earthquakes along the West Coast. But earthquakes can occur anywhere there are stresses in underlying rocks.

Four out of five of the world's earthquakes take place along the rim of the Pacific Ocean, a zone called the Pacific Ring of Fire. Alaska, California, Mexico, the west coasts of Central and South America, and the east coasts of China, Japan, and New Zealand are all located within the Pacific Ring of Fire. Another major earthquake zone stretches through Italy, Greece, and Turkey to the Middle East and into Asia.

In the United States, almost half of the quakes each year occur in southern California. In other sections of the United States, earthquakes are rare. About the only places that have never recorded an earthquake are the southern parts of Florida, Alabama, and Texas.

Go On

6 Which of the following causes earthquakes to occur?

○ landslides and mudslides

○ stresses in underlying rocks

○ friction holding rocks in place

○ buildings falling down

7 Where do most earthquakes occur in the United States?

○ Texas

○ Florida

○ Alabama

○ California

8 Read the following sentence from the article.

The colliding plates are what causes most of the earthquakes along the West Coast.

Which word means about the SAME as *colliding*?

○ burning

○ bumping

○ standing

○ smoothing

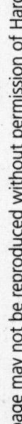

Go On

9 Which of the following sentences from the passage contains a simile?

○ Cracks in the rocks, called faults, run through the crust.

○ But finally, like a stretched rubber band, the rocks suddenly snap past each other.

○ Sometimes one side of a fault will slip higher than the other.

○ The plates float slowly about on the mantle up to four inches a year.

10 Read the following sentence from the passage.

The shocks may last for less than a second for a small quake to several minutes for a major one.

What is the meaning of the word *shocks* as it is used in this sentence?

○ stalks of corn set up in a field

○ a violent shaking

○ physical condition after an accident

○ a sudden surprise

Go On

For Number 11, read the paragraph and then follow the directions.

11   Using a video camera is fun and easy. The first thing you need to do is connect the power source. If you're filming inside in one location, you just connect the power cord to the camera and to a plug in the wall. If you're filming outside or moving around, you need to put in the battery pack. _____ Then you remove the lens cover and press the "record" button. Look through the viewfinder to see your subject. When you're finished, push the "record" button again to turn the camera off.

Choose the sentence that MOST LIKELY fits in the blank.

○   The next step is to read the video camera manual.

○   The next step is to watch the tape on your television.

○   The next step is to put in the tape, which is like film.

○   The next step is to focus the camera on your subject.

For Number 12, choose the sentence that shows the correct punctuation.

12   ○   Kathy didnt' fold her clothes.

○   Kathy didnt fold her clothes.

○   Kathy didn't fold her clothes.

○   Kathy didnt fold her clothe's.

Go On

For Number 13, choose the sentence that shows the correct punctuation.

13　○　My favorite poem is called "Mr. Grumpledump's Song."

　　　○　My favorite poem is called Mr. Grumpledump's Song.

　　　○　My favorite poem is called *Mr. Grumpledump's Song.*

　　　○　My favorite poem is called *"Mr. Grumpledump's Song."*

14　Read the following sentence.

Trying to walk quickly on the floor she was and dropped the eggs and butter.

Which is the BEST way to rewrite this sentence?

○　She was trying to walk quickly, but she dropped the eggs and butter on the floor.

○　Dropping the eggs and butter trying on the floor to walk quickly she was.

○　She was dropping the eggs and butter trying to walk quickly on the floor.

○　She was too quick for the eggs and butter she dropped on the floor.

15　Choose the BEST way to combine the following sentences.

Prudy went to the dentist.
Her tooth hurt.
The dentist did not find any cavities.

○　Prudy went to the dentist who did not find any cavities because her tooth hurt.

○　Prudy went to the dentist because her tooth hurt, but the dentist did not find any cavities.

○　Because her tooth hurt, the dentist did not find any cavities and Prudy went to the dentist.

○　The dentist did not find any cavities, and Prudy went to the dentist because her tooth hurt.

Test 2: English/Language Arts

In Test 2, you will read a poem and an article. Then you will answer questions based on each passage. After responding to these questions, you will answer more questions about writing, research, spelling, and grammar.

This poem is called "The Visitor." It requires the reader to use his or her imagination. Read the poem. Then do Numbers 1 through 5. Refer back to the poem as often as you like.

The Visitor

it came today to visit
and moved into the house
it was smaller than an elephant
but larger than a mouse

first it slapped my sister
then it kicked my dad
then it pushed my mother
oh! that really made me mad

it went and tickled rover
and terrified the cat
it sliced apart my necktie
and rudely crushed my hat

it smeared my head with honey
and filled the tub with rocks
and when i yelled in anger
it stole my shoes and socks

that's just the way it happened
it happened all today
before it bowed politely
and softly went away

—by Jack Prelutsky

Go On

1 Based on the clues in the third stanza of the poem, who MOST LIKELY the speaker in the poem?

   ○ a dog

   ○ a boy

   ○ a mother

   ○ a monster

2 What was the cause of all the trouble in the poem?

   ○ The cat was terrified.

   ○ The tub was full of rocks.

   ○ The speaker became angry.

   ○ The visitor came to the house.

3 Read the following lines from the poem.

   it went and tickled rover
   and terrified the cat

   Based on the clues in the lines above, "rover" was probably a

   ○ cat

   ○ dog

   ○ elephant

   ○ mouse

Go On

4 Which of the following is the MOST likely reason the speaker yelled at the visitor?

○ The speaker wanted to take a bath and the visitor interrupted him.

○ The speaker was angry about the visitor's rude behavior.

○ The speaker had told the visitor not to come into the house.

○ The speaker was upset about having his shoes and socks stolen.

5 Read the following lines from the poem.

> **it sliced apart my necktie**
> **and rudely crushed my hat**

Which of the following words means the OPPOSITE of *crushed*?

○ smoothed

○ ruined

○ destroyed

○ squeezed

Go On

English/Language Arts

Have you ever actually seen a bald eagle? Sometimes you can see bald eagles that have been rescued in the zoo. The bald eagle is our national bird. In the passage from the book *Soaring with the Wind: The Bald Eagle*, you will learn more about this interesting bird. After reading the passage, you will answer questions about what you have read. Then you will answer more questions about writing, punctuation, capitalization, and spelling.

Now read the passage from *Soaring with the Wind: The Bald Eagle* and do Numbers 6 through 10. Refer back to the passage as often as you like.

Go On

from Soaring with the Wind: The Bald Eagle

by Gail Gibbons

The bald eagle is a raptor. Raptors are birds of prey, which means they eat meat. The name raptor comes from the Latin word *rapere,* meaning "to grasp or seize by force." Bald eagles are excellent hunters, gripping their prey with claws, also called talons, that are razor sharp and four inches long.

A bald eagle isn't bald. Its name comes from *balde,* an Old English word meaning "white." With its gleaming white head and tail feathers, the bald eagle cannot be mistaken for any other bird. It belongs to the group of eagles called fish and sea eagles that lives near water and eats mostly fish and water birds.

An adult bald eagle is about three feet tall from head to tail and weighs about eleven pounds. Often the female is bigger than the male. They both have the same basic characteristics.

The bald eagle is one of the largest hunting birds in North America. Its body is perfectly designed for flight and for catching prey. The entire skeleton of a bald eagle weighs only about half a pound. Each bone is hollow and filled with air. Braces, also called struts, inside the bone give it strength.

There are about 7,000 feathers on a bald eagle's body. Together, they weigh a little less than one and one-half pounds. They overlap one another to create a lot of air space in between. This helps to insulate, or protect, the bird's body from heat and cold.

The feathers are strong because they are made of keratin, just like your fingernails. Each feather is held together by a pattern of barbules. More than 350,000 hooked barbules are attached to bowed barbules to give each feather its particular shape. The covert feathers shape the wing so that air moves faster over the top than under the bottom. The difference in air pressure gives the eagle better lift. The tail feathers are used for stopping and steering.

Like all birds, eagles are streamlined for flight. Their wingspread can be as wide as seven and a half feet. The wings are flatter on the bottom than on top, just like an airplane's wings. The bald eagle uses its wing feathers to lift off and change direction, and it can dive down through the air at 100 miles an hour!

Go On

6 Which of the following sentences from the article is an OPINION?

○ Raptors are birds of prey, which means they eat meat.

○ With its gleaming white head and tail feathers, the bald eagle cannot be mistaken for any other bird.

○ An adult bald eagle is about three feet tall from head to tail and weighs about eleven pounds.

○ There are about 7,000 feathers on a bald eagle's body.

7 What does the Latin word *rapere* tell you about raptors?

○ They have hollow bones.

○ They have strong feathers.

○ They seize their prey by force.

○ They eat mostly fish and water birds.

8 Which of the following is an effect of eagles' feathers overlapping?

○ It makes the feathers strong.

○ It gives each feather its shape.

○ It makes the feathers very light.

○ It protects the eagle from heat and cold.

Go On ➡

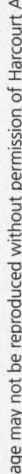

9 Read the following sentence from the article.

Like all birds, eagles are streamlined for flight.

What does the word *streamlined* mean in this sentence?

○ big and heavy

○ well organized

○ smoothly shaped

○ new and modern

10 Look at the following idea web and then follow the directions.

Raptor
excellent hunter; eats meat;
grasps prey by force

Body
7000 feathers; overlapping
feathers create insulation;
streamlined for flight

Bald Eagles

——————
3 feet tall; 11 pounds;
7 1/2 foot wingspan

Which heading BEST completes the bottom circle?

○ Size

○ Skeleton

○ Feathers

○ Hunters

Go On

For Number 11, read the paragraph and then follow the directions.

11   Dogs can be trained to help people with disabilities. Seeing eye dogs lead their owners across streets and around obstacles. Hearing dogs alert their owners to sounds such as alarms, doorbells, and telephones. Other service dogs open doors, turn on lights, pick up dropped objects, and fetch wheelchairs. _____ .

Choose the sentence that MOST LIKELY comes next.

○   It's nice to have a dog in the house.

○   Service dogs can learn to do many new tricks for their owners.

○   Some training organizations get all of their dogs from animal shelters.

○   In addition to providing needed help, the dogs provide friendship and love.

For Number 12, read the paragraph and then follow the directions.

12   ¹ In January 1925, some people in a small town in Alaska got sick. ² It was too risky to fly an airplane in the winter weather. ³ They needed medicine quickly or many people would die. ⁴ However, the medicine they needed was hundreds of miles away. ⁵ People organized dog teams. ⁶ Each team carried the medicine for long miles over the freezing, snowy trails. ⁷ They traveled 700 miles in six days. ⁸ The brave men and their strong dogs had saved the town!

Where should sentence 2 be moved to better fit in the paragraph?

○   After sentence 3

○   After sentence 4

○   After sentence 6

○   After sentence 7

Go On

For Number 13, choose the sentence that shows the correct punctuation.

13 ○ Mr. Smith's favorite hobby is fishing; he doesn't like swimming, though.

○ Mr. Smiths favorite hobby is fishing; he doesnt like swimming, though.

○ Mr. Smith's favorite hobby is fishing; he does'nt like swimming, though.

○ Mr. Smiths favorite hobby is fishing; he doesn't like swimming, though.

For Number 14, choose the sentence that shows the correct capitalization.

14 ○ My mom reads a magazine called *living well*.

○ My art class is studying a painting called *Starry, Starry Night*.

○ "The Star-spangled banner" has always been one of my favorite songs.

○ The group mothers against hunger works to raise money to help starving people.

For Number 15, choose the word that is spelled correctly and BEST completes the sentence.

15 My father looked very _____ in his favorite chair.

○ comfortable

○ comfertable

○ comfortible

○ comfitible

STOP

ISTEP+

Indiana Statewide Testing for Educational Progress

Practice Test

Applied Skills Assessment
English/Language Arts
Grade 5

 This icon means that you will be doing a writing activity. The writing that you do will be scored on how well you address the prompt, the organization of your ideas, how well you express yourself, and your consistent use of correct paragraphs, grammar, spelling, and punctuation. It will not be scored on your personal opinions.

Do not use slang or jargon in your writing. Use the rules of Standard English for formal writing.

My Favorite Hobby

Read the writing prompt below and complete the writing activity.

 Write an essay about your favorite hobby or about a hobby you would like to try. Describe your hobby and explain why you like it. Write in a way that will convince your audience to try your hobby. Be sure to include details in your story.

Be sure to include

- a description of your hobby

- an explanation of why you enjoy your hobby

- statements that might convince your audience to try your hobby

- an introduction, a body, and a conclusion to your essay

Go On

The Pre-Writing/Planning space on the next two pages, or a separate sheet of paper, can be used for notes, outlines, lists, or any other tools to help plan your writing. When you have finished planning, write your essay neatly on pages 70–73 in this book. Your final essay on the lined pages will be the only writing scored. Be sure to create a title for your essay. Proofread your essay using the Editing Checklist on page 73. The Editing Checklist will help you check your writing for correct paragraphing, spelling, grammar, and punctuation, and for the use of Standard English.

Pre-Writing/Planning

Go On

Go On

Essay

Title: _____

_____

_____

_____

_____

_____

_____

_____

_____

_____

_____

_____

_____

_____

_____

_____

_____

_____

_____

_____

_____

_____

Go On

Go On

_Go On_ ➡

_____

_____

_____

_____

_____

_____

_____

_____

_____

_____

_____

Check your writing with the Editing Checklist.

Editing Checklist

1   Have you checked capitalization and punctuation?

2   Are all words spelled correctly?

3   Are there any run-on sentences or fragments?

4   Have you kept verb tense consistent?

5   Do the subject and verb agree?

6   Is your essay written according to the rules of Standard English?

7   Do you use paragraphs correctly?

Test 4: English/Language Arts

You will read a story and an article in Test 4. Next, you will answer questions based on what you have read. Then you will write about a related topic.

Have you ever ridden a beautiful horse? The first story you will read is about a horse named Black Beauty. Next you will read an article about light pollution and what causes it.

Now read this chapter adapted from the book *Black Beauty.* Then do Numbers 1 through 6. Refer back to the story as often as you like.

Go On

My Early Home

from *Black Beauty* by Anna Sewell

The first place that I can well remember was a large pleasant meadow with a pond of clear water in it. Some shady trees leaned over it, and rushes and water-lilies grew at the deep end. Over the hedge on one side we looked into a plowed field, and on the other we looked over a gate at our master's house, which stood by the roadside; at the top of the meadow was a grove of fir trees, and at the bottom a running brook overhung by a steep bank.

While I was young I lived upon my mother's milk, as I could not eat grass. In the daytime I ran by her side, and at night I lay down close by her. When it was hot we used to stand by the pond in the shade of the trees, and when it was cold we had a nice warm shed near the grove.

As soon as I was old enough to eat grass my mother used to go out to work in the daytime, and come back in the evening.

There were six young colts in the meadow besides me; they were older than I was; some were nearly as large as grown-up horses. I used to run with them, and had great fun; we used to gallop all together round and round the field as hard as we could go. Sometimes we had rather rough play, for they would frequently bite and kick as well as gallop.

One day, when there was a good deal of kicking, my mother whinnied to me to come to her, and then she said:

"I wish you to pay attention to what I am going to say to you. The colts who live here are very good colts, but they are cart-horse colts, and of course they have not learned manners. You have been well-bred and well-born; your father has a great name in these parts, and your grandfather won the cup two years at the Newmarket races; your grandmother had the sweetest temper of any horse I ever knew, and I think you have never seen me kick or bite. I hope you will grow up gentle and good, and never learn bad ways; do your work with a good will, lift your feet up well when you trot, and never bite or kick even in play."

I have never forgotten my mother's advice; I knew she was a wise old horse, and our master thought a great deal of her. Her name was Duchess, but he often called her Pet.

Our master was a good, kind man. He gave us good food, good lodging, and kind words;

Go On

he spoke as kindly to us as he did to his little children. We were all fond of him, and my mother loved him very much. When she saw him at the gate she would neigh with joy, and trot up to him. He would pat and stroke her and say, "Well, old Pet, and how is your little Beauty?" I was a dull black, but he called me Beauty; then he would give me a piece of bread, which was very good, and sometimes he brought a carrot for my mother. All the horses would come to him, but I think we were his favorites. My mother always took him to the town on a market day in a light gig.

There was a plowboy, Dick, who sometimes came into our field to pluck blackberries from the hedge. When he had eaten all he wanted he would have what he called fun with the colts, throwing stones and sticks at them to make them gallop. We did not much mind him, for we could gallop off; but sometimes a stone would hit and hurt us.

One day he was at this game, and did not know that the master was in the next field; but he was there, watching what was going on; over the hedge he jumped in a snap, and catching Dick by the arm, he gave him such a box on the ear as made him roar with the pain and surprise. As soon as we saw the master we trotted up nearer to see what went on.

"Bad boy!" he said, "bad boy! to chase the colts. This is not the first time, nor the second, but it shall be the last. There—take your money and go home; I shall not want you on my farm again." So we never saw Dick any more. Old Daniel, the man who looked after the horses, was just as gentle as our master, so we were well off.

Go On

1 The title of the passage is "My Early Home." Who is telling the story?

○ Beauty

○ Duchess

○ Dick

○ Old Daniel

2 Why does the master yell at Dick and tell him to go home?

○ The master is upset because Dick ate so many of his blackberries.

○ The master is an impatient man who goes into rages unexpectedly.

○ The master is angry because Dick did not finish plowing the fields.

○ The master is angry that Dick was throwing stones at the horses.

3 Based on the advice Beauty's mother gives him, what do you know about Beauty?

○ He does not like to work hard.

○ His grandfather was a cart-horse.

○ He comes from a strong, kind family.

○ His grandmother still lives on the farm.

Go On

4   Which of the following is the an example of personification in the passage?

○   Dick eating blackberries

○   Duchess working in the fields during the day

○   Beauty, the colt, telling the story

○   Old Daniel taking good care of the horses

5   Give TWO examples from the story that show how the master is a good man.

1) _____

_____

2) _____

_____

6   Duchess says that Beauty is "well-bred and well-born." Then she tells him why she thinks that. On the lines below, list TWO examples that Duchess gives to Beauty about why he is from a good family.

1) _____

_____

2) _____

_____

Go On

English/Language Arts

This passage is an article called "Light Pollution." Have you ever heard of light pollution? Do you know it can harm animals? For an explanation and for some other interesting facts about light pollution, read the article. Then do Numbers 7 through 13. Refer back to the article as often as you like.

Go On

Light Pollution

This satellite image of Earth was taken at night. The bright spots in the image are all man-made sources of light, except for the Northern Lights. These are natural "curtains" of light that make up the bright strip near the top left.

When chemicals from big companies are dumped into streams and rivers, that is water pollution. Have you ever seen smoke pouring out of a car's tailpipe? That's air pollution. Litter on the side of the road is another kind of pollution. But what is light pollution?

Light pollution is when there is too much man-made light in the night sky. How much is too much? Different people have different answers. But light pollution does have some negative effects. Among these is the inability of astronomers and other people to see many of the planets and stars that fill our skies.

Effects on Star-Gazing

People who study the stars and planets are affected by light pollution. Even though they use powerful telescopes to help them see, too much man-made light makes it difficult for them to do their work.

About two-thirds of the people in the United States live in places where they cannot see the tremendous Milky Way galaxy. There is too much light in the night sky for them to see the billions of stars above them. While it is nice to be able to see where you're going at night, it is also important to be able to see the same stars that our ancestors could see.

Go On ➡

Effects on Human Body

Medical studies show that people have a natural rhythm that affects their behavior and health. This rhythm is like an inner clock that operates on a 24-hour cycle. It is able to match up with the outside world by outer signs, like the sun. This rhythm is interrupted if there is too much man-made light. Behaviors such as sleeping and being awake are affected. This, in turn, can change mood and productivity. People need to maintain their natural rhythms in order to stay healthy.

Effects on Animals

Light pollution affects animals too. Many migrating birds have been killed by flying into tall buildings. They are probably attracted to the light inside and on the buildings. However, they cannot see the glass, so they fly into it.

Sea turtles lay their eggs on the beach. The eggs hatch when it is dark. The baby turtles usually scurry toward the light when they hatch. This is a good thing when it is the natural light of the horizon found over the ocean. However, light pollution can confuse the turtles. If they move toward man-made light, this can lead them away from the ocean. When this happens, fewer baby turtles survive. They might starve or be eaten by other animals or get run over by cars.

What Can Be Done?

While it might sound like light pollution is hopeless, there are things that can be done. A first step is just to turn off outside lights at night. Another option is to use lights that come on only when they detect motion.

Bird lovers have asked owners and residents of tall buildings in some cities to turn off their lights during the migration months. This has saved the lives of thousands of birds.

Rangers at many of our national parks are also working to keep the wilderness dark. Bryce National Park is located in southern Utah. Visitors enjoy some of the darkest skies in the country at Bryce.

Some cities and towns have laws that limit the use of lights at night. They require that outside lights point downward, so that the light is not shining up into the dark sky. They also require that people use weaker lights. This keeps the skies darker, and it saves energy at the same time!

Go On

7   Which of the following is an OPINION from the article?

○   People who study the stars and planets are affected by light pollution.

○   About two-thirds of the people in the United States live in places where they cannot see the tremendous Milky Way galaxy.

○   While it is nice to be able to see where you're going at night, it is also important to be able to see the same stars that our ancestors could see.

○   Medical studies show that people have a natural rhythm that affects their behavior and health.

8   The word *astronomer* comes from the Greek root *ast*, meaning *star*. What does *astronomer* mean in the following sentence?

Among these (negative effects) is the inability of astronomers and other people to see many of the planets and stars that fill our skies.

○   a person who designs airplanes

○   a person who flies to outer space

○   a scientist who studies stars and planets

○   a scientist who studies plants and animals

9   Based on the map, where is the author MOST LIKELY to say people should go to study the stars and planets?

○   on one of the oceans

○   in a dark land area

○   near the Northern Lights

○   near a big city

Go On

10 Which of the following is the MAIN idea of the section titled "Effects on Star-Gazing"?

○ Our ancestors could see the stars more easily.

○ There are billions of stars in the Milky Way galaxy.

○ Light pollution makes it harder for people to look at the stars.

○ It would be easier to see where you are going at night without light pollution.

11 Fill in the chart below by identifying TWO different effects of light pollution. Give ONE example from the article that suggests a way to fix EACH of the effects.

Effects of light pollution	Ways to fix the problem

12 Give TWO examples of laws the article mentions that help lessen light pollution. Give ONE example from the article that explains how EACH of the laws helps to decrease light pollution.

First Law: _____

How the first law helps decrease light pollution: _____

_____

Second Law: _____

How the second law helps decrease light pollution: _____

_____

Go On

13 Write a summary of the article "Light Pollution." In your summary, be sure to include the main ideas of the article and the most important details. Remember to put the information in your own words.

Use the Pre-Writing/Planning space below to plan your writing. Only the essay on pages 85–86 will be scored. The Editing Checklist on page 86 will help you proofread your writing for correct paragraphing, spelling, grammar, and punctuation, and the use of Standard English. **Your essay should have an introduction, a body, and a conclusion and should be well organized.**

Pre-Writing/Planning

Go On

Summary

_____

_____

_____

_____

_____

_____

_____

_____

_____

_____

_____

_____

_____

_____

_____

_____

_____

_____

_____

_____

_____

_____

Go On

_____

_____

_____

_____

_____

_____

_____

_____

_____

_____

Check your writing with the Editing Checklist.

Editing Checklist

1 Have you checked capitalization and punctuation?

2 Are all words spelled correctly?

3 Are there any run-on sentences or fragments?

4 Have you kept verb tense consistent?

5 Do the subject and verb agree?

6 Is your essay written according to the rules of Standard English?

7 Do you use paragraphs correctly?